Economics of Irish Forestry:
Evaluating the Returns to Economy and Society

J. Peter Clinch

Published by COFORD,
the National Council for Forest Research and Development,
University College Dublin, Belfield, Dublin 4, Ireland.

© COFORD, 1999.

First published in 1999 by COFORD

Title: Economics of Irish Forestry: Evaluating the Returns to Economy and
Society

Author: J. Peter Clinch

Citation: Clinch, J. Peter (1999), Economics of Irish Forestry: Evaluating the
Returns to Economy and Society, Dublin: COFORD.

ISBN 1 902696 03 4

Cover Design by Magner Communications

For my family and friends

Foreword

In the *Economics of Irish Forestry*, Peter Clinch provides a comprehensive analysis of the economic value of Irish forestry with a particular focus on plantation forestry and the economic analysis of its interaction with the environment. It is now almost 20 years since the publication of the National Economic and Social Council report on Irish Forestry Policy and 13 years since the publication of the findings of the Review Group on Forestry. Apart from these studies there have been few economic analyses of Irish forestry and there has been no comprehensive analysis of the value of the non-timber benefits and costs of forestry. In addition, since their publication, the nature of forestry in Ireland has changed markedly. The focus of Forest Policy is now firmly on afforestation shown most clearly in the Government's Strategic Plan for the Forestry Sector which proposes the doubling of the forest estate by 2030. It is therefore timely that this book is published as it provides a comprehensive analysis of the social costs and benefits of investments in afforestation with a particular focus on valuing non-wood outputs such as carbon sequestration, recreation and tourism, biodiversity, landscape and water impacts.

The principal results of an analysis of the economic value of afforestation show that its net environmental benefits are positive and significant, amounting to 18 percent of the timber value of the Government's Strategic Plan. By carrying out a complete cost benefit analysis, the study shows that the Plan itself, if fully implemented, can be expected to give a rate of return of between four and five percent depending upon various assumptions.

In addition to a comprehensive analysis of both wood and non-wood benefits, the book provides the results of the first national survey of public attitudes to afforestation and the environment. This shows that over two-thirds of the public has a favourable attitude to afforestation although those who are against tend to have stronger feelings. A further survey shows that opinions vary considerably from region to region. The book also contains the results of the first comprehensive assessment of the extent of visits to Irish forests by the public and by tourists. The estimated total of 8.5 million visits is considerably higher than was thought previously.

The *Economics of Irish Forestry* ends by raising some concerns regarding the extent and rationale for the high level of subsidisation of afforestation and poses some challenging questions to those advocating the Government's Strategic Plan. In a time when the Common Agricultural Policy is being reformed, this comprehensive analysis of the economic value of Ireland's afforestation programme provides a model which can be applied to alternative land uses so that we can begin to have a factually based assessment of their costs and benefits. In this publication, the Forestry Sector has shown the way.

Fergal Mulloy
Director, COFORD
November 1998

Acknowledgements

There are a number of people who have assisted in the production of this book: Frank Convery and Anthony Murphy of UCD provided important contributions to the contents. Fergal Mulloy and Eugene Hendrick of COFORD gave most excellent advice and assistance throughout the project without being implicated in its findings. Tomás O'Leary and Art McCormack of UCD improved the scope of the book through their co-operation on the landscape survey. Colin Price and Rob Willis of the University of Wales at Bangor gave permission to use CARBMOD and gave general advice on matters relating to carbon sequestration. Wendy Clinch advised on ecological aspects of the study. Bengt Kriström of the Swedish University of Agricultural Sciences in Umeå provided helpful advice on matters relating to contingent valuation. Julia Barrett and Sheila Byrne of the UCD Richview library were of great assistance in tracking down obscure publications. Mike Bulfin of Teagasc and Dermot O'Brien of Coillte provided helpful advice on matters relating to forest practice. Trevor Champ of the Central Fisheries Board gave useful information on matters relating to water resources. Ken Byrne of UCD provided helpful articles on carbon sequestration. Ted Farrell of UCD gave guidance on matters relating to forest ecosystems. Helpful comments by David Pearce of UCL are greatly appreciated. Two anonymous referees helped to correct a number of flaws in the original drafts. Any remaining errors are the responsibility of the author and the conclusions of the book do not necessarily reflect the views of those named above.

Peter Clinch
University College Dublin
National University of Ireland, Dublin

Contents

	Foreword	v
	Acknowledgements	vi
	Contents	vii
	List of Tables	ix
	List of Figures	xvii
	Summary	xix
Chapter 1	Introduction	1
Chapter 2	Literature Review	7
Chapter 3	Methodology	13
Chapter 4	Policy Instruments	25
Chapter 5	Timber	35
Chapter 6	Inputs	69
Chapter 7	Carbon Sequestration	77
Chapter 8	Water	91
Chapter 9	Recreation and Tourism	107
Chapter 10	Biodiversity	123
Chapter 11	Landscape	139
Chapter 12	Other Considerations	149
Chapter 13	Public Preference Assessment	155
Chapter 14	Contingent Valuation	167
Chapter 15	Cost Benefit Analysis	177
Chapter 16	Summary and Conclusions	183
	References	197
Appendix 1	Appendix Tables	221
Appendix 2	Technical Description of Methodology	233
Appendix 3	Maps	261
Appendix 4	Subsidy Assessment	265
	Index	269

List of Tables

Table	Title	Page
1.1	Forest Area, 1922, 1938 and 1996	3
3.1	Classification of Forest Benefits	21
4.1	Forest Service Guidelines	27
4.2	Scope of Environmental Designations	28
4.3	Western Package Achievements	29
4.4	Afforestation Grants	31
4.5	Forest Premium Scheme	32
5.1	Calculating MSY and Yield Class for Sitka Spruce	36
5.3	Global Forest Estate	38
5.4	EU Forest Estate	39
5.5	Global Production of Selected Industrial Woods, 1991 and Percentage Change Since 1971	39
5.6	World Trade in Forest Products, 1993	40
5.7	EU 12 and EU 15 Forest Products and the Economy, 1991	41
5.8	Forecasts of Global Consumption of Forest Products	42
5.9	US Forest Products Forecasted Consumption	42
5.10	Consumption of Forest Products in Europe, 1979 to 1981 with Estimates to 2000 and 2020	43
5.11	Forecast of Japan's Demand for Wood Products to 2004	43
5.12	Great Britain Planting, 1971 to 1996	45
5.13	Volumes of UK Imports, Production and Apparent Consumption of Wood and Wood Products	46

5.14	UK Imports of Softwood Lumber	47
5.15	Past and Future Wood Production in Britain	48
5.16	UK Forecast of Annual Production to 2050	49
5.17	UK Demand for Wood Forecast to 2050	49
5.18	State Sales of Wood by Volume and Value	51
5.19	Trade Balance for Selected Timber Products	53
5.20	Cork and Wood (Div. 24), Pulp and Waste Paper (Div. 25), Cork and Wood Manufactures (excl. furnit) (Div 63) Exports, 1992	55
5.21	Value and Percentages of Selected Irish Timber Exports to EU, Great Britain, Northern Ireland and Total	56
5.22	Timber Value of Strategy under Various Assumptions	66
5.23	Possible Economic Security Value of Strategy under Various Assumptions	66
6.1	Shadow Price of Land	70
6.2	Land Costs of the Strategy at Test Discount Rates	70
6.3	Labour Costs per 1000 ha of *Sitka spruce* Afforestation	72
6.4	Labour Costs per 1000 ha of Oak Afforestation	73
6.5	Labour Costs per 1000 ha of *Sitka spruce* Reforestation	73
6.6	Labour Costs per 1000 ha of Oak Reforestation	74
6.7	Labour Costs of the Strategy at Test Discount Rates	74
6.8	Non-Labour and Land Costs per ha of *Sitka spruce* Afforestation and Reforestation	75
6.9	Non-Labour and Land Costs per ha of Oak Afforestation and Reforestation	75
6.10	Non-Labour and Land Costs of the Strategy at Test Discount Rates	76

7.1	Predictions of General Circulation Models of the Climate Effects of a Doubling of the Atmospheric Level of CO_2	78
7.2	Estimates of CO_2 Emission Costs	82
7.3	Carbon Sequestration Benefits of the Strategy with a Permit Price per tonne of Carbon of £15	88
7.4	Carbon Sequestration Benefits of the Strategy with a Permit Price per tonne of Carbon of £10	89
7.5	Carbon Sequestration Benefits of the Strategy with a Permit Price per tonne of Carbon of £20	89
7.6	Global Carbon Sequestration Benefits of the Strategy	90
8.1	Suspended Sediments in Streams	92
8.2	Application Rates of Fertilisers in the UK	93
8.3	Losses Following Application of Fertiliser	94
8.4	Interception Loss as a Percentage of Incoming Rainfall	96
8.5	Current Demand for Water in the Greater Dublin Area	101
8.6	Future Demand for Water	101
8.7	Possible Approaches to Increasing Dublin's Water Supply	101
8.8	Potential Water Supply and Probable Loss due to Afforestation	102
8.9	Water Restriction Cost of the Strategy	103
8.10	Water Pollution Costs of the Strategy	105
8.11	Total Cost of Water Supply Effects of the Strategy	105
9.1	Number of Visits to Forest Parks, 1972 to 1976	108
9.2	Day Visits to Coillte Forest Parks for which a Charge is Levied, 1993.	109
9.3	Forest Usage	109
9.4	Annual Domestic Forest Visitor Estimates	111

9.5	Annual Forest Visits by Overseas Tourists	112
9.6	Total Annual Visits to Irish Forests	112
9.7	Coillte Costs and Revenues from Forest Recreation	114
9.8	NI Forest Service Costs and Revenues from Forest Recreation	114
9.9	Entrance Fees Charged at Coillte Forest Parks	114
9.10	Progress of Planned Recreational Forestry Scheme	117
9.11	Estimates of British Forestry Recreational Values using the Travel Cost Method	117
9.12	Admission Charges Respondents Paid to Irish Forests	119
9.13	Admission Charge Respondents would have been Willing to Pay	119
9.14	Actual and Potential Revenue from Foreign Tourist Recreational Visits and the Partial External Benefit	120
11.1	Awareness of Forest Strategy	146
11.2	Approval of Forest Strategy	146
11.3	Preferred Species Type	146
11.4	Mean WTP for Broadleaf Afforestation on the Part of Those Preferring the 'Fund' under Different Scenarios	147
13.1	"Is Afforestation Good for the Countryside?"	157
13.2	"Is Afforestation Good for the Countryside?" by Age	158
13.3	"Is Afforestation Good for the Countryside?" by Education	158
13.4	"Is Afforestation Good for the Countryside?" by Occupation	158
13.5	"Is Afforestation Good for the Countryside?" by Children	159

13.6	"Is Afforestation Good for the Countryside?" by Locality	159
13.7	"Is Afforestation Good for the Countryside?" by Environmental Concern	159
13.8	"Is Afforestation Good for the Countryside?" by Use	159
13.9	"Is Afforestation Good for the Countryside?" by County Area Afforested	160
13.10	Significance of Covariates with "Is Afforestation Good for the Countryside?"	160
13.11	"How Will Afforestation Affect the Landscape?"	160
13.12	"How Will Afforestation Affect the Landscape?" by Occupation	161
13.13	"How Will Afforestation Affect the Landscape?" by Locality	161
13.14	"How Will Afforestation Affect the Landscape?" by Environmental Concern	162
13.15	"How Will Afforestation Affect the Landscape?" by County Area Afforested	162
13.16	"How Will Afforestation Affect Wildlife?"	162
13.17	"How Will Afforestation Affect Wildlife?" by Occupation	163
13.18	"How Will Afforestation Affect Wildlife?" by Locality	163
13.19	"How Will Afforestation Affect Wildlife?" by Environmental Concern	163
13.20	"How Will Afforestation Affect Recreation?"	164
13.21	"How Will Afforestation Affect Recreation?" by Use	164
13.22	Importance of Protecting the Environment by Frequency of Viewing/Listening to Nature Programme of TV/Radio	165
14.1	Division of the Total Sample	174

xiv

14.2	Percentage of Respondents Presented with Each Cost Level	174
14.3	Landscape, Wildlife and Recreational Value of the Strategy at Test Discount Rates	175
15.1	Costs and Benefits of Strategy	178
15.2	Costs and Benefits of Strategy if EU Funds "Free"	178
15.3	Net External Benefits of Strategy	179
15.4	Financial Analysis of Strategy	179
15.5	Costs and Benefits of Strategy, Higher Timber Prices	180
15.6	Costs and Benefits of Strategy, Low Timber Prices	180
15.7	Costs and Benefits of Strategy including Economic Security Value	180
15.8	Costs and Benefits of Strategy with Reduced Shadow Wage	181
15.9	Best Case Costs and Benefits of Strategy	181
15.10	Worst Case Costs and Benefits of Strategy	182
A1.1.	Afforestation, 1984 to 1995.	221
A1.2	Forest Strategy Planting Statistics	222
A1.3	Forest Strategy Financial Statistics	223
A1.4	Cork and Wood (Div. 24) Net Exports 1975 to 1992	224
A1.5	Pulp and Waste Paper (Div. 25) Net Exports 1975 to 1992	225
A1.6	Cork and Wood Manufactures (excluding furniture) (Div. 63) Net Exports, 1974 to 1992	226
A1.7	ROI, NI and British Timber Real Price Indices Compared	227
A1.8	ROI CSO "Rough Timber" and "Other Timber" Real WPIs	228
A1.9	Selected UK Forest Products Real Price Indices	229

A1.10   Selected ROI Real Export Price Indices   230

A1.11   UK Cork and Wood Softwood Lumber Real Import   231
Price Indices

A4.1   'IDA Advised' Subsidy and Actual Subsidy to Strategy   266

A4.2   Value of Parameters for Equation A7.6 under Various   267
Assumptions

A4.3   Recommended Subsidy to Strategy   268

List of Figures

Figure	Title	Page
1.1	Afforestation, 1984-1995	5
5.1	Volume Increment of an Even-Age Stand of *Sitka spruce*	36
5.2	Softwood Cutting Potential of Selected Regions	44
5.3	Future Demand for and Supply of Wood and Wood Products in the UK	50
5.4	Destination of Coillte Log Sales, 1992	52
5.5	Cork and Wood (CSO Div. 24) Net Exports: Quantity and Real Value	53
5.6	Pulp and Waste Paper (CSO Div. 25) Net Exports: Quantity and Real Value	54
5.7	Cork and Wood Manufactures (excluding furniture) (CSO Div. 63) Net Exports: Quantity and Real Value	54
5.8	Global Softwood Real Prices since 1900	58
5.9	ROI, NI and British Standing Timber Real Price Indices	59
5.10	ROI CSO "Rough Timber" and "Other Timber" Real WPIs	60
5.11	Selected UK Forest Products Real Price Indices	60
5.12	Selected Real Export Price Indices	61
5.13	UK Imported Cork and Wood and Imported Softwood Lumber Real Price Indices	62
7.1	Optimal Level of CO_2 and Associated Permit Price	83
7.2	Optimal and Non-Optimal Abatement Levels and Associated Permit Prices	84
7.3	China: Optimal and Non-Optimal Abatement	85
7.4	United States: Optimal and Non-Optimal Abatement	86

7.5	Net Sequestration Benefits of a ha of Afforestation	88
14.1	Outline of Main Body of CV Questionnaire	170
14.2	Proportion of Respondents Presenting Zero and Positive Bids in Each Contingent Market	174
16.1	Discounted Net Social Benefit of Strategy	184
16.2	Components of Net Social Benefit of Strategy	185
16.3	Actual and Recommended Subvention of Strategy	191
16.4	Actual and Recommended Subvention of Strategy: EU Funds "Free"	192
A2.1	`Surplus Measures for a Change in Quantity	238
A3.1	Forestry Production Potential in Ireland	261
A3.2	Natural Heritage Areas	262
A3.3	Acid Sensitive Areas	263

Summary

INTRODUCTION

Since the early 1980s there has been a dramatic increase in afforestation in Ireland. This has been primarily the result of heavy subvention by the Irish Government and the European Union (EU). In June 1996 the Government published a Strategic Plan for the Forestry Sector (the 'Strategy') which proposes that the forest estate be doubled over the next 35 years at a cost of over £3 billion (75 percent funded by the EU). This would be the most comprehensive and costly afforestation programme in the history of the State. The "Strategic Goal" of the Strategy is "to develop forestry to a scale and in a manner which maximises its contribution to national well-being on a sustainable basis and which is compatible with the protection of the environment".

It is well recognised that afforestation brings with it many more benefits than timber, such as the provision of areas for recreation, the potential for contributing positively to the landscape scenery etc. While there is no doubt that further afforestation in Ireland will make positive contributions to the economy and to society, even before the publication of the Strategy, there had been some concern about possible negative environmental impacts. Prior to this study, no comprehensive assessment of the magnitude of the non-timber costs and benefits of afforestation (external effects) had been undertaken. Therefore, the net contribution that investments in forestry make to the economy and to society had not been assessed, even in the Strategic Plan, which has the objective of maximising such a contribution. This book attempts to fill such gaps in knowledge by calculating the economic value of investments in forestry and thereby testing the hypothesis that investments in afforestation in Ireland are socially efficient, i.e. whether they will make a positive contribution to the economy and society.

METHODOLOGY

In order to assess the social efficiency of afforestation in Ireland, the Strategic Plan for the Forestry Sector is taken as a case study. This plan is assessed using Cost Benefit Analysis. In undertaking the Analysis, the Total Economic Value framework is employed. Using this approach, adjustments are made for the existence of market failure whereby certain forestry outputs are not captured within markets and so do not have an obvious 'price' by which they may be valued. Therefore, these externalities (costs and benefits of forestry to members of society other than the forest owner) of forestry must be estimated using non-market valuation techniques, i.e. techniques which enable a monetary value to be placed on these outputs. Benefits and costs are adjusted for time using five test discount rates. In the absence of agreement amongst researchers of an appropriate discount rate, a five percent discount rate is used for the purposes of policy analysis, as it is the Irish Government's test discount rate for public sector projects.

COMPONENTS OF TOTAL ECONOMIC VALUE

Timber

The principal marketed output of the Forest Strategy will be timber. The plan is to afforest 725,000 ha of trees, 80 percent of which will be conifers. Prior to calculating the value of the timber, appropriate assumptions must be made regarding timber prices. A survey of timber markets and prices shows that there has been no secular tendency for real timber prices to increase over time in Ireland and the UK and it would be unwise to predict a rise in the real price of Irish standing coniferous timber in the long term.

The *potential* exists for Coillte to act as a monopoly supplier and thereby inflate prices. However, the evidence is unclear as to whether this potential is exploited. Given that price distortion may occur, price series provided by Coillte are not reliable as indicators of the social value of Irish timber.

Using British prices as a proxy for the world price, the value of the timber that will be produced under the Forest Strategy is estimated to be worth £887 m in present value terms. The expansion of the EU from 12 to 15 member states and the consequent shrinking of the timber deficit renders the economic security value of Irish timber close to zero.

Inputs

The inputs required for afforestation consist of land, labour and other inputs such as plants, fertiliser, and materials for roads. Heavy subsidisation of agriculture and forestry has resulted in a distortion of the price of land such that the market price is no longer a true reflection of the opportunity cost to society of using the land. The opportunity cost of using land for forestry can be measured by the agricultural output forgone valued at world prices. Using this approach, the cost of the land required for the targets of the Forest Strategy to be reached is calculated to be £552 m in present value terms. The shadow price of labour is considered to be equal to the market price of labour (net of taxes and social insurance) reflecting the assumption that an expansion in the forest estate is unlikely to reduce unemployment. The present value of the labour required under the Strategy amounts to £136 m. The cost of other inputs amounts to £169 m. The total cost of inputs into the Forest Strategy therefore amounts to £857 m.

Carbon Sequestration

Trees absorb (sequester) carbon dioxide (CO_2) and store it in the wood. The carbon is released when the wood, or the products that have been made from the wood, decay. In this way forests delay the release of CO_2 to the atmosphere and may, therefore, assist in reducing the damage that might result from global warming. The benefits to the Irish nation as a result of carbon sequestration by forests planted under the Forest Strategy when measured in terms of the avoided damage from global warming may not be very large. However, Ireland has signed an EU agreement to stabilise emissions of CO_2. If emissions are calculated net of carbon sequestered by forests, it is clear that the carbon sequestered by the forests to be planted under the Forest Strategy will be of considerable value in terms of the reduced cost of complying with international agreements. However, the net sequestration effect of forests on peat soils is still unknown. A conservative estimate of total sequestration benefits can be calculated by assuming peat oxidation rates are fast such that there are no net sequestration benefits on peat soils. Using a five percent discount rate, this gives a total value of carbon sequestration benefits of the Forest Strategy of £46 m.

Water
Plantation forestry can have a number of effects on the water supply including acidification in poorly buffered areas as a result of 'scavenging', pollution from fertilisers, and restriction of the water supply. These effects are some of the most difficult externalities to value as they tend to be very localised. However, a reasonable approximation suggests that the cost of the effects on water of afforestation planted under the Forest Strategy would amount to about £10 m which, in comparison with the timber value, is relatively small. However, this figure assumes an acidification cost of zero. This assumption is only reasonable if grant aid is supplied to areas of yield class 14 or above only (as promised in the Strategy) and if afforestation is prohibited in Natural Heritage Areas (as it is presently) such that areas prone to acidification are avoided. This should be borne in mind when interpreting the results of the final cost benefit analysis.

Recreation and Tourism
It is clear that there has been a serious deficiency in data on forest use. However, the figures available prior to this study suggested that there has been little growth in forest park patronage. This study supplements the available data using two surveys. The first, a household survey, resulting in an effective sample of over 2,800, produced an estimate for annual visits by Irish residents to forests of 7.7 million. However, it should be borne in mind that respondents may vary in their interpretation of the term "forest". This figure is much higher than expected given that only 42 percent of households visit forests but seems to be explained by a high frequency of visits probably as a result of location and tastes. It is unclear as to whether this result implies that there has been rapid growth in forest visits or whether previous measures were simply inaccurate. A survey of 1000 tourists resulted in an estimate for total visits to forests by overseas tourists of just fewer than 744 thousand giving a total annual number of forest visits of 8.5 million. Age is negatively correlated, and household income and the presence of children, are positively correlated with forest visits. Urban households are more likely to visit forests than are rural households.

The limited fee revenues generated by forest recreation do not cover the costs of provision. In addition, costs are tending to increase driven by public liability costs. The difficulty of 'capturing' the benefits of forest recreation is demonstrated by the fact that, out of the 31 percent of overseas tourists who visit forests, only 22 percent are charged admission such that the 'uncaptured' (external) benefit amounts to nearly £1.2 million. Benefit transfer using results from the travel cost method is inappropriate for estimating the recreational value of future afforestation. Rather, the contingent valuation method, which elicits in a survey the value that the public puts on such a benefit (or cost), is the most appropriate technique.

Biodiversity
The afforestation that is planned under the Forest Strategy has the potential to destroy valuable habitats if planting takes place in 'sensitive' areas. However, if planting is kept out of NHAs (as it is presently) and sensitive areas to be designated by local authorities, the threat to biodiversity is low such that one rather limited diversity will be replaced by another limited diversity. The valuation of biodiversity is extremely difficult when existence values are thought to be significant. This is because there is often a lack of knowledge of the precise effects a proposed development will have on an ecosystem and there is also the difficulty of describing these effects in a contingent valuation questionnaire. In addition, there are a number of other difficulties with contingent valuation. Nevertheless, at this point in time, it is the most appropriate method.

Landscape
The visual impact of afforestation is probably the most controversial external effect of afforestation in Ireland. This is primarily the result of the predominance of coniferous forestry and *Sitka spruce* in particular. A survey of 795 individuals consisting of 403 from Leitrim and 392 from Wicklow was undertaken to assess attitudes to the landscape impact of afforestation. The results suggest that the extent of awareness of the Government's plans to double the forest estate is low. It appears that large regional variations in attitudes to afforestation exist. This suggests that the distribution of costs and benefits of the Strategy will be rather uneven. A survey suggests that broadleaves are valued more highly than conifers in terms of their contribution to the landscape. Awareness of biodiversity arguments for broadleaves is minimal. A national contingent valuation survey is the most appropriate method of valuing the landscape effects of an expansion in the forest estate.

Other Considerations
The most vocal concerns about the increase in afforestation have come from farming organisations despite the fact that over 75 percent of private sector afforestation is actually undertaken by farmers. Their principal complaint is that the availability of subsidies for afforestation has driven up the price of land. It is clear that the subsidisation of afforestation and the consequent increase in the price of land suitable for forestry will be a disbenefit to those farmers who

wish to expand their land under traditional agriculture. However, it is also true that the land they already own will become more valuable as a result of such price increases. However, annual subsidies to agriculture are much higher than afforestation subsidies and so have a much greater impact on the price of land.

It was not possible to calculate the community integrity value of the Forest Strategy, i.e. the contribution that forestry makes to stabilising rural populations. Neither was it possible to value the external cost of forestry development on archaeology which may be quite significant. The absence of both these values should be borne in mind when interpreting the results of the final cost benefit analysis.

PUBLIC PREFERENCE ASSESSMENT

A survey of 2,895 households suggests that a majority (70 percent) of the public feels that further afforestation of the type that is presently taking place will improve the landscape and provide better habitats for wildlife. Fewer are convinced of the merits of afforestation for recreational opportunities. Over two thirds of the population believe that, on balance, afforestation will have a beneficial effect of the countryside. Younger people are more favourably disposed to forestry than are older generations. A high correlation between environmental concern and a positive attitude towards forestry suggests that forestry is seen as an environmental good rather than an agricultural good. This view is supported by the finding that those households with children have a more positive attitude towards afforestation and are also more concerned about the environment. In addition, urban dwellers are much more positive than are those living in rural areas. Not surprisingly, those who use forests for recreation are more favourably disposed to afforestation particularly in relation to its recreational value. The more favourable response to afforestation from counties with a low or medium level of forest cover compared with those with a high level of forest cover suggests that there are diminishing external benefits of forestry. While farmers are the least well disposed to afforestation, just over half have a favourable attitude to the environmental impact of afforestation.

CONTINGENT VALUATION

Contingent valuation, which elicits the value that individuals place on environmental goods by asking them in a survey for their willingness to pay for the good, was considered to be the only appropriate way to calculate the landscape, wildlife and recreational benefits of the trees to be planted under the Forest Strategy. Given that the views of the Irish public differ regarding the environmental impact of forestry in Ireland it was necessary to allow people to express a positive or negative willingness to pay. Those who 'liked' afforestation were asked to 'bid' for an increase in the forest estate while those who 'dislike' forestry were asked to 'bid' to preserve the present land use and thereby avoid forestry. Mean willingness to pay increased taxes to avoid forests was significantly higher that mean willingness to pay for forests suggesting that, as a result of an expansion in the forest estate, those who dislike forestry will, on average, endure a greater welfare loss than the average increase in welfare experienced by those who like forestry. Mean willingness to pay for an expansion in the forest estate was £14.50 per annum for ten years. This indicates that the net present value to the Irish population of the landscape, wildlife and recreational benefits of the Forest Strategy amounts to £129 m.

COST BENEFIT ANALYSIS

Bringing together the various components of the Total Economic Value of the Forest Strategy shows it to return a rate of approximately 4 percent. This is below the Government's test discount rate of 5 percent. Net external benefits amount to 18 percent of the timber value of the Strategy at a 5 percent discount rate. The main results of the cost benefit analysis are presented in the table below. At a 5 percent discount rate, net external benefits range between £131 m and £350 m depending on assumptions regarding the absolute size and the growth in the price of carbon emissions permits. A conservative estimate of £165 m is 18 percent of the value of timber benefits.

Costs and Benefits of Strategy (£m).

	Discount Rate (%)				
	0	*3*	*5*	*8*	*10*
Timber	89,839	3,065	887	204	84
Land	-17,183	-1,193	-552	-250	-167
Labour[1]	-3,105	-258	-136	-74	-55
Other inputs	-2,690	-326	-169	-136	-97
Landscape, wildlife, recreation	168	143	129	112	103
Carbon[2]	261	101	46	16	9
Water	-95	-15	-10	-6	-5
Excess Burden from All Funds	-1,558	-881	-636	-419	-331
Excess Burden from Irish Funds	-389	-220	-159	-105	-83
Net Social Benefit	65,638	636	-441	-553	-459
Net Social Benefit (EU funds free)	66,807	1,279	36	-239	-211

If it could be argued that, because funding for forestry is part of CAP reform and, therefore, the EU portion of the afforestation subsidies will not be made available for an alternative use, the Excess Burden could be calculated on Irish Exchequer funds alone. In this instance, the Strategy would pass the cost benefit test at a 5 percent discount rate and, therefore, it would be deemed to be economically efficient and beneficial to the society as a whole. The difficulty for the Irish Government in justifying such an approach is that is that it contradicts its own Guidelines for appraisal in the public sector.

POLICY IMPLICATIONS

Subsidy Assessment

One of the limitations of cost benefit analysis is that it does not give an indication of the appropriate size of the subsidy that should go to the programme being assessed. It is clear that afforestation on the scale that is planned under the Forest Strategy would not take place without the provision of subsidies by the Government.

The rationale for transfer payments is to correct failures in the market system. Otherwise there is no justification for giving one activity a subsidy while leaving another without. It is likely that a cost benefit analysis of many activities such as banks, supermarkets and restaurants would show a higher rate of return than does forestry, but it is not suggested that the government subsidise these activities. Contrasting the actual level of subvention that is required for the Strategy to be implemented with the recommended subsidy level based on the rationale of correcting market failure, at all discount rates the level of subvention of the Forest Strategy is far in excess of that which is justified (over £1 billion in excess at a 5 percent discount rate). Thus, while it has been shown that the net external benefits of the Forest Strategy are significant (18 percent of the timber value at a 5 percent discount rate), the cost of obtaining them far outweighs their value.

The inclusion of EU funds in the calculation of the total subsidy relies on the belief that, if the Forestry Plan were not implemented, Ireland would receive the funds for an alternative use subject to an appropriate plan being put to the Union. In defence of the Forestry Plan, it has been suggested that the EU would not provide any of the funds for an alternative use. If this were true, the subsidy for purposes of comparison should be calculated net of EU funds, i.e. only the 25 percent contribution by the Irish Government should be included as a cost. However, at a five per cent discount rate, the Irish Government's subsidy alone is over one and a half times greater than the appropriate subsidy.

The standard welfare economics approach to subsidy analysis perhaps ignores that policy is operating in a second best world where there is already a high level of subsidisation which is not based on the rationale of correcting for market failure. It is clear that, without large-scale subvention, forestry, on the scale envisaged, would not be able to compete with agriculture and thereby assist the political aim of reducing agricultural production as part of the reform of the Common Agricultural Policy (CAP).

In addition, it is sometimes suggested that subsidisation of forestry is simply a mechanism for compensating farmers for loss of income resulting from CAP reform and a politically acceptable way of reducing agricultural production. If the Strategy were designed as a means of compensating farmers, such a benefit of the scheme would not be reflected in the subsidy assessment above. All else being equal, it seems that such large transfers to forestry are not justified. However, all else is rarely equal and if, under CAP reform, there would be fewer people employed on the land, then the justification for subsidising forestry would be greater as the number of otherwise underemployed people would be greater.   However, to justify the forestry scheme for the purposes of compensation to farmers it would be necessary to assess whether providing forestry grants is the most efficient method of compensation. In addition, just under half of all afforestation is undertaken by non-farmers comprising the semi-state forestry company Coillte (25 per cent) and private individuals/companies (22.5 per cent) so a substantial proportion of the funds do not go to farmers.

The "Strategic Goal" of the Forestry Plan is "to develop forestry to a scale and in a manner which maximises its contribution to national well-being on a sustainable basis and which is compatible with the protection of the environment" (Department of Agriculture, Food and Forestry, 1996). This suggests that increasing the welfare of Irish society is the principal aim of the project. Using the Government's test discount rate of five per cent, the Forestry Plan fails to pass a cost benefit analysis and even if 4 per cent is considered a reasonable return, the subsidy is far in excess of that which is justified. This questions the validity of growing timber in Ireland at huge expense to the exchequer rather than importing it from abroad and freeing up the funds for an alternative project or projects which might make better use of the funds.

A weakness of this study is that it is limited to assessing the efficiency of the Governments existing plan and, thus, it does not show whether some other package of measures to promote afforestation would provide a higher (or lower) rate of return and thereby provide a greater justification for the use of the funds. Such measures could include a reduced level of planting, a different species mix, longer rotation periods etc. However, an analysis would have to be carried out to see if this would be a better use of the funds.

It is important to note that this study should not be used as a basis for criticising the Strategy on *environmental* grounds since it has shown that, if the Forest Service enforces its rules and regulations, net environmental benefits will be positive at approximately £165 m. It cannot, therefore, be argued using these figures that, overall, the Strategy will be "bad" for the environment. While there will be some negative environmental impacts of the plan these figures should not be quoted out of context as they are small relative to the other benefits.

Concerns
It has been assumed in this book that the planting and timber production targets set out in the Strategy will be achieved. However, even if the planting targets are met, this does not guarantee that timber production targets will be achieved. In addition, in order to sustain timber output it will be necessary for sites to be reforested after felling.   However, the Strategy makes no provision for

reforestation grants and, while the law requires sites to be reforested once felled, it remains to be seen as to whether this will be enforced. There is also some concern regarding the long-term physical sustainability of the forest resource.

There is a serious question mark over the ability of the Forest Service to ensure that afforestation is carried out in the most socially efficient manner. This results from the poor quality of information provided by the Forest Service (see below), the lack of an effective monitoring procedure of the location and extent of afforestation, the lack of statutory backing for the forestry Guidelines, and the lack of any *ex post* evaluation to ascertain the effectiveness of the Guidelines.

Whether or not the Strategic Plan is fully implemented depends in part upon EU approval and financial support.

Future Areas for Research
Given that the level of subsidies the Strategic Plan seeks to commit to afforestation does not seem not to be justified, it would be desirable for further research to be undertaken to assess the optimal use of these funds. However, if the Strategic Plan is to be implemented, a greater effort should be made to provide the optimal mix of forest outputs under the present scheme in order to endeavour to maximise the social benefits of afforestation. Certain areas of research would greatly assist this process. These include the design of fiscal incentives to achieve optimal forest outputs, a national survey of the attitudes of the public to the landscape impact of afforestation and the development of new landscape guidelines, the net carbon sequestration gain from afforestation of peat, research on water-forest relationships, and the extent to which forestry can contribute to community stability.

Information
Information on most aspects of the Irish forest industry is extremely difficult to acquire. The flow of information has deteriorated since the transfer of State forestry from the Forest Service to Coillte in 1989. The Forest Service is failing in its duty to provide information such as the size and location of the forest estate, the location of planting, the species types planted, and annual average timber prices. The difficulty of obtaining such basic information and the reliance upon Coillte to provide information regarding State forestry where it is the duty of the Forest Service to make such information available, seriously hampers research efforts. In view of the huge sums of public money being given in subsidies to Coillte and the private sector it is unacceptable that information is not more freely available. Records of compliance and non-compliance with zoning and the Guidelines (which should be given statutory backing) should be kept in a fashion which facilitates public access and *ex post* evaluation.

CONCLUSION

To conclude, the study has shown that, if the Forest Strategy is implemented, the resulting expansion of the forest estate will provide a rate of return of approximately 4 percent. This is below the Government's test rate of 5 percent. This result relies upon the assumption that EU funds committed to afforestation as part of the Strategic Plan could be made available for an alternative use. However, if the EU funds would not be available for an alternative use, the Strategy would pass a cost benefit analysis at a 5 percent discount rate and, therefore, it would be predicted that its implementation would improve the welfare of Irish society as a whole. However, even if a convincing argument was made that EU funds should be considered as "free", there is still a serious doubt as to whether the social benefits of the programme justify the level of subvention required.

If Strategic Plan for the Forestry Sector in Ireland is to be justified, a number of issues will need to be clarified: are EU funds restricted to this project and, if so, is there an opportunity cost of using them? Is forestry a more viable prospect than an alternative agricultural land use? Will forestry subsidies merely replace agricultural subsidies such that there is no net increase in the use of public funds? Are subsidies to forestry designed purely to provide income support for farmers and, if so, should Coillte and non-farmers be excluded from the scheme? Is funding forestry the best way of transferring income to farmers? Would such a plan take the long term unemployed off the dole queue?

The Strategy document does not provide convincing answers to any of these questions. With certain answers to these questions, forestry could be shown to be a wise investment of public funds particularly in comparison to other land uses. However, without such answers, public financing of the Strategic Plan for the Development of the Forestry Sector in Ireland is questionable.

CHAPTER 1

INTRODUCTION

This objective of this book is to examine whether investments in forestry in Ireland, which are heavily subsidised by the Government and the European Union (EU), are socially efficient, i.e. whether they make a positive contribution to the economy and society. In order to carry out this test, the principal objective is to calculate the Total Economic Value of investment in forestry in Ireland[1] by:

1.   Developing a methodology which allows the value of both market (e.g. timber) and non-market (e.g. recreation etc.) forestry outputs to be calculated;
2.   Identifying each of these forestry outputs;
3.   Estimating the value of each of these outputs;
4.   Calculating the cost of the inputs into afforestation;
5.   Estimating the net benefit of investment in afforestation.

CONTEXT

Forestry as a land use in Ireland involves a paradox: the rate of tree growth is among the fastest in Europe[2] and neighbouring Great Britain is the continent's largest wood importer, yet forests comprise only 8 percent of the State's land area, the lowest proportion in the European Union. There are a number of possible reasons for this phenomenon, which can be summarised as follows:

Once the indigenous forests were cleared towards the end of the seventeenth century, those who controlled the cleared land rarely felt that the financial and other returns from tree planting justified the cost. To invest in anything having a pay-off extending fifty and more years into the future, certain conditions are necessary for those who control the land: they must have, or at least think that they have, security of tenure and expect to retain it indefinitely; they must have resources which can be invested today without prospects of financial return for a generation (such a long view is encouraged if interest rates are low); they must have sufficient land to achieve economies of scale, and have the resources and the authority to limit access; it helps if the other options for using land which yield immediate returns are commercially unattractive to them (opportunity costs are low); they must have a certain faith that the outputs of the forest will be marketable in the distant future.

---

[1] Éire/the Irish State/the Republic of Ireland is referred to as "Ireland" throughout this book.
[2] Average growth rates for *Sitka spruce* (*Picea sitchensis*) are nearly four times the European average (Government of Ireland, 1991).

In Ireland in the past, these conditions were met only for a relatively short time towards the end of the 18th century and the first half of the 19th century, and then only on the part of a small number of landowners. Estate forestry in this period, although modest in scale, was of great and continuing importance in providing the beginning of a forestry culture, and in endowing the country with a few woodlands which today are of great aesthetic and environmental significance (Neeson, 1991). But most of these forest estates did not survive the transfer of the estates from landlord to tenant. The new owners did not have the economies of scale needed to practice effective forestry; they did not have the resources would allow them an investment with long-deferred returns; farming became increasingly synonymous with cattle-farming, and livestock farmers everywhere tended to have an antagonistic view of trees as a crop; and finally forestry was identified as an avocation of the 'landlord class', a group regarded by many as symbolic of a suppressive past rather than as models to be emulated.

The Twentieth Century
The position of forestry in this century has been well summarised by Gillmor (1993), from whom much of the discussion of this period is drawn. The State took the lead in restoring forests as a land use. Progress depended on a combination of political will, the associated willingness to provide the necessary resources, and the ability to afforest without 'intruding' on land perceived as being suitable for agriculture. The capacity to expand the boundaries of forest conservation was enhanced dramatically by the discovery in the 1940s of ploughing techniques which allowed peatlands and podzolised soils to be successfully drained and planted, and the associated development of knowledge of the North American species *Sitka spruce* and *lodgepole pine*. With appropriate drainage and fertiliser application these species could withstand very low-nutrient-status upland sites which were very exposed and therefore of little value or interest for farming. In Ireland, the emergence of this knowledge coincided with very strong political backing for forestry, supported by the rationale that the financial constraint could be relaxed owing the post war availability of Marshall Funds. An annual planting target of 10,000 hectares (ha) was set. Frequently, however, this target was not reached.

There has been a steady increase in forest area in this century, concentrated mainly on relatively high-elevation and poor-nutrient sites, which were not perceived as being of value for farming, with much of the expansion concentrated in the western counties. Farrell (1983) has explained how the constraints on land acquisition were designed to confine afforestation to very low-yielding land and succeeded in doing so up to the early 1980s. In the years immediately following membership of the European Community (now European Union) in 1973, the boom in farming resulted in an escalation in the real price of land and this put further pressure on the land effectively available to the State. Forestry could not compete with highly subvented farming alternatives. By 1980 the rate of planting in Ireland had fallen to 6,000 ha.

Throughout this period, the motivation in tree crop establishment was primarily to produce wood, with the subsidiary objective of generating rural employment. However, the use of forests as public recreation areas developed also, with a series of forest parks being established throughout the 1960s and 1970s (Kennedy and McCusker, 1983). However, the context of Irish forestry was about to change. During the past decade, one could observe unprecedented alterations in both the magnitude and the location of forestry and the emergence of environmental considerations as public concerns. Table 1.1 demonstrates the increase in the forest estate over this century.

TABLE 1.1. Forest Area, 1922, 1938 and 1996.

Year	State Forests 000s ha	Private Forests 000s ha	Total 000s ha
1922	8	92	100
1938	14	86	100
1996	392	178	570

Source: Mulloy, 1992; Department of Agriculture, Food and Forestry, 1996.

Forestry in Ireland since 1980
The past decade has seen very striking changes in forestry in Ireland and they have been driven by the country's membership of the EU. When the Single European Act was ratified in 1987, part of the package was a programme of transfers to the poorer members of the Union (the "Cohesion Countries") namely Greece, Ireland, Portugal and Spain. These transfers were called Structural Funds and were aggregated into an integrated programme called a Community Support Framework (CSF) agreed between the Commission of the European Communities and each member state. As part of the CSF a number of Operational Programmes were developed which set out the rationale, targets and means of subvention for each sector.

At the time the Structural Funds were being put in place reform of the EU's Common Agricultural Policy was on the agenda stimulated by the need to agree a new General Agreement on Tariffs and Trade (GATT). The objective was to reduce agricultural output using a "stick and carrot" approach, i.e. reducing agricultural price support on the one hand and introducing subsidies for alternative land uses on the other. In Ireland, where there was a high dependency on traditional agriculture and a paucity of trees (woodland as a percentage of the total land area was the lowest in the EU), forestry was an obvious target for structural fund support. Trees were seen as an alternative land use with a certain permanency such that land would not come quickly back into farm production.

Underpinned by these rationales, a very ambitious programme of afforestation[3], was proposed in the Forestry Operational Programme, to be implemented over

---

[3] Afforestation is the planting of trees on land formerly under some other use.

the 1989-93 period at a total cost of over £163 million[4] (Government of Ireland, 1991). This coincided with the establishment of Coillte Teoranta (Coillte) under the Forestry Act of 1988 which charged the new company with managing the State's forest resource (heretofore managed by a Civil Service Department) on a more commercial basis. However, the focus was firmly on the private sector. Generous planting grants, tax free timber revenues, and annual payments for farmers combined with growth rates of timber among the fastest in Europe to make investments in forestry seem most attractive[5]. These returns seemed particularly attractive relative to the falling returns from traditional farming. Sheehy (1992) has shown that the real price per unit of value added in farming fell on average at a rate of 5.5 percent annually over the 1978 to 1991 period. These dramatic falls in prices combined with the introduction of a milk superlevy and quotas to put pressure on returns and limit the attractiveness of farming on land judged to be commercially marginal for agriculture. This combination of factors led Ireland to have the highest rate of afforestation in the EU with most of the planting being undertaken by the private sector (Figure 1.1).

The success of the first Operational Programme led the Irish Government to introduce another round of even more generous subsidies in 1994 under the Operational Programme for Agriculture, Rural Development and Forestry at a total cost of over £108 million, three quarters of the funds coming from the EU (Government of Ireland, 1994). Under this programme the proportion of land under forestry is expected to rise to ten percent by the year 2000. In 1996, the Minister for Agriculture, Food and Forestry proposed that £3 billion (75% funded by the EU) be committed to increase forestry to over 18 percent of the total land area by 2030[6] (Department of Agriculture, Food and Forestry, 1996).
It is clear that what is planned amounts to a massive land use change. There has been considerable controversy regarding this change. A battle has raged in the national newspapers between those advocating forestry and the opponents of forestry. The controversy surrounds the externalities produced by an expansion in the forest estate, i.e. the effects of plantation forestry on the environment particularly with regard to its effects on the landscape, water, recreation, the greenhouse effect and wildlife which tend to effect, positively or negatively, members of society other than the forest owner. Yet, despite the proposed investment of billions of pounds of public funds in forestry, no estimate of the total economic value of these investments has been produced, so that little is known of the magnitude of forest externalities.

---

[4] '£' refers to Irish Pounds. At time of printing £1 = €1.27 = 0.85 Pounds Sterling = 1.38 US Dollars.
[5] O'Connor and Conlon (1993) estimate that a one unit increase in grant aid per ha can be expected to bring about a six unit increase in the private afforestation index.
[6] This involves increasing the forest area from 570,000 ha in 1996 to 1.29 million ha by end 2030 by planting 25,000 ha per annum to the year 2000 and 20,000 ha per annum thereafter.

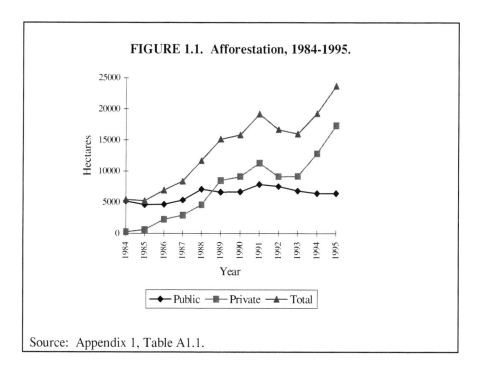

FIGURE 1.1. Afforestation, 1984-1995.

Source: Appendix 1, Table A1.1.

In addition, there is evidence which suggests that the case for subsiding afforestation on commercial grounds may be weak. Clinch (1994) undertook a financial analysis of sites planted in 1991 under the EC Forestry Operational Programme 1989-93. The results show that, under average historical timber prices, in the absence of subsidies the rate of return to the private investor from investing in forestry falls well below five percent which is the minimum required rate of return for public sector investment[7]. If subsidies are required to make an investment in forestry commercially viable this begs the question as to whether the net external benefits of forestry are sufficient to justify subvention and the wider question as to whether the investments in forestry as a whole are justified on social efficiency grounds. There has been no study that addresses these questions.

This book attempts to rectify this gap in knowledge. It does so by assessing whether the government target of doubling the forest estate in Ireland over the next 35 years is efficient from the point of view of society. In so doing, it attempts to shed some light on the disagreements surrounding the environmental effects of afforestation and the magnitude of forest externalities. In addition to estimating the external effects of afforestation, the book contains the first ever survey of the attitudes of the Irish public to afforestation and an

---

[7] See Department of Finance, 1994 for details of the required rate of return for public sector investments.

assessment of the regional differences in such attitudes and it also provides estimates of the numbers of domestic and tourist visits to the existing forest estate.

OUTLINE OF STUDY

Chapter 2 provides a brief review of the literature on the Total Economic Value of forestry with a view to pointing out the gaps in the literature which necessitated this piece of research.   Chapter 3 formulates the overall methodology to be employed in the remaining chapters. Chapter 4 provides an outline of the policy instruments used to promote and control afforestation. Chapters 5 to 14 examine the components of the Total Economic Value of forestry. These components are brought together in a Cost Benefit Analysis in Chapter 15.   The study is summarised and the conclusions and policy implications outlined in Chapter 16.

CHAPTER 2

LITERATURE REVIEW

This chapter reviews the literature on the Total Economic Value of forestry. The objective of the chapter is to highlight the gaps in the literature which necessitate the body of research in this book. The literature relevant to each component of the economic value of forestry in Ireland is not included in this chapter but can be found in the appropriate chapters. The literature upon which the methodology is based can be found in Chapter 3.

UNDERLYING THEORY

The classical 'problem' of the optimal rotation period for forestry, i.e. that, if the rate of time preference is greater than zero, the optimal harvest time for a forest is sooner than the time at which the timber output is maximised, was formulated firstly by Faustmann (1849) and then solved by Preßler (1860) and Ohlin (1921). Samuelson (1976) provides an excellent synthesis of this literature. However, this approach focused entirely on timber as the sole output of a forest. Gregory (1955) first modelled the multiple outputs that forests produce but the Hartman model (1976) has become the model most associated with multiple use forestry. Hartman considered the various non-market amenity services such as recreation, wildlife and waterflow which are influenced by alterations of the standing timber stock. Thus he accounted for market failure and thereby formulated the socially optimal (as opposed to the privately optimal) forest rotation. A synthesis of this literature can be found in Chapter 3.

NON-MARKET VALUATION AND FORESTRY

The literature on the non-market costs and benefits of forestry varies in its quality. Pearce (1996) states that the results are a "mixture of legitimate and illegitimate valuation procedures" while Godoy et al. (1993) recommend that future valuations be undertaken using a common format so that comparison will be made easier. Due to the varied quality of the research, this review outlines the focus of the research on forestry externalities rather than listing the values obtained which are mostly of limited relevance to the Irish case.

Developing World
A large number of studies of the total economic value of forestry have been undertaken in developing countries. Most of these have been concerned with the destruction of indigenous forests and the associated loss of non-timber benefits rather than by any concern regarding the supply of timber (Pearce, 1996). Thus, a large body of research has focused upon tropical forests and

their provision of such external benefits as bush meat, fire-wood, nuts and berries, and medicinal plants. Few researchers concerned themselves with the valuation of non-timber tropical forest products until 1988 when a report of the International Tropical Timber Organization called for a rigorous study of these products. A summary of this research can be found in Godoy *et al.* (1993), Lampietti and Dixon (1995) and Pearce (1996). This research examines three values:

1.   Extractive Values
2.   Non-extractive Values
3.   Preservation Values

Extractive Values
Research on extractive values has been concerned with valuing goods which are extracted from the forest such as meat products from hunting (e.g. Caldecott, 1987; Ruitenbeek, 1988 and 1989; Thorbjarnarson, 1991; Wilkie, 1989; Wilkie and Curran, 1991) and fishing (e.g. Kumari, 1994) and plant products such as rubber (e.g. Anderson and Ioris, 1992; Pinedo-Vazquez, 1992; Schwarzman, 1989), nuts and berries (e.g. Alcorn, 1989; Chopra, 1993; Grimes *et al*, 1993; Mori, 1992; Pinedo-Vazquez, op cit.) and medicines (e.g. Balick and Mendelson, 1992; Chopra, 1993 Grimes *et al*, 1993.).

Non-Extractive Values
Research on non-extractive values is concerned with placing values on the ecological functions of trees such as watershed protection (e.g. Cruz *et al.*, 1988; Magrath and Arens, 1989; Ruitenbeek, 1989), carbon sequestration (e.g. Brown and Pearce, 1994; Pearce and Warford, 1993) and recreation and tourism (e.g. Brown and Henry, 1989; Tobias and Mendelson, 1991; Kramer *et al.*, 1995).

Preservation Value
Preservation value is the value placed by society on the preservation of natural environments. Pearce (1996) states that only one study of the preservation value of forests in the developing world has been published which was carried out by Kramer *et al.* (1995).

Developed World
Despite much of the work on forestry valuation being concerned with tropical forests there is an extensive literature focused on woodland in developed countries. Summaries of this research can be found in Wibe (1995) and Prins *et al.* (1990). Most of the research has been carried out in North America although there is a considerable body of literature from the Nordic countries and the United Kingdom (this region is considered separately below).

Wibe (1995) breaks down his summary into use values and existence values.

Use Values

Use values derive from the actual use of the environment (Pearce and Turner, 1990). The most studied non-timber benefit of forestry in developed countries is recreation with much of the work based on the seminal work of Clawson and Knetsch (1966). Wibe (1995) lists details of ninety five studies of forest recreation carried out in the USA between 1965 and 1993. These consist of studies of basic recreation such as hiking and walking (see examples such as Englin and Mendelson, 1991, Halsted *et al.* 1990, Walsh *et al.*, 1985), camping (e.g. Walsh *et al.*, 1980) and hunting of deer (e.g. Bishop *et al.*, 1988; Loomis and Cooper, 1988) and other animals. A number of studies, most of which are related to hunting, have been carried out in Canada (see Adamowicz, 1992). Research on forest recreation in the Nordic countries has focused on moose hunting (e.g. Johansson, 1990; Sodal, 1989) as well as general recreation (e.g. Mattsson, 1990). Estimates of the value of trees as carbon sinks have also been made in developed countries (e.g. Sedjo, 1989; van Kooten *et al.*, 1993) as have studies of forest management for increased water yields (Bowes *et al.*, 1986).

Existence Values

Existence Values are values that humans place on the environment due to a sense of stewardship or responsibility for preserving it. Wibe (1995) outlines a number of studies which value this sense of stewardship including a study by Kriström (1989) which measures the value people place on preserving virgin forests in Sweden and a study by Johansson (1989) which assesses the value that Swedes place on endangered species in Swedish forests.

Great Britain

British literature deserves a separate section in this review because of its relevance to the Irish case. This is because much of the research has been concerned with plantation forestry, which is the area of concern of this book, and also because Irish and British climate and geography are similar.

The first in-depth cost benefit analysis of forestry in Britain was an interdepartmental study published in 1972 which was "designed to clarify what the nation gets in return for accepting such low rates of return" as shown in financial analyses of forest investments (H.M. Treasury, 1972). This analysis included estimates of the general amenity services of the nation's forests as well as an estimate of the cost of reduced water flow due to forestry. The study concluded that it was not justified to value the wildlife benefits of the forests.

In a study published in 1991, Pearce provided a most useful framework for analysing investments in forestry using the Total Economic Value method. In calculating the rate of return to eight silvicultural options he included just two externalities, i.e. recreation and carbon fixation. However, while not valued, the costs that forestry may impose on the water supply were analysed in an impact matrix. Bateman (1992) attempted to calculate the Total Economic Value of Government investment in forestry in Great Britain. His calculations included the use value of preservation based upon studies in other countries but excluded water impacts and existence values. Whiteman (1991) undertook a cost-benefit analysis of forest replanting in East England using ten forest districts as a sample. While the study was a financial analysis it did include estimates for recreation, carbon fixation, use value of nature conservation, and water effects. Whiteman and Sinclair (1994), undertook a similar study of three community forests in England. London Economics (1993) examined the costs and benefits of the National Forest which included values of recreational benefits, landscape effects and carbon sequestration benefits. An interesting analysis of twenty five years of forestry cost benefit analysis in Britain can be found in Price (1997).

The studies above lean on a substantial and growing body of research on individual forest externalities which includes such works as Anderson (1991) and Price and Willis (1993) on carbon sequestration, Willis, Benson and Whitby (1988), Willis and Benson (1989), Hanley (1989), Benson and Willis (1990), Benson and Willis (1991), Willis and Garrod (1991), and Bateman *et al.* (1995) on recreation, Barrow *et al.* (1986) on water, Hanley and Common (1987), Hanley and Craig (1991) and Hanley and Ruffell (1993) on preservation use values, and Garrod and Willis (1992), Willis and Garrod (1992) and John Clegg and Co. (1993) on landscape values.

Among the few studies of existence values are Hanley and Craig (1991) and Hanley *et al.* (1996).

Ireland
It is worth outlining all the literature on the economics of forestry in Ireland, given that this is the country in question in this study. The key literature is limited to approximately fifteen works.

One of the first studies since the foundation of the State was that of H. J. Gray in 1963 which looked at the financial returns to forestry but did not refer to non-market costs or benefits. Convery (1972) examined the changes in employment and income that would occur if agriculture were to be replaced by forestry. However, although the social efficiency of the alternative investments was analysed, the analysis did not include estimates of externalities.

The most detailed financial appraisal of state forestry in Ireland was undertaken in a confidential study by the Forest and Wildlife Service (1974). This provided details of the rates of return to a sample of sites. While it made adjustments for what it called the social effects of the use of labour and land, it did not include any estimates of environmental externalities. Rea (1976) undertook a profitability analysis of the development of a pulpwood industry in Ireland. However, the external effects of timber production were not analysed.

Hickey and Bulfin (1978) contrasted the private rates of return to forestry on different site types in Leitrim with the returns to agriculture. However, non-market costs and benefits were excluded from the analysis.

The most comprehensive published work on forestry in Ireland is NESC report no. 46 (Convery, 1979) which covers most areas of forest policy, yet while it refers to forest externalities, these are not quantified.

In November 1985, the Review Group on Forestry published a report (Review Group on Forestry, 1985) to the Minister for Fisheries and Forestry which included an estimated value of the forests under the ownership of the State at that time. However, the costs and benefits measured excluded all externalities. Bulfin (1987) undertook an analysis of the economics of private planting of forestry in disadvantaged areas but this did not include non-market values.

Convery (1988) analysed the rate of return to a hypothetical privately afforested site in the Republic of Ireland. While he makes reference to the amenity aspects of forestry, his analysis was purely financial thus omitting estimates for externalities. O'Connor and Kearney (1993) followed a similar approach and, when analysing the impact of forestry on rural communities, the same authors also omitted externalities from the analysis (Kearney and O'Connor, 1993) and did not use shadow pricing. In a thematic evaluation of EU financed forestry measures, duQuesne (1993) made no attempt to value external costs and benefits.

Clinch (1994) used a representative sample of actual sites planted and detailed sensitivity analysis to examine the rates of return that can be expected on sites privately afforested under the Forestry Operational Programme 1989-93. While this was the most in-depth analysis of the *financial* returns from forestry in Ireland, the analysis was from the point of view of the private investor so that externalities were excluded.

In its strategic plan for the forestry sector, the Department of Agriculture, Food and Forestry (1996) gave an estimate of £21 million for annual non-timber benefits of Irish forests, however, no estimates are included for external costs and the method of calculation of the benefits is not explained[8].

There has only been one piece of research which attempts to provide data on the external benefits of forestry. This was part of a project exploring the socio-economic impact of afforestation on rural development (Ní Dhubháin et al., 1994). The study provided an estimate of the recreational value of the present forest estate using travel cost and on-site contingent valuation. In addition, the study made an important first step in assessing the value of alternative options for increasing afforestation using contingent valuation. However, the sample size of 75 people is not large enough to be considered representative of the population. The authors themselves suggest that the work should be considered as "a very detailed pilot study".

---

[8] It is thought that this figure is the result a rather suspect benefits transfer approach.

CONCLUSIONS

The results from the literature on the Total Economic Value of forestry suggest that externalities are significant and can sometimes be of magnitudes greater than the timber benefits of forests. This illustrates the need to include them in any analysis of the efficiency of investments in forestry. Yet, as pointed out in Chapter 1, despite the investment of billions of pounds of taxpayers' money in forestry in Ireland, no attempt has been made to provide a reliable estimate of the externalities associated with forestry.

While it has been shown that there is a substantial literature on the economic value of forestry in other countries, most of the research is related to deforestation and the associated loss of non-timber benefits. In Ireland, the nature of forestry is markedly different. Temperate commercial afforestation brings with it quite different externalities and the consideration of external costs is most important. While some of the British literature focuses on this type of forestry, most of the valuation is of non-market benefits alone and much of the literature is site specific and cannot be applied to Ireland. Literature which values the external costs of forestry is extremely rare.

CHAPTER 3

METHODOLOGY

This study employs a case study approach. The most comprehensive and costly investment in afforestation ever undertaken in Ireland will take place as part of the Government's Strategic Plan (the 'Strategy') for the Forestry Sector in Ireland. The "Strategic Goal" of the Strategy is "to develop forestry to a scale and in a manner which maximises its contribution to national well-being on a sustainable basis and which is compatible with the protection of the environment" (Department of Agriculture, Food and Forestry, 1996).

The principal elements of the Strategy include:

- afforesting 25,000 ha per annum from 1996 to 2000 and then 20,000 ha per annum thereafter until 2030;
- an increase in the total productive forest area from 464,000 ha to 1.2 m ha;
- 80 percent of the trees planted would be conifers, 20 percent broadleaves;
- the total cost of the project would amount to more than £3 billion over 34 years. The project would be cost shared by the EU at a rate of 75 percent. The money will finance afforestation subsidies.

Details of planting and financial statistics of the Strategy are given in Appendix 1, Tables A1.2. and A1.3 respectively.

The Total Economic Value of the afforestation financed under this programme is estimated using both market and non-market valuation procedures. The estimates are then included in a Cost Benefit Analysis in order to test the hypothesis that the investment in afforestation under this programme is socially efficient. The implications of the results for policy are then analysed, conclusions are drawn and areas for future research are suggested.

The remainder of this chapter explains the techniques used to estimate the economic value of investments in forestry. This section may be skipped should the reader be willing to trust that the techniques used are based on widely accepted and best practise! Details of a more technical nature are provided in Appendix 2.

COST BENEFIT ANALYSIS

Cost Benefit Analysis (CBA) is applied welfare economics. It is a way of organising and analysing data as an aid to thinking. It provides a set of procedures for comparing benefits and costs and is traditionally associated with government intervention and with the evaluation of government action and government projects (Zerbe and Dively, 1994). Price (1997) defines it as the appraisal of all the costs and all the benefits, whether marketed or not, to whomsoever accruing, both present and future, in so far as possible in a common unit of account.

The underlying rationale for CBA is rational choice, i.e. a rational agent will weigh up the costs and benefits of any proposed activity and will only undertake the activity if the benefits exceed the costs. The basic principle is simple, if one has to decide whether to do A or not, the rule is: do A if the benefits of this action exceed the benefits of the next best alternative action. This can be simplified further by referring to the next best alternative to A as the cost of undertaking A (the opportunity cost) and hence the rule becomes: do A if its benefits exceed its costs, and not otherwise (Layard and Glaister, 1994). However, CBA differs from financial analysis in that it assess the costs and benefits to the whole of society rather than to a portion of society. In this study, that society is considered to be the population of Ireland.

History of Cost Benefit Analysis
Detailed histories of CBA can be found in Pearce and Nash (1981) and Hanley and Spash (1993), however, the essence is as follows: in 1808, the US Secretary of the Treasury, Albert Gallatin, gave what is believed to be the first recommendation for the employment of CBA in public decision making when he suggested that the costs and benefits of water related projects should be compared. In 1936, the US Flood Control Act introduced welfare economics into public decision making by deeming flood control projects as desirable if "the benefits to whomsoever they may accrue, are in excess of the costs". Thus, unlike financial appraisal, CBA is concerned with the costs and benefits to *society*. In 1950, after a debate on the foundations of CBA in welfare economics, the US Federal Inter-Agency River Basin Committee published a guide to CBA known as the Green Book. From then on there was a considerable interest in CBA and the development of cost benefit rules with seminal contributions by Marglin *et al.* (1972), Little and Mirrlees (1968; 1974) and Squire and van der Tak (1975). Mishan (in 1971 - see Mishan, 1988) provided a discussion of theoretical issues. A historical perspective of the rise and fall of CBA was given by Little and Mirrless in 1994 (Little and Mirrlees, 1994). While the distortions created by government intervention in the 1970s provided much room for the application of CBA, Honohan (1995) points out that the technique went through a lull in the early 1980s when structural reform replaced piecemeal intervention and it was thought that this would address market failures. However, CBA has made a come-back since then mainly as a result of increased public awareness of environmental degradation and the associated demand that this cost be accounted for in analyses of projects and policies.

Cost Benefit Methodology

<u>Welfare Criterion</u>
In using CBA to assess the costs and benefits of a project or policy to society, it is first necessary to define the social efficiency criterion. This study relies predominantly on allocative efficiency as a measure of social efficiency. Allocative efficiency reflects the possibility of reallocating resources so as to achieve an increase in the net value of output produced by those resources and is measured using the Kaldor-Hicks test (Kaldor, 1939 and Hicks, 1939).

The Kaldor-Hicks test embodies the potential compensation principle. Kaldor categorised an action as efficient if those who gain from the action could compensate the losers and still be better off. Hicks framed the question slightly differently and labelled the action efficient if the potential losers from the action could compensate the potential beneficiaries of the action for not going ahead. In both cases the action is an improvement *regardless of whether the compensation is actually paid*. The potential compensation principle differs from the welfare criterion known as Pareto Optimality which requires that an action which makes one person better off leaves nobody else feeling worse off. For an investment to pass the Pareto Optimality test, compensation must be paid to those bearing the costs so as to leave them indifferent between their welfare *ex post* and *ex ante*. Most policies and investments leave somebody worse off and thus most would fail to meet the Pareto criterion. However, Freeman (1993) points out that the Kaldor-Hicks criterion is essentially one of *potential* Pareto improvement since if the compensation were paid nobody would be worse off.

Whether or not this potential payment is enough to show that a project is good for society has been the matter of much debate but the reader of this book will be spared the details. Suffice to say that, as Layard and Walters (1994) suggest, despite the shortcomings of the Kaldor-Hicks criterion, it is often useful to measure the effects of a change in the total value of output independently of the distribution of output, however, in judging the social efficiency of a project equity aspects should also be considered. A two part test would be best whereby, as suggested by Little (1957), a project or policy is put to the Kaldor-Hicks test and then tested to see if it improves the distribution of income. Approaches that consider questions of equity[9] therefore allow the possibility of acceptance of a project or policy which returns a negative figure for the sum of individual welfare changes if the gains from income distribution outweigh these losses. However, the difficulty when considering equity is the assignment of weights to individual welfare changes according to the relative 'deservingness' of the different individuals (Freeman, 1993). Given this difficulty, this study does not attempt to explicitly address equity considerations in an attempt to judge 'deservingness'.

---

[9] See Pearce and Nash, 1981 and Layard and Glaister, 1994 for an outline of various approaches.

Welfare Measures
In order to assess the costs and benefits of a project or policy it is necessary to examine the strength of consumers' preferences for or against the project (Pearce and Nash, 1981). The standard approach is to measure the benefit an individual obtains from a project or policy by the maximum willingness to pay on his or her part for such a benefit or the maximum willingness to accept compensation for not getting such a benefit. Similarly, a cost can be measured by the maximum willingness to pay on the part of an individual to avoid such a cost or the maximum willingness to accept compensation for such a cost being imposed on them. A technical explanation of welfare measures in contained in Appendix 2.

Temporal Considerations
Account must be taken of the fact that costs and benefits arise at different time periods. Thus future costs and benefits must be discounted so they can be compared with present costs and benefits. A technical discussion of discounting and its controversies is contained in Appendix 2.

The rate of return to an investment in forestry is strongly affected by the discount rate given the long time span involved. Thus, the choice of discount rate is most important. Yet, with the enormous literature on discounting it seems a difficult task to calculate the social rate of discount. However, since economists have been unable to provide a definitive figure for the social rate of discount, it has become something to be chosen rather than something that is measured (Heal, 1981) and as Leslie (1989) states, "all views on discount rates are opinions". In reality, the discount rate used to assess government projects is chosen via the political system. Hanley and Spash (1993) state that the UK rate of 5 percent that was used until recent years was a compromise arrived at by civil servants as a value lying somewhere between the rate of return on private investments and the consumption rate of interest. This 5 percent rate is used by the Irish civil service[10]. More recent UK Treasury guidelines for the opportunity cost of public investment take the rate of return to marginal private sector investment as 6 percent. For pricing output sold commercially public sector agencies are expected to achieve a required average rate of return of 8 percent to be consistent with the private sector (Newbery, 1992).

In the USA recommended rates for investment projects vary. The Office of Management and Budget recommends a rate of 10 percent while the General Accounting Office prefers a rate of 2.5 percent based on government bond yields (Cline, 1993). The World Bank uses an 8 percent rate in project analysis and, while two of their employees (Birdsall and Steer, 1993) recognise that the opportunity cost of capital may be lower in industrialised countries, they recommend a rate of at least 6 percent.

---

[10] Department of Finance, 1994.

The UK Treasury makes an exception for the Forestry Commission, which is required to have a real target rate of return of 3 percent and if non-market benefits are included a rate of 6 percent is suggested (Newbery, 1992). In Ireland, the Review Group on Forestry (1985) considered a real rate of return of 3 percent to be "desirable and achievable" (although State forestry was estimated to have a real rate of return of just 2 percent at that time).

Given the conflicting views of the magnitude of the social rate of discount, this study adopts the standard practice of using a number of 'test' discount rates. The World Bank's rate of 10 percent is taken as an upper bound and the Review Group's target of 3 percent is taken as the lower bound. The Department of Finance rate of 5 percent is used as an appropriate rate for policy analysis. Results using zero percent and 8 percent discount rates are also reported.

Uncertainty

Investments with long time horizons are subject to uncertainty, particularly in relation to future prices. Sensitivity analysis is used in this study to account for uncertainty whereby results are calculated for various scenarios. In relation to public goods such as forest recreation, it is assumed that using the contingent valuation method will capture the option value[11] people place on these goods (see below).

Shadow Prices

Shadow prices must be used when there are distortions within an economy which render certain prices invalid as indicators of social opportunity costs or values (Drèze and Stern, 1994).

In the real world, market prices may not reflect the social value of goods or services because of distortions in the market such as monopoly power (which inflates price), indirect taxes and subsidies (unless they are correcting some other distortion) and unemployment. Thus, when calculating each value of a project, it is necessary to assess the appropriateness of using the market value and, where necessary, these values should be adjusted for market distortions. It is important to note that just as market prices vary over time, so too will shadow prices.

A technical discussion of shadow prices is contained in Appendix 2.

Externalities and Public Goods

Shadow prices adjust for one form of market failure. However, a CBA must also take into account the existence of externalities and public goods. An external cost (benefit) is a cost (benefit) resulting from an activity which is not borne (captured) by the person engaging in that activity. These externalities can be placed in two categories:

---

[11] This concept is defined under Total Economic Value below.

a) Depletable Externalities such as drift wood from a ship (an external benefit) which, if consumed by one individual, is not available for consumption by any other individual. There are few examples of this type of externality;

b) Undepletable Externalities such as poor air quality (an external cost) which is harmful to the population of a town will be equally harmful to each person even if the town's population were to grow. Most externalities feature this 'non-rivalry' in consumption.

A Public Good is both non-rivalry in consumption but also has 'non-exclusion' as a feature, e.g. even if a lighthouse is provided for one ship, it is not possible to exclude other ships from benefiting from its provision. In some cases, public goods can exhibit rivalry in consumption past a certain point e.g. a public park may be a public good when there are only a few people using it but congestion may set in after a certain point, this could be thought of as an 'impure' public good. A Public Bad is something which even at a zero price, consumers would wish to have less of it (Freeman, 1993) such as some activity which has a negative effect on the landscape.

The State provides many public goods due to the difficulty of excluding people from consumption and the associated incentive to free ride. In the case of externalities, the market system unchecked will cause a misallocation of resources. If, by undertaking an activity, individual A imposes a cost on individual B, the cost to individual A of undertaking that activity, the private cost, does not include the cost to individual B. Thus, there is a divergence between the private cost of the activity and the cost to society, i.e.

$$\text{Social Cost} = \text{Private Cost} + \text{External Cost} \qquad (3.1)$$

If, by undertaking an activity, individual A confers a benefit on individual B, the benefit to individual A of undertaking that activity, the private benefit, does not include the benefit to individual B. Thus, there is a divergence between the private benefit of the activity the benefit to society, i.e.

$$\text{Social Benefit} = \text{Private Benefit} + \text{External Benefit} \qquad (3.2)$$

An individual undertaking an activity that produces an external cost will, if not forced to bear that cost, engage in a higher level of the activity than is socially optimal. Conversely, an individual undertaking an activity that produces an external benefit will, if not compensated for that benefit, engage in a level of that activity that is below the socially optimal level. For a more complete discussion of externalities, the reader is referred to Baumol and Oates (1988).

This sub-optimal outcome in the presence of externalities can be explained in the context of the rotation of a forest. For example, if the benefits of carbon storage by trees were appropriated by forest owners, the forest rotation would be longer as larger trees store more carbon. However, because such a benefit accrues to society as a whole rather than to the forest owner, there is no incentive for him or her to delay clearfelling the forest. A mathematical treatment of the effect of externalities on the optimal forest rotation is contained in Appendix 2.

The existence of forestry externalities makes it essential to use what is known as the Total Economic Value approach when carrying out a CBA.

TOTAL ECONOMIC VALUE

The Total Economic Value (TEV) approach expands the traditional Neoclassical concepts of value to include option values and existence values. Environmental assets such as forests have both 'use' and 'non-use' values. Use values derive from the actual use of the asset. These values can be broken down further into direct use values such as timber from a forest and indirect use values such as the value of a forest for carbon sequestration. Direct and indirect use values can be combined and called 'actual use' value (Pearce and Turner, 1990). Another use value is 'option value'. This notion of option value was first put forward by Weisbrod (1964). Friedman (1962) had suggested that, if a national park closed down when run by a profit maximising entrepreneur because gate receipts would not cover operating costs, this is not a failure of the market. However, Weisbrod pointed out that this decision would ignore an option value, i.e. people would be "willing to pay something for the option to consume the commodity in the future" since "there is no practical mechanism by which the entrepreneur can charge non-users for this option". Thus, "user charges are an inadequate guide to the total value of the park". In his seminal piece *Conservation Reconsidered*, Krutilla (1967) defined option demand as "a willingness to pay for retaining an option to use an area or facility that would be difficult or impossible to replace and for which no close substitute is available. Moreover, such a demand may exist even though there is no current intention to use the area or facility in question and the option may never be exercised". Option value[12] can be broken down into a number of components (Pearce and Turner,1990): the value individuals place on the preservation of an asset so that they may have the option of using it in the future (value of future options for the individual), the value they attach to preserving the asset because it can be used by others[13] ('vicarious value'), and the value they attach to preserving the asset so that future generations have the option of using it ('bequest value'). Thus, total use value is defined as,

Total use value = Direct use value + Indirect use value + Option value   (3.3)

where

---

[12] The reader is referred to an excellent exposition on option value by Bishop (1982).

[13] In the late eighteenth century, Adam Smith in his *Theory of Moral Sentiments* (1790) drew attention to this "sympathy principle" (Kriström, 1990).

Option value = Value of future options for the individual + Vicarious value + Bequest value   (3.4)

Non-use values are 'existence' values. Existence values reflect the benefit to individuals of the existence of an environmental asset although those individuals do not actually use the asset. These values may exist due to sympathy for animals and plants and/or some human approximation of the intrinsic value of nature, i.e. these values reflect a sense of stewardship on the part of humans towards the environment. Evidence of these values is shown in the willingness of people to contribute to charities which preserve wildlife. While many of the donors are unlikely to ever see these animals in the flesh, they just value the fact that they exist. Krutilla (1967) first introduced the concept of existence value: "there are many persons who obtain satisfaction from mere knowledge that part of wilderness North America remains even though they would be appalled by the prospect of being exposed to it". There has been some disagreement regarding existence values. McConnell (1983) sees the concept as "far fetched" and that "existence value occurs only insofar as bequest or altruistic notions prevail", thus it is a use value. However, it is clear that individuals often contribute to animal charities not because they want animals to be preserved for others or for future generations but because they gain utility themselves from knowing that the animals are being preserved. Thus, following Krutilla's definition, existence value is classed as a non-use value such that Total Economic Value (TEV) is defined as:

$$TEV = \text{Actual use value} + \text{Option value} + \text{Existence value}   (3.5)$$

It is important to note that the TEV approach attempts to encapsulate all aspects of a resource which enter into *human's* utility functions, i.e. it is anthropomorphic. Thus, it does not attempt to find an intrinsic value for the environment where 'intrinsic' means the value that resides in something which is unrelated to human beings altogether (Pearce and Turner, 1990), however, it does attempt to include the intrinsic value which humans bestow on nature.

There is no agreement on the exact breakdown of the values in the TEV framework, however, the important thing in CBA is to account as best as possible for all these values. Following closely the analysis of Pearce (1991), a forest can have the following outputs:

1. T = Timber values;
2. G = Carbon sequestration (reducing the 'greenhouse effect');
3. W_f = Restriction of water flow;
4. W_p = Water pollution (by forestry practice or 'acidification stripping');
5. R = Recreation;
6. A = Biodiversity/Wildlife Value (as a habitat);
7. L = Landscape Value (aesthetic value);

8. S = Economic Security (avoidance of uncertainty regarding the supply of timber from abroad);

9. C_s = Community Integrity (avoidance of the decline of rural communities).

Thus the benefit (B) of afforestation is measured by,

$$B = T + G + W_f + W_p + R + A + L + S + C_s \qquad (3.6)$$

Some of these components may be negative, i.e. external costs are included as negative benefits.

In order to assess the efficiency of the project using CBA, the costs of the inputs into afforestation must be subtracted from these benefits as shown earlier.

Since externalities are not captured within markets, they do not have an obvious 'price' which can be included in a CBA. Thus, what are known as "non-market" valuation methods must be used to calculate some of the components of TEV.

NON-MARKET VALUATION METHODS

Table 3.1 shows a classification system for forest benefits and the appropriate techniques for valuing them.

TABLE 3.1 Classification of Forest Benefits.

Total Economic Value			
Direct use values	*Indirect use values*	*Option values*	*Existence values*
Timber	Biodiversity	Biodiversity	Biodiversity
Recreation	Water Restriction	Recreation	Landscape
Biodiversity	Water Pollution	Community Stability	
Economic Security	Carbon Sinking		
Landscape	Community Stability		
Valuation Technique			
Market prices	Production function	Contingent	Contingent
Hedonic prices	approaches	valuation	valuation
Travel cost			

Source: Adapted from Pearce, 1991.

Production Function Approaches
Production Function Approaches are indirect methods of valuing externalities. Environmental goods often enter into the production functions of firms and households e.g. a fishery combines water quality with purchased inputs. Thus,

if forestry causes a deterioration in water quality production of fish will be reduced. This cost can be estimated in two ways:

1.   By the cost of the increase in other inputs which would be necessary to achieve the same level of output after the reduction in water quality as before e.g. by liming a river to reduce acidification (Defensive Expenditures/ Avoided Cost Approach) or by the cost of restoring the damage done e.g. restocking a river (Replacement Cost).

2.   By the value of productivity changes, i.e. the value of the lost output of fish (Dose-Response Functions);

These techniques are outlined in greater detail in Appendix 2.

Contingent Valuation

The Contingent Valuation Method (CVM) is the only direct non-market valuation approach. The CVM collects preference information by asking households how much they are willing to pay for some change in the provision of a public good, or the minimum compensation they would require if the change was not carried out (Johansson, 1993). The advantage of the CVM is that, unlike other methods, it can elicit option and existence values.

<u>CVM Steps</u>
A Contingent Valuation (CV) study consists of the careful selection of a sample which is considered to be representative of the population whose valuation of a public good is being elicited. The interview technique is then selected (face-to-face, telephone or mail) and a questionnaire is developed. This questionnaire contains (Mitchell and Carson, 1989):

1.   A detailed description of the good being valued and the hypothetical circumstance under which it is made available to the respondent, i.e. the researcher constructs a hypothetical market which is communicated to the respondent in a realistic scenario including a plausible method of payment.

2.   Questions which elicit the respondents' willingness to pay for the good being valued. These are constructed to facilitate the valuation process.

3.   Questions about the respondents' characteristics (e.g. age and income), their preferences relevant to the good being values (e.g. how concerned or interested are they in the environment), and their use of the good. This information is used in a regression equation for the good. If these variables 'explain' the valuations of the individuals as the theory would suggest then this is a partial test of reliability.

The study is pre-tested using a pilot survey and then the full survey is carried out. The mean and median willingness to pay (accept) can then be calculated and the results generalised to the population.

The CVM is the most controversial of all non-market valuation methods. Therefore, a detailed explanation of the method and the controversies surrounding it is contained in Appendix 2.

Hedonic Pricing and Travel Cost
As with production function approaches, the Hedonic Price Method (HPM) and the Travel Cost Method (TCM) are indirect benefit measures. While these methods are not employed in this study, reference is made to them and thus, it is worth providing a brief explanation.

The HPM developed by Griliches (1971) and Rosen (1974) is used to estimate the implicit prices of the characteristics which differentiate closely related products (Johansson, 1993). The value of an asset is measured by the stream of benefits which flow therefrom. This is best explained using an example. The value of a forest park will be partially reflected in the difference in price between a house beside the park and one further away from the park. However, in addition, the price of the house is likely to be a function of a number of other variables. The extent to which changes in the environmental variable (the forest park) 'explains' changes in the property price can be estimated by econometric techniques and people's willingness to pay for the environmental commodity can then be derived.

The TCM uses costs of travel to an environmental asset as a proxy for the value of that asset. This was first proposed by Hotelling but first used by Clawson in 1959 (see Clawson and Knetsch, 1966). In the example of the forest park, the recreational value can be estimated using the direct costs of people's travel to the site such as petrol, depreciation of their car etc. and the opportunity cost of the trip, i.e. time. These costs reflect the willingness to pay on the part the individuals for a site visit. The sum of the consumer surpluses gives the recreational value of the forest park.

Neither HPM nor TCM are employed in this book since these methods are more useful in the analysis of site specific case studies. In addition, neither of these methods can estimate satisfactorily existence values. Thus, in this study, CVM is used to estimate option value, existence value and future use value while production function approaches are used to estimate other externalities. In this way double counting is avoided as best as possible.

CONCLUSIONS

In conclusion, before embarking on the analysis, it is important to note the limits of the scope of this study: the efficiency criteria employed is based on the Kaldor-Hicks *potential* compensation principle and, therefore, distributional issues are ignored. In addition, the concept of economic value includes only human values.

CHAPTER 4

POLICY INSTRUMENTS

This chapter examines the policy instruments which are employed to promote and control forestry in Ireland.

LEGISLATIVE FRAMEWORK AND ORGANISATIONAL STRUCTURE

The Forestry Acts of 1946 and 1988 provide the legislative framework for forestry in Ireland. Overall responsibility for forestry rests with the Department of Agriculture, Food and Forestry and is discharged by a division of the Department known as the Forest Service (Department of Agriculture, Food and Forestry, 1996). Its responsibilities include overall forest strategy, administration of grant and premium schemes, and forestry awareness and promotion.

Coillte Teoranta, a semi-state company established under the Forestry Act of 1988, manages the State's forests on a commercial basis. The company owns approximately 70 percent of the forest area and is actively engaged in afforestation.

PUBLIC INFORMATION

Public information with regard to forestry is provided by the Forest Service. The Service provides information on grant and premium schemes for forestry and also provides separate leaflets which outline guidelines with regard to forestry and its impact the environment (see below). Information on grant schemes is also provided in the Department of Agriculture, Food and Forestry's Schemes and Services brochure[14]. Information on taxation provisions as described below is also freely available. The Forest Service provides no information on expected returns to afforestation and does not publish statistics on private or public forestry. Information on most aspects of forestry is very difficult to acquire.

ENVIRONMENTAL REGULATION

Planning Regulations
Under Section 4 of the Local Government (Planning and Development) Act of 1963, the use of land for forestry is exempt from the need for planning

---

[14] Department of Agriculture, Food and Forestry, 1995.

permission except in the case of the following forestry developments which require an Environmental Impact Assessment (EIA) (Department of the Environment, 1997a):

- Initial afforestation where the area involved, either on its own or taken together with any adjacent area planted by or on behalf of the applicant within the previous three years, would result in a total area planted exceeding 70 hectares. An area is deemed to be adjacent if its nearest point lies within 500 metres if any part of the area involved;
- the replacement of broadleaved high forest by conifer species where the area involved would be greater than 10 ha.

The first threshold was reduced from 200 ha by the Minister for the Environment on 1st October, 1996 in response to concerns regarding the effect of afforestation on the environment, as were the procedures regarding plantations built up on an incremental basis. The other initiatives announced include (Department of the Environment, 1996, 1997a):

- A system of notification of local authorities for all applications for grant aid of projects over 25 ha. However, the Forest Service will remain responsible for final decision on the application;
- Local authorities have been asked to designate areas as sensitive to afforestation with regard to landscape, water quality, rural isolation and protection of the natural and archaeological heritage by the end of March 1997[15]. Once these designations have been made, the Forest Service will notify the local authorities of *all* proposals for afforestation in these designated areas regardless of size. Once again, the Forest Service will remain responsible for the final decision on the application;
- It has been suggested that each local authority develop an indicative forest strategy for their area;
- The EIA thresholds are to be reviewed in 1999.

In addition, afforestation proposals which include areas listed in the Sites and Monuments Records of the Department of Arts, Culture and the Gaeltacht are subject to the agreement of the Department (Department of the Environment, 1997a).

The Forest Strategy (Department of Agriculture, Food and Forestry, 1996) has amended the minimum distance between grant assisted afforestation and dwellings, buildings and roads as follows:

- Dwellings/Buildings: 60 metres in place of the current 30 metres except with the agreement of the owner, where a 30 metre rule will apply;

---

[15] As of May 1997 this deadline has passed and the areas have not been designated as yet.

- Public Roads: 20 metres for conifers, 10 metres for broadleaves.

Forest Service Guidelines

Guidelines regarding forestry and fisheries, archaeology, and the landscape (as shown in Table 4.1) are provided to those who apply for grant-aid. Implementation of the Guidelines is a general condition of grant aid in every case. Certain forestry contractors, including Coillte, are allowed to carry out the assessment process on the ground and they must indicate to the Forest Service whether the work complies with the three sets of guidelines. In all other cases, the assessment is carried out by the Forest Service. A certain percentage of the cases are inspected at various stages by Forest Service inspectors with a view to inspecting every site (including those belonging to Coillte) at least once in its first four years of the rotation. Forest plantations are subject to the provisions of the Forestry Act 1946 which controls the felling of trees and a felling licence is required before the trees can be clearfelled. The effectiveness of the guidelines and the inspection system is unclear as, unlike in Britain, no ex post evaluation of the guidelines has been carried out.

In the Forest Strategy, the Forest Service commits itself to producing new guidelines covering wildlife and habitat diversity, harvesting and clear felling, amenity and recreation, and the use of chemicals and herbicides.

TABLE 4.1. Forest Service Guidelines.

Brochure Title	Publication Date
Forestry and Fisheries	January, 1992
Forestry and Archaeology	January, 1992
Forestry and Landscape	September, 1992

Source: Forest Service, 1994b.

Land Categorisation

There are a number of categories of sites designated as environmentally sensitive which have implications for afforestation. Hickie (1996) provides a full list and explanation of the designations. The scope of each of these designation is shown in Table 4.2.

Natural Heritage Areas (NHAs) have been designated with the objective of conserving plants, animals and wildlife habitats under the forthcoming Wildlife Act (Amendment Bill). NHAs encompass all other designations. The Forestry Operational Programme (Government of Ireland, 1991) specifically excluded areas of ecological importance (now identified as NHAs) and therefore, the Forest Service has generally refused to give grants for afforestation in these areas (Hickie, 1996). A map of the NHAs can be found in Appendix 3.

Special Areas of Conservation (SACs) have been designated with the intention of conserving plants, animals and wildlife habitats of EU importance under EU Directive 92/42/EEC (Habitats Directive) with responsibility resting with the National Parks and Wildlife Service, the Department of Arts, Culture and the

Gaeltacht and the Commission of the European Communities.   SACs will effectively result in land owners having to apply to the EU if they wish to engage in any potentially damaging land use activity.   It is therefore be expected that afforestation will be ruled out in all of these areas except where it involves the maintenance or restoration of natural habitat.   In addition, the Habitats Directive prohibits activities which take place outside SACs but which may damage them (Hickie, 1996).

Special Protection Areas (SPAs) are designated under the Birds Directive.   The habitat requirements of listed bird species must be taken into account in development activities, including development in areas outside designated sites (Hickie, 1996).

TABLE 4.2. Scope of Environmental Designations.

Designation	Number	Coverage (Proposed)
Natural Heritage Area	1,251	400,000ha (approx 6% land)
Special Area of Conservation	approx 400	100,000ha
Special Protection Area	74	157,628 ha
Statutory Nature Reserve	78	18,095 ha
National Park	5	33,956 ha
Refuge for Fauna	7	figures not available
Wildfowl Sanctuary	68	figures not available
Ramsar Site	21	12,562 ha
Biogenetic Reserve	14	6,587 ha
UNESCO Biosphere Reserve	2	11,500 ha
Salmonid Water	22	n/a
Sensitive Areas for Urban Wastewater	10	n/a
Sensitive Areas for Fisheries and Forestry	n/a	approx 5% land
Special Control in County Development Plans	n/a	figures not available
Special Amenity Area Order	2	under 2,000 ha
Tree Preservation Order	151	n/a
World Heritage Site	1	780 ha
Environmentally Sensitive Area	2	7,653 ha
Designated Areas under Rural Environmental Protection Scheme	n/a	West Mayo and Galway, parts of Donegal, Sligo and Kerry. All NHAs and Salmonid Waters

Source: Hickie, 1996.

PRICE INCENTIVES

There is no price support for timber in Ireland or in the EU.

FISCAL INCENTIVES

Sources and Extent of Funding

Costs of afforestation are subsidised primarily by the EU and thereafter by the Irish Government. The Community Strategy and Action Programme for the Forestry Sector[16] summarises EU forestry policy (duQuesne, 1993):

- to provide an alternative land-use to reduce food surplus in the Union;
- to develop employment and arrest population declines in rural areas;
- to protect existing forests;
- to reduce the Union's trade deficit in timber and forest products[17].

The Western Package

Pressure by the Irish Government on the European Commission led to the first direct EU supported grant aid for forestry being introduced in Ireland in 1981 with the introduction of the *Western Package Forestry Scheme*. This was a ten year package introduced to address problems of development in the rural areas of twelve western counties covered by the Agricultural Development Programme under Regulation (EEC) no. 1820/80. Total investment under the Western Package was £41.63 m. Public sector investment was £17.473 m, private sector investment was £9.365 m and EC aid totalled £17.793 m (Mulloy, 1992). A summary of the impact of the Western Package is shown in Table 4.3.

TABLE 4.3. Western Package Achievements.

	Private	*Public*	*Total*
Afforestation			
Area (ha)	23,403	5,840	29,243
Cost (£)	29.650 m	11.667 m	41.31 m
Private Forest Roads			
Cost (£)		321,000	
EC Funding (£)		135,000	
Total Programme Cost (£)			
	41.631 m		

Source: Mulloy, 1992.

The Forestry Operational Programme 1989-1993

The Single European Act which came into operation in July 1987 provided the impetus for an increase in EU structural funding and this combined with a

---

[16] Document COM(88) 255 final.

[17] This objective became more-or-less redundant when Sweden and Finland joined the EU.

continuing timber deficit in the member states led to the introduction of the Forestry Operational Programme 1989-1993 (Government of Ireland, 1991) funded by the European Community Support Framework and the consequent National Development Plan (of 1989).

The Forestry Operational Programme covered the whole of Ireland and lasted five years (terminating in December 1993). Measures included: afforestation, woodland improvement and reconstruction, forest roads, harvesting and back-up measures. The total cost amounted to £163.24 m (Government of Ireland, 1991).

Forest Premium Scheme
The Forest Premium Scheme was introduced in 1990 to provide farmers with an extra annual payment on top of the basic grant scheme. It was later expanded to non-farmers. Full details of the present scheme are provided below.

Other Schemes
Other schemes which include some forestry components are InterReg, the Rural Development Operational programme, Stride, the Operational Programme for Science and Technology, and Eurofortech. Full details of these schemes can be found in a paper by Mulloy (1992).

Operational Programme for Agriculture, Rural Development and Forestry 1994-1999
In 1994, the Irish Government and the Commission of the European Communities agreed a second round of funding for forestry under the Operational Programme for Agriculture, Rural Development and Forestry. The total cost of the programme amounts to £108 m, 75 percent of which is funded by the EU (Government of Ireland, 1994). However, some of this money pays for second instalment grants committed by the Forest Service under the first Operational Programme.

Strategic Plan for the Development of the Forestry Sector
The Strategic Plan for the forestry sector which was published in 1996 proposes to commit over £3 billion to finance grants and premium schemes for forestry. A seventy-five percent funding rate is being sought from the EU. Details of the financial statistics of the Strategy can be found in Appendix 1, Tables A1.2 and A1.3.

Fiscal Instruments
In Ireland, schemes to promote afforestation can be categorised as follows:

(1)   Cost-sharing grant schemes;
(2)   Annual payments (forest premium scheme);
(3)   Taxation incentives to promote and maintain conversion to forest cover.

Grant Schemes

The Afforestation Grant Scheme applies to afforestation of land suitable for agriculture. The aid is given in two parts after the applicant receives pre-planting approval, an establishment grant (in the year of establishment) and a maintenance grant (after 4 years). Total grants range from £1,300 per ha to £3,000 per ha depending on the species type and quality of the land[18]. Applicants receive higher grants for planting broadleaves and/or planting land formerly used for agriculture (enclosed/improved land). The minimum areas for broadleaves and conifers are 0.1 ha and 1 ha respectively. To be eligible for the grants the planting must adhere to the environmental guidelines referred to above. Only approved tree species may be planted (Forest Service, 1994a and 1996). Afforestation grant and maintenance levels are shown in Table 4.4.

TABLE 4.4. Afforestation Grants.

	Afforestation Grant (£/ha)	Maintenance Grant (£/ha)	Total Grant (£/ha)
Unenclosed Land[1]	975	325	1,300
Enclosed and Improved Land			
Non-Diverse Species[2]	1,125	375	1,500
Diverse Species[3]	1,350	450	1,800
Broadleaf/Conifer Mixtures[4]:			
40% stocking of broadleaf	1,500	500	2,000
50% stocking of broadleaf	1,575	525	2,100
60% stocking of broadleaf	1,650	550	2,200
75-100% stocking of broadleaf	1,800	600	2,400
Oak/Beech Species[5]:			
50% stocking of Oak/Beech	1,950	650	2,600
60% stocking of Oak/Beech	2,100	700	2,800
75-100% stocking of Oak/Beech	2,250	750	3,000

Notes:
[1] Land never improved or enclosed by man made boundaries for agricultural use other than extensive grazing.
[2] *Sitka spruce* and Lodgepole Pine in excess of 60% of total area.
[3] Not more than 60% *Sitka spruce* and Lodgepole Pine and 10% broadleaves.
[4] Minimum 40% stocking of broadleaves.
[5] Minimum 50% stocking of Oak and Beech.

Source: Forest Service, 1994a.

In addition to the basic afforestation grants there is a grant schemes to promote afforestation in urban areas by local authorities and a scheme to encourage the planting of amenity forestry (see Forest Service, undated a and b).

---

[18] It is interesting to compare these grants with those provided by the Forestry Commission in Britain which are £615 to £1005 per ha for conifers and £975 to £1575 per ha for broadleaves depending on the area planted (Forest Authority, 1993). It is clear that Irish establishment grants are much more generous.

Annual Payments
The Forest Premium Scheme provides a tax free annual income to farmers and non-farmers who plant forestry. The premium levels for farmers range from £130 per ha to £300 per ha depending on the species type and former land use. Premium levels for non-farmers range from £80 per ha to £120 per ha[19]. The premium lasts for 15 and 20 years for non-farmers and farmers respectively (Forest Service, 1994a). Full details of the annual payments are given in Table 4.5.

TABLE 4.5. Forest Premium Scheme.

Farmers (£/ha/annum)				
Unenclosed Land		130		
Enclosed and Improved Land	Conifers		Broadleaves	
	non-diverse	diverse	non-diverse	diverse
More Severely Handicapped[1]	155	190	220	235
Less Severely Handicapped[2]	190	220	250	265
Non-Disadvantaged[3]	220	255	280	300
Others (£/ha/annum)				
Unenclosed Land		80		
Enclosed and Improved Land (Conifers)		100		
Enclosed and Improved Land (Broadleaves)		120		

Notes:
[1,2,3] These categories are defined under EC Directives 85/350/EEC.
For the interpretation of all other definitions, see Table 4.4.

Source: Forest Service, 1994a.

Taxation
There are significant tax incentives for investing in forestry. Grants, premia and profits are exempt from tax, but earnings from forestry are taken into account when making social welfare assessments. Details of woodland taxation are outlined below[20].

Income Tax
Profits accruing to an individual or company from the occupation of woodlands managed on a commercial basis and with a view to making a profit are exempt from income tax and corporation tax. The grants and annual premia under the Operational Programme are not taxed. Dividends paid by corporations out of exempt woodland income are exempt income to the recipients.

Capital Gains Tax
Individuals upon disposal of woodlands pay tax only on the land (however, chargeable gains are restricted to the surplus over inflation adjusted cost), trees

---

[19] Annual premia in Britain for conifers are £10 to £15 per ha and £25 to £35 per ha for broadleaves for 5 years (Forest Authority, 1993). It is clear that Irish premia are far in excess of these levels.
[20] Taken from Forest Service, 1992d and O'Hegarty, 1994.

are not so chargeable. Capital sums received by an individual under an insurance policy in respect of the destruction of trees or damage to them are free from capital gains tax. The tax is not applicable to a disposal on death. Corporations are not exempt from the tax.

Value Added Tax (VAT)
Forestry is regarded as an agricultural activity for VAT purposes. Hence persons whose sales consist exclusively of their own agricultural produce are not required to register for VAT (i.e. are exempt). If unregistered an individual is entitled to an addition of 2.5 percent to his or her selling price of timber to VAT registered purchasers.   If the individual undertakes another non-farming business that is taxable or supplies agricultural services the turnover from which exceeds £15,000 per annum he or she must register. Henceforth any supply by the woodland, including disposal, will incur VAT.

Gift and Inheritance (Capital Acquisitions) Tax
Commercial woodlands are treated as agricultural property for the purposes of gift and inheritance tax. The value used for the purposes of tax calculation is 10 percent of the market value.

Stamp Duty
Any deed executed under seal is subject to stamp duty, so a licence to enter and cut timber is liable to £10 stamp duty. The 1990 Finance Act introduced an exemption from stamp duty on the value of trees providing they are commercial.

CHAPTER 5

TIMBER

This chapter calculates the value of the timber which will be produced as a result of the expansion in the forest estate under the Forest Strategy. Appropriate assumptions for the calculation of timber output are firstly outlined. Then a survey of timber markets and prices is undertaken to assess the appropriate timber price assumptions. The necessity for shadow pricing timber is examined. The value of the timber for economic security is then analysed. Finally, timber value projections are made.

TIMBER OUTPUT

Production Functions for Timber

Production functions for timber are listed in Yield Tables. In essence, these tables list the quantity of timber (volume) produced from a stand of trees as a function of time.

Measuring Yield Class

Cumulative production of timber from a hectare of *Sitka spruce* is shown in column (2) of Table 5.1, measured in 5 year intervals over the age of a stand. This yield rises but at a diminishing rate. Column (3) shows the mean annual increment (MAI). This is the average yield of each even-age stand over time. MAI is calculated by dividing cumulative production (2) by age (1) at each time.

The maximum MAI defines the maximum average rate of volume increment which a particular stand can achieve. It is clear that to achieve this, trees should remain standing so long as the marginal yield (CAI) exceeds the average yield MAI. MAI is at a maximum when it equals marginal yield[21]. Marginal yield, known to foresters as Current Annual Increment (CAI), is calculated in column 4 of Table 5.1 and is plotted against MAI in Fig 5.1.

The age that maximises MAI is found by inspection. In this example the time period is equal to 50 years. Thus, following an MSY regime, each hectare will yield approximately $20m^3$ over bark. This figure shows the stand to be of yield class 20. Research by the British Forestry Commission has produced estimates

---

[21] This can be shown to be at the Maximum Sustained Yield (MSY) harvesting age. This is what is often called the biological harvesting decision. It ignores the opportunity cost of delaying harvest, i.e. interest forgone. All else equal, so long as the interest rate is positive, the Faustmann rotation length derived in Chapter 3 will be shorter that the MSY rotation.

of yields broken down by species and yield class. These Yield Tables are also used by Irish foresters.

TABLE 5.1. Calculating MSY and Yield Class for *Sitka spruce*.

Age (Years) (t)	Cumulative Prod'n (m³/ha)	Mean Yield (m³/ha) MAI	Marginal Yield (m³/ha) CAI
(1)	(2)	(3)	(4)
15	84	5.6	
20	189	9.4	21.0
25	322	12.9	26.6
30	468	15.6	29.2
35	616	17.6	29.6
40	753	18.8	27.4
45	876	19.5	24.6
50	984	19.7	21.6
55	1079	19.6	19.0
60	1162	19.4	16.6
65	1235	19.0	14.6
70	1298	18.5	12.6
75	1353	18.0	11.0
80	1408	17.5	11.0

Note:
Cumulative production figures from Edwards and Christie, 1981.

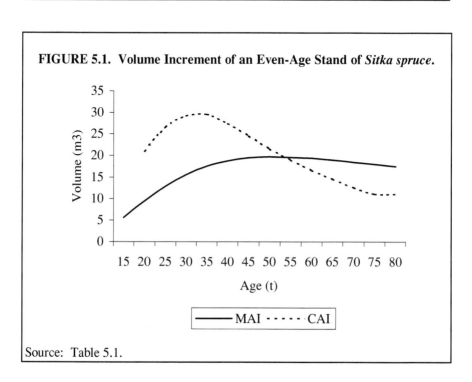

FIGURE 5.1. Volume Increment of an Even-Age Stand of *Sitka spruce*.

Source: Table 5.1.

Profit Maximising Investors and the Harvesting Age
When calculating the timber yield from forest investments, it is important to base the calculations on the Faustmann solution rather than the Hartmann solution. This is because a private investor has a different production function than would a social planner. As explained in Chapter 3, a private forest owner normally benefits from timber production alone. Forest externalities do not enter into his or her production function and the rotation length will be based solely on the value of the timber. The profit maximising investor will factor in subsidies and tax breaks when calculating the optimal harvest age and will value inputs and outputs at market prices rather than shadow prices[22]. *Sitka spruce* of yield class 18, other conifers of yield class 14 (see species and yield class assumptions below) and broadleaves of yield class 6 are calculated to have profit maximising rotation lengths of 40, 55 and 80 years respectively.

Assumptions Regarding Species Planted
The Forest Strategy (Department of Agriculture, Food and Forestry, 1996) has a target of planting 725,000 ha of trees (see Appendix 1, Table A1.2). It projects that 80 percent of these will be conifers and the remainder broadleaves. 60 percent of total planting will be *Sitka spruce* and 20 percent of broadleaf planting will be oak. No further details of species types are provided.

Assumptions Regarding Yield Class
The minimum yield class eligible for grant aid under the Forest Strategy is a *Sitka spruce* equivalent 14 for conifers. The Forest Strategy predicts that the average yield class for *Sitka spruce* will be 18. This is a reasonable assumption given present planting, land availability and eligibility for grant aid. The average yield class for broadleaves is assumed to be 6 (Department of Agriculture, Food and Forestry,1996). No prediction is made of the average yield class for conifers other than *Sitka spruce*. However, for the purposes of calculation, yield class 14 is assumed.

TIMBER MARKETS AND PRICES

Prior to calculating the timber value of the Forest Strategy it is necessary to make assumptions regarding timber prices. This section examines the long-term supply and demand for timber and forecasts the likely movement of timber prices. The study concentrates on global, European and domestic markets but also examines the UK in some depth due to its relative importance as a trading partner.

---

[22] A grant in period zero will shorten the rotation all else equal as will an exemption from sales tax on timber. See Kula, 1988a for some simple examples of this.

Timber Markets

Global and European Wood Markets
It is difficult to find up to date figures for global and European wood markets. Most studies rely on data collected by the Food and Agriculture Organization of the United Nations. However, most of the data in their most recent publication on timber trends (FAO, 1996) does not go beyond 1990. The tables below present the most recent data comparable across countries and regions.

Global Forest Estate
The Global Forest Estate covers approximately 3,411 m ha and accounts for 26 percent of the total land area. South American forests account for 26 percent of the Estate and cover 51 percent of the continent. The former USSR, Africa and North/Central America account for a further 22 percent, 16 percent and 16 percent respectively. Europe's 140 m ha of woodland cover 30 percent of the continent comprising a mere 4 percent of the World's woodland. It is notable that Japan's forest estate covers 64 percent of the country (Table 5.3).

TABLE 5.3. Global Forest Estate, 1991.

	Forest (000s ha)	% Land Area	ha per 1000
North/Cent. America	530,744	25	1,240
Europe	140,196	30	280
Former USSR	754,958	34	2,609
Japan	24,158	64	196
Other Asia	439,063	18	149
South America	898,148	51	3027
Africa	535,848	19	835
Oceania	87,700	10	3,278
WORLD	3,410,815	26	644

Source: FAO (1), 1993.

European Union Woodland
The forest area of the fifteen member States of the EU covers just over 112 m ha. The percentage of the Union covered by the Estate stands at 35 percent. However, prior to the expansion of the Union, the average was just under the world average despite the suitability of land quality and climate of those twelve countries. Austria, Finland and Sweden, the new members of the EU, contain almost half of the Union's woodland. The UK, the Netherlands and Ireland exhibit the lowest percentage of land coverage (Table 5.4)

World Timber Production
Annual timber production stands at approximately 3,400 m m^3. Global production by region of selected timber products is shown in Table 5.5. Saw

TABLE 5.4. EU Forest Estate, 1992.

	Forest (000s ha)	% Land	% Conifers	% B'leaves	% State	% Private
Austria	3,900	47	78	22	15	8
Belgium	617	20	47	53	11	53
Denmark	493	11	63	37	30	66
Finland	28,000	69	90	10	28	69
Germany	10,844	30	69	31	31	44
Greece	5,755	44	19	81	73	15
Spain	12,511	25	48	52	6	65
France	14,688	27	30	70	10	72
Ireland	327	5	90	10	79	20
Italy	6,410	21	25	75	6	60
Lux.	89	34	34	66	8	54
N'lands	330	8	65	35	30	53
Portugal	2,986	32	46	54	3	83
Sweden	23,000	62	93	7	31	69
U.K.	2,297	9	73	27	43	57
EU15	112,247	35	66	34	26	60

Note: Residual of % State and % Private is % "other forests under public law".

Source: CEC, 1995.

TABLE 5.5. Global Production of Selected Industrial Woods, 1991 (000s units) and Percentage Change since 1971.

	ConiferSaw & Veneer Logs (m^3)	Conifer Pulp Wood (m^3)	Conifer SawnWood (m^3)	Fibre Board (m^3)	Paper & Paper Board (mt)	Wood Pulp (mt)
N/C	324,200	130,334	133,874	7,158	92,389	82,679
America	29%	23%	31%	-10%	56%	53%
Europe	118,551	77,585	65,945	4,612	67,781	35,698
	9%	5%	2%	7%	76%	34%
Former	114,000	41,600	62,500	4,160	9,590	8,662
USSR	-21%	22%	-41%	192%	36%	23%
Japan	15,796	2,808	25,075	929	29,053	11,722
	-26%	-18%	-20%	40%	125%	30%
Other	38,244	7,201	22,459	1,718	31,358	4,568
Asia	73%	170%	62%	336%	378%	157%
South	26,657	16,761	10,960	948	7,747	6,691
America	139%	378%	107%	140%	157%	361%
Africa	5,836	3,456	2,322	133	2,711	2,282
	57%	36%	40%	-18%	190%	159%
Oceania	11,773	7,502	3,518	542	2,843	2,387
	54%	223%	49%	107%	85%	120%
WORLD	655,208	287,247	326,652	20,201	243,472	154,691
	15%	26%	0%	30%	88%	51%

Source: FAO, 1982 and 1993b.

and veneer logs comprise over 70 percent of all industrial wood of which 70 percent is harvested from conifers.

Timber output in most regions grew by approximately 13 percent in the 1980s while growth in production in the USSR and Japan was sluggish and for some products negative. The south temperate zone enjoyed marked growth (Arnold, 1991).   While some regions have had higher growth rates, by its sheer magnitude of output, North America has been influential in the increase in production of coniferous saw and veneer logs and sawnwood.

World Trade
World trade in forest products is shown in Table 5.6. The three main trading areas are Europe, North America and Asia-Pacific. Trade principally takes place between Canada and the USA, within Europe, within the Asia-Pacific region and between North America and Asia-Pacific. Canada, the Nordic region, the USA and Southeast Asia are the largest exporters (Arnold, 1991). Approximately one third of industrial wood enters world trade flows in the form of processed wood products.

TABLE 5.6. World Trade in Forest Products, 1993 (£m).

From:	*Europe*	*North America*	*Ex-USSR*	*Latin America*	*Asia-Pacific*	*Africa*	*Other*	*Total*
To:								
Europe	21,754	2,940	676	675	775	801	153	27,774
North America	1,012	9,947	16	581	653	45	8	12,262
Latin America	323	1,428	1	460	37	21	8	2,278
Asia-Pacific	2,439	6,574	574	724	9,433	367	10	20,121
Africa	712	145	7	63	72	43	8	1,050
Other	27	1	12	3	272	0	0	315
TOTAL	26,267	21,035	1,286	2,506	11,242	1,277	187	63,800

Source: FAO, 1996.

Forest Products in the European Union
Table 5.7 shows the extent to which the EU was a net importer of wood prior to the entry of Austria, Finland and Sweden. When these countries signed up, the EU cut its deficit by over 70 percent. The UK has the largest production deficit and therefore it is the largest net importer. Apart from the new members, Portugal is the only country with a production surplus.

TABLE 5.7. EU 12 and EU 15 Forest Products and the Economy, 1991.

	Prod'n (£m) (i)	% GDP	Imports (£m) (ii)	Exports (£m) (iii)	% Trade	Cons'n (£m) (iv)=(i)+ (ii)-(iii)	Net Prod'n (£m) (i)-(iv)
Belg/Lux	1,253	1	2,380	1,328	2	2,305	-1,052
Denmark	403	0	1,218	288	1	1,333	-930
France	6,433	1	4,243	2,650	2	8,026	-1,593
Germany	11,519	na	8,667	4,703	2	15,483	-3,964
Greece	308	1	689	69	1	928	-620
Ireland	128	0	322	94	1	356	-228
Italy	3,408	0	4,252	1,254	1	6,406	-2,998
Ne'lands	1,518	1	3,034	1,678	2	2,874	-1,356
Portugal	1,360	3	509	834	7	1,035	+325
Spain	3,015	1	1,920	772	2	4,163	-1,148
UK	2,912	0	6,106	1,191	1	7,826	-4,915
EU 12	32,257	na	33,342	14,861	na	50,735	-18,479
Sweden	7,418	4	806	6,809	18	1,414	+6,003
Finland	6,179	7	353	5,681	36	850	+5,328
Austria	2,923	2	1,074	2,266	8	1,732	+1,191
EU 15	48,777	na	35,573	29,617	na	54,731	-5,957

Source: FAO, 1993a.

Demand Projections

Arnold (1991) summarises global demand projections as follows: World demand for industrial wood will grow at rates of between 15 percent and 40 percent over the next 15 years and between 35 percent and 75 percent over the next 50 years. Jaakko Pöyry's (1994) forecasts of global demand for softwood raw material predict that demand for coniferous sawlogs and veneer logs will increase by 95 m m^3 (a growth of 16 percent) between 1990 and 2010. Coniferous pulpwood and other industrial roundwood demand will rise by 120 m (18 percent) over the same period. Per annum growth rates for softwood log demand and softwood pulpwood demand are projected to be 0.9 percent and 1.0 percent respectively. Per annum growth rates of coniferous forest products will be higher: paper and paperboard, 2.5 percent, sawnwood, 1.2 percent, and wood-based panels, 2.8 percent. Table 5.8 provides some other growth rate estimates. It is notable that the FAO estimates (1993a) are surprisingly high and are not consistent with other estimates.

**TABLE 5.8. Forecasts of Global Consumption of
Forest Products (millions m³).**

Product	Forecaster	1995	2000	2010	Implicit growth rate/annum
Sawnwood	WRA (1988)	530	570	---	1.4%
	FAO (1988)	532	588	---	1.9%
	WB (1988)	---	538	---	1.0%
	FAO (1993)	---	---	745	2.6%
Pulp & Paper	FAO (1988)	255	304	---	3.0%
	RISI (1987)	254	297	---	2.9%
	Chase (1987)	246	285	---	2.6%
	WRA (1988)	240	270	---	2.3%
	FAO (1993)	---	---	443	3.2%
Wood Panels	WRA (1988)	140	154	---	2.4%
	FAO (1988)	162	202	---	4.4%
	WB (1988)	---	145	---	2.3%
	FAO (1993)	---	---	313	5.5%

Notes:

[1] RISI (Resource Information Services Inc.); WRA (Woodbridge Reed & Associates); WB (World Bank); Chase (Chase Econometrics); FAO (Food & Agriculture Organisation).

Source: Murphy, 1994.

Over the next 50 years demand for all timber products in the USA is projected to increase (Table 5.9). Consumption of coniferous sawnwood is expected to rise by 21 percent, coniferous plywood by 10 percent and coniferous roundwood by 89 percent over 1986 levels by the year 2040.

TABLE 5.9. US Forest Products Forecasted Consumption (millions m³).

	1986	2000	2020	2040
Sawnwood				
Softwoods	110.4	106.9	128.1	133.1
Total	131.5	130.7	156.7	164.3
Structural Panels				
Softwood plywood	18.2	15.0	17.6	20.1
Total	21.3	22.4	29.1	34.2
Pulpwood				
Softwood roundwood	128.0	176.9	209.2	241.8
Total roundwood	207.0	305.2	391.9	451.7
Total	338.6	406.4	515.5	574.9

Source: Arnold, 1991.

TABLE 5.10. Consumption of Forest Products in Europe, 1979 to 1981 with Estimates to 2000 and 2020 (million units).

	1979-1981 Average	2000 Low	High	2020 Low	High
Sawnwood (m^3)	102.3	119.0	140.8	123.0	148.0
Wood-based panels (m^3)	35.6	49.6	58.5	52.0	60.0
Paper and paperboard (mt)	49.2	67.2	92.0	68.0	95.0

Source: Arnold, 1991.

Projections for Europe give upper and lower bounds for growth in demand for paper and paperboard over the same years of 93 percent and 38 percent respectively, an average of 65.5 percent. For wood-based panels and sawnwood the corresponding figures are 68 percent and 41 percent, 45 percent and 20 percent respectively (Table 5.10). Demand for sawn hardwood will grow faster than for sawn softwood (Arnold, 1991).

TABLE 5.11. Forecast of Japan's Demand for Wood Products to 2004 (million m^3 roundwood equivalent)

	1984	1994	2004
Sawnwood	45	43-45	42-45
Plywood and panels	15	17	19
Pulpwood	31	35	40
Other	4	4	5
TOTAL	94	99-101	104-108

Source: Arnold, 1991.

Growth in Japanese consumption is estimated to have been in the magnitude of 6 percent in the decade prior to 1994 and is projected to grow a further 6 percent in the next decade (Table 5.11).

Consumption by developing countries is forecast to increase and this is the justification for the FAO's (1993a) optimistic figures. Most forecasts predict a slowing of the consumption growth rate after 2010. There will be some substitution away from solid to reconstituted products causing the slowest growth in demand for sawnwood and the fastest growth in demand for pulp and paper products. Demand for non-coniferous products will grow faster than for coniferous products (Arnold, 1991).

Supply Projections
Supply predictions indicate a growth in timber supply of 53 percent over the period 1986 to 2040 in the USA. Nordic supply is expected to rise by 25 percent between 1980 and 2020 while an increase of 47 percent is expected in the rest of Europe. Japanese output is projected to rise by 17 percent between 1990 and 2004. Supply predictions such as these are difficult to compare as they are calculated under differing assumptions and over various time spans. Arnold (1991) predicts that the increases in temperate resources will be offset

by a continuing decline in supply from the tropics such that growth in output will match the growth in demand.

Global Demand/Supply Equilibrium
Demand for coniferous wood will increase as a result of rising consumption of forest products. Increased recycling and more efficient use of raw materials make estimates for the growth in demand for standing coniferous timber lower than for corresponding forest products (Jaakko Pöyry, 1994). There are large global resources, in particular in Europe and Canada, which can be exploited to match any growth in demand notwithstanding conservation of some natural forests in North America. There is also a substantial untapped forest estate in the former USSR which can act as a backstop (Figure 5.2). Structural adjustment due to political changes and a move to the market system may inhibit any increase in production in the short term. In addition, unexploited forest resources may suffer from a competitive disadvantage due to higher costs of extraction.

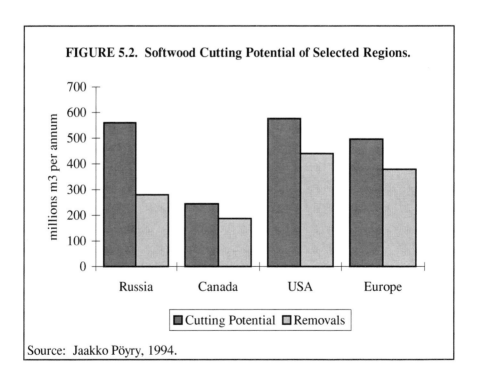

FIGURE 5.2. Softwood Cutting Potential of Selected Regions.

Source: Jaakko Pöyry, 1994.

It must be noted however, that while total growth in demand may be matched by the growth in output, the composition of the timber market will be altered e.g. the ratio of softwood to hardwood may increase and have a consequent effect on prices (see below).

United Kingdom Wood Market

British Forest Estate
The British forest estate spans 2,297,000 ha covering 9 percent of the land area, one of the lowest in the EU. Forty three percent is under the ownership of the Forestry Commission. Conifers comprise 73 percent of the estate (CEC, 1995). Planting in Great Britain over the last twenty years is described Table 5.12. Following a fall in annual planting in the late 1970s the rate had recovered somewhat by the late 1980s but seems to have peaked in 1989.

TABLE 5.12. Great Britain Planting, 1971 to 1996 (000s ha).

Year	State Aff[1].	State Ref[2].	Private Aff.	Private Ref.	State Total	Private Total	Total Aff.	Total Ref.	Total Total
1971	23.3	5.1	19.2	3.8	28.4	23.0	42.5	8.9	51.4
1972	21.7	4.5	20.2	4.3	26.2	24.5	41.9	8.8	50.7
1973	19.4	3.8	20.8	3.7	23.2	24.5	40.2	7.5	47.7
1974	18.4	3.3	19.8	3.9	21.7	23.7	38.2	7.2	45.4
1975	19.6	3.5	18.7	3.0	23.1	21.7	38.3	6.5	44.8
1976	17.2	3.3	10.0	2.6	20.5	12.6	27.2	5.9	33.1
1977	15.5	3.1	7.5	2.1	18.6	9.6	23.0	5.2	28.2
1978	14.1	3.1	6.5	2.2	17.2	8.7	20.6	5.3	25.9
1979	11.8	3.6	8.1	3.0	15.4	11.1	19.9	6.6	26.5
1980	15.8	5.7	8.6	3.1	21.5	11.7	24.4	8.8	33.2
1981	11.6	5.0	8.7	3.3	16.6	12.0	20.3	8.3	28.6
1982	11.0	5.5	12.6	3.5	16.5	16.1	23.6	9.0	32.6
1983	9.0	5.8	12.5	3.2	14.8	15.7	21.5	9.0	30.5
1984	8.4	6.7	16.9	3.2	15.1	20.1	25.3	9.9	35.2
1985	5.2	6.0	16.6	3.2	11.2	19.8	21.8	9.2	31.0
1986	4.3	7.3	19.4	4.6	11.6	24.0	23.7	11.9	35.6
1987	5.3	8.0	19.4	4.6	13.3	24.0	24.7	12.6	37.3
1988	5.0	8.1	24.0	5.0	13.1	29.0	29.0	13.1	42.1
1989	4.1	8.5	25.4	4.9	12.6	29.6	29.5	30.4	42.9
1990	4.1	7.9	15.6	6.3	12.0	21.9	19.7	14.2	33.9
1991	3.5	7.7	15.5	7.1	11.2	22.6	19.0	14.8	33.8
1992	3.0	8.3	14.3	7.9	11.3	22.2	17.3	16.2	33.5
1993	2.3	8.6	15.5	8.2	10.9	23.7	17.8	16.8	34.6
1994	1.4	7.9	15.9	8.5	9.3	24.4	17.3	16.4	33.7
1995	0.9	7.9	18.5	6.2	8.8	24.7	19.4	14.1	33.5
1996	0.4	7.5	15.3	5.8	15.7	21.1	15.7	13.3	29.0

Notes:
[1] Afforestation
[2] Reforestation

Source: Forestry Commission, 1976-1996.

UK Trade in Forest Products
The UK is the largest net importer of forest products in the EU. In 1991 net imports amounted to £4,915 m. Total imports have increased over the past 20 years (Table 5.13). Canada, Finland, Sweden and the former USSR supply the UK with over 80 percent of its imports of softwood lumber (Table 5.14).

TABLE 5.13. Volumes of UK Imports, Production and Apparent Consumption of Wood and Wood Products (millions m³ WRME).

Year	Wood	Pulp	Panel Products	Paper	Total Imports	UK Prod'n	Apparent Cons'n
			Imports				
1970	18.3	11.7	2.5	3.5	36.0	2.7	37.9
1971	18.6	12.7	3.3	4.5	39.1	3.0	41.3
1972	15.9	13.7	3.4	7.3	40.3	3.2	42.3
1973	15.7	11.7	4.0	8.8	40.2	3.3	42.6
1974	16.1	11.9	3.7	10.6	42.3	3.3	44.0
1975	10.3	9.4	3.3	7.9	30.9	3.2	33.1
1976	13.6	10.7	3.8	8.9	37.0	3.5	39.3
1977	13.2	10.2	3.6	9.1	36.1	3.8	38.6
1978	12.4	10.0	4.5	10.2	37.1	3.8	39.7
1979	14.1	11.6	4.8	10.8	41.3	4.1	43.9
1980	11.5	9.8	3.6	9.8	34.7	3.9	36.3
1981	10.6	8.6	4.2	11.1	34.5	4.3	36.3
1982	13.6	7.5	4.1	10.7	35.9	4.1	37.8
1983	14.5	8.0	4.8	9.1	36.4	3.9	38.0
1984	13.1	8.6	4.7	12.3	38.7	3.8	39.7
1985	12.3	8.1	4.7	12.4	37.5	4.7	39.9
1986	14.6	8.3	4.7	13.0	40.6	5.2	43.0
1987	19.1	8.5	4.5	15.4	47.5	5.4	49.4
1988	18.6	9.2	6.8	13.9	48.5	6.0	50.7
1989	18.6	8.9	6.1	14.4	48.1	6.4	50.3
1990	20.3	8.6	5.7	13.8	48.5	6.4	50.2
1991	16.0	8.7	4.9	13.6	43.2	6.5	44.7
1992	15.6	8.7	4.9	14.3	43.5	6.6	45.0
1993	15.0	7.8	4.8	14.6	42.2	6.8	44.5
1994	17.4	8.7	5.1	16.4	47.6	7.4	49.2
1995	14.0	9.1	5.1	15.9	44.2	7.7	45.9

Source: Forestry Commission, 1976-1996.

UK Timber Production and Consumption
Production of wood and wood products has risen steadily over the past 20 years. Conifer wood production has increased from 2.3 m m³ over bark in 1970 to just under 7.5 m m³ in 1995. Hardwood production has been relatively stable (Table 5.15). On the other hand, a substantial deficit has remained between

apparent consumption and production (Table 5.13) such that the UK relies on domestic production for 12 percent of its wood requirements (Whiteman, 1991a).

TABLE 5.14. UK Imports of Softwood Lumber (000s m^3)

	Canada		Sweden		F. USSR		Finland		Ireland		Total
Year	Qty.	%	Qty.	%	Qty.	%	Qty.	%	Qty.	%	Qty.
1982	1,427	24	1,568	26	1,066	18	877	14	68	1	6,085
1983	1,418	19	2,093	29	1,210	17	1,069	15	78	1	7,155
1984	1,238	19	1,958	29	1,079	16	898	13	100	2	6,686
1985	907	15	1,855	30	1,051	17	877	14	91	2	6,111
1986	1,537	22	1,949	28	1,062	15	968	14	80	1	7,024
1987	2,332	29	1,856	23	1,286	16	1,059	13	105	1	8,123
1988	2,992	33	1,709	19	1,227	14	1,217	14	145	2	9,014
1989	2,865	34	1,579	19	1,260	15	1,074	13	135	2	8,514
1990	3,151	40	1,218	15	1,171	15	851	11	144	2	7,923
1991	2,250	37	1,278	21	630	11	665	11	158	3	6,021
1992	2,007	33	1,735	28	616	10	816	13	207	3	6,287
1993	719	11	264	41	673	11	1,163	18	211	3	6,384

Source: Irish Timber Growers Association, 1995.

UK Supply Projections
Forecasts in Table 5.15 show that hardwood production is expected to return to the average of the past 20 years during the next two decades and to show an increase in the following 40 years. Conifer wood production forecasts show a rise of 5.3 m m^3 in per annum output by the year 2011 and of a further 4 m m^3 after another 40 years.

Whiteman (1991a) expresses demand as a roundwood equivalent and hence studies the balance between supply and demand. Production forecasting techniques were used to predict future timber production from the UK forest estate to the year 2050. The results are shown in Table 5.16.

Annual production of wood is predicted to rise by 184 percent of the 1991 level to peak at 19.6 m m^3 over bark in the period 2022-2026. Annual production of coniferous sawlogs is expected to rise by 342 percent over the same period. It is predicted that total annual wood production will fall back to about 12 million m^3 over the following 24 years.

TABLE 5.15. Past and Future Wood Production in Britain
(000s m^3 over bark).

Year	Conifer	Broadleaf	Total
1970	2,310	1,300	3,610
1971	2,370	1,300	3,670
1972	2,390	1,300	3,690
1973	2,430	1,300	3,730
1974	2,400	1,300	3,700
1975	2,280	1,300	3,580
1976	2,710	1,300	4,010
1977	2,890	1,400	4,290
1978	2,710	1,400	4,110
1979	2,940	1,400	4,340
1980	3,300	1,300	4,600
1981	3,260	1,300	4,560
1982	3,550	1,100	4,650
1983	3,710	1,000	4,710
1984	4,000	1,000	5,000
1985	4,170	1,000	5,170
1986	4,490	1,100	5,590
1987	4,970	1,000	5,970
1988	5,250	1,260	6,510
1989	5,250	1,280	6,630
1990	5,460	1,120	6,580
1991	5,560	1,110	6,670
1992	6,140	910	7,050
1993	6,520	830	7,350
1994	7,350	1,000	8,340
1995	7,440	1,030	8,470
1997/2001	8,200	1,200	9,400
2002/2006	9,790	1,200	10,990
2007/2011	12,100	1,200	13,300
2050	15,260	1,707	16,967

Notes:

(i)   Forecasts for 1997-2011 represent an average annual figure for each five year period.

(ii) Forecast for 2050 assumes conifers and broadleaves yield 10 m^3 and 3 m^3 per ha per annum respectively on land presently under forest.

Source: Forestry Commission, 1976-1996; Forestry Trust.

**TABLE 5.16. UK Forecast of Annual Production to 2050
(millions m³ over bark).**

Year	Coniferous sawlogs	Coniferous small roundwood	Non-coniferous sawlogs	Non-coniferous small roundwood	Total
1987-1991	2.6	3.2	0.9	0.2	6.9
1992-1996	3.4	4.0	0.9	0.2	8.5
1997-2001	4.8	4.8	1.0	0.1	10.8
2002-2006	6.1	5.7	1.0	0.1	13.0
2007-2011	8.1	6.5	1.0	0.1	15.8
2012-2016	9.6	6.9	1.0	0.1	17.7
2017-2021	10.4	6.8	1.1	0.1	18.4
2022-2026	11.5	6.9	1.1	0.1	19.6
2027-2031	11.0	6.3	1.1	0.1	18.4
2032-2036	10.2	5.7	1.1	0.1	17.1
2037-2041	8.4	4.7	1.1	0.1	14.3
2042-2046	6.5	4.4	1.1	0.1	12.0
2047-2050	6.6	4.6	1.1	0.1	12.4

Source: Whiteman, 1991a.

UK Demand Projections
Supply and demand predictions are presented in Table 5.17. Demand is forecast to increase steadily over the next 50 years in the case of both high and low Gross Domestic Product (GDP) growth. Annual demand for wood is predicted to rise by between 42 percent and 60 percent by 2025 and by between 51 percent and 95 percent by 2050. However, the forecast shows a fall in the demand for sawnwood.

**TABLE 5.17. UK Demand for Wood Forecast to 2050 (millions m³
WRME).**

	Actual 1989	GDP growth rate	Year 2000	Year 2010	Year 2025	Year 2050
Wood-based	6.6	H	8.3	9.8	12.6	14.3
panels		L	8.3	9.4	10.8	11.6
Paper and	20.8	H	28.4	33.5	43.8	58.1
paperboard		L	28.4	32.4	37.3	40.3
Sawnwood	18.8		16.8	17.0	17.2	17.7
Other roundwood	0.4		0.5	0.4	0.4	0.3
TOTAL	46.4	H	54.1	60.8	74.2	90.5
		L	54.1	59.4	65.9	70.1

Source: Whiteman, 1991a.

UK Domestic Demand/Supply Balance
The demand and supply forecasts are shown graphically in Figure 5.3. While domestic supply will rise it will be unable to close the gap between domestic

demand and production. Rather, the gap is likely to widen and the UK will have to rely even more on imported wood. However, Tables 5.16 and 5.17 suggest that the gap between domestic production and consumption of coniferous sawnwood will shrink considerably over the next thirty years.

Irish Wood Market

The available data on the Irish wood market are very poor. It is necessary to rely on the FAO for much of the statistics which, as stated before, does not provide data for the last few years. An additional problem is that, in 1993, the Irish Central Statistics Office (CSO) changed the categories of timber products in each trade division. For this reason some of the tables and figures presented below omit figures for the mid 1990s.

Irish Forest Estate

The extent and growth of the Irish forest estate and afforestation rates are discussed in detail in Chapter 1.

Domestic Supply

The rapid growth in planting has been reflected by an increase in timber production. Total wood production from forests is currently 2.2 m m^3 per annum (Department of Agriculture, Food and Forestry, 1996). Coillte's wood sales have doubled in the last ten years. Coillte forecasts wood sales to rise by over 50 between 1997 and 2006 (Table 5.18).

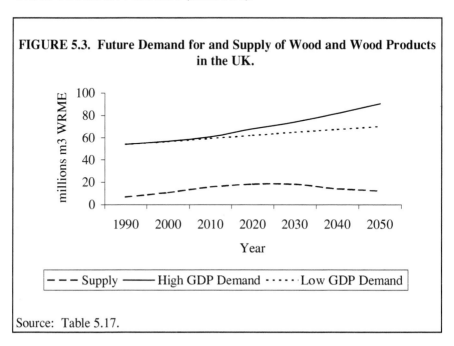

FIGURE 5.3. Future Demand for and Supply of Wood and Wood Products in the UK.

Source: Table 5.17.

Pulpwood production will rise but there will be particularly large increases in small and large sawlog output: 93.5 percent and 145.5 percent increases respectively between 1992 and 2005. Crude estimates suggest that the private sector will add a further 40 percent to pulpwood production, 18 percent to small sawlog production and 9 percent to large sawlog output (duQuesne, 1993).

Domestic Demand
Domestic demand for raw wood comes from about 100 sawmills, four panel board manufacturers and a number of timber distributors. The sawmilling sector is dominated by 10 large mills which process between 70,000 m^3 and 250,000 m^3 annually. At present, these mills handle 80 percent of timber supply. Domestic overcapacity in sawmilling is running at 30 percent. Irish sawmills provide 60 percent of construction timber used domestically (Department of Agriculture, Food and Forestry, 1996). Approximately fifty percent of the raw wood going to sawmills converts to sawn timber, 30 percent to clean chips , 12 percent to sawdust and 8 percent to bark.

TABLE 5.18. State Sales of Wood by Volume and Value.

Year	Volume (000s m^3)	Value (£ million)
1983	1,000	9.4
1984	1,013	13.1
1985	1,218	16.1
1986	1,263	16.8
1987	1,374	19.4
1988	1,450	22.5
1989*	1,503	27.3
1990	1,444	31.6
1991	1,537	33.1
1992	1,840	32.9
1993	1,854	31.5
1994	2,052	45.3
1995	2,140	na
1996	2,190	na
1997	2,062	na
1998**	2,755	na
2000**	3,000	na
2006**	3,181	na

Notes:
* The first year of Coillte operations.
** Forecasts

Source: Irish Timber Growers Association, 1995; Coillte Teoranta.

There are four primary purchasers of pulpwood. Medite Europe Ltd. in Clonmel, Co. Tipperary produced 230,000 m^3 of medium density fibreboard (MDF) in 1995 but this is expected to rise to 300,000 m^3. Finsa Ltd in Scarriff, Co. Clare produces 90,000 m^3 of chipboard per annum. The recently opened

Louisiana Pacific Coillte Ireland Ltd. in Waterford is expected to produce 350,000 m³ of OSB (a substitute for plywood) per annum.

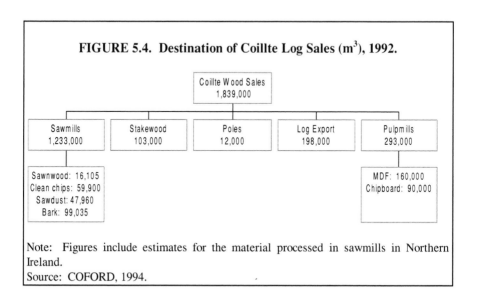

FIGURE 5.4. Destination of Coillte Log Sales (m³), 1992.

Note: Figures include estimates for the material processed in sawmills in Northern Ireland.
Source: COFORD, 1994.

Masonite Corporation in Carrick-on-Shannon, Co. Leitrim is expected to come into production in 1997 and will produce 120,000 m³ of moulded door facings per annum (Department of Agriculture, Food and Forestry, 1996).

In Northern Ireland there are two principal sawmills (Balcas Timber Ltd. in Derry and Fermanagh) and a panelboard mill (Spanboard Products Ltd. in Derry) which account for much of the exported raw timber to that jurisdiction. Figure 5.4 shows the destination of Coillte's wood sales in 1992.

Trade
In 1991 forest products accounted for 1 percent of total Irish trade. Ireland consumed £356 m worth leaving a production deficit of £228 m (Table 5.7). A trade balance for selected forest products is shown in Table 5.19. The majority of imported forest products come from the Nordic countries, the former USSR and Canada. Figures 5.5, 5.6 and 5.7 show the quantity and real value (1991£) of net exports for Central Statistics Office (CSO) trade divisions 24, 25 and 63. These show that in the 1980s and early 1990s net exports in terms of quantity were positive. However, in value terms there is a trade deficit. This demonstrates that the majority of exports are low priced products as a result of resource quality limitations. The predominance of *Sitka spruce* limits access to higher value markets.

TABLE 5.19. Trade Balance for Selected Timber Products, 1995 (m³).

	Production (i)	Imports (ii)	Exports (iii)	Cons'n (iv)=(i)+ (ii)-(iii)	Net Prod'n (i)-(iv)
Soft S'wood	706,000	326,000	248,000	784,000	-78,000
Hard S'wood	10,000	77,000	7,000	80,000	-70,000
MDF	240,000	52,000	149,000	143,000	97,000
Chipboard	90,000	38,000	32,000	96,000	-37,000
Plywood	na	76,000	3,000	na	na
Pulp and Paper[1]	32,000	588,000	52,000	568,000	-536,000

Note:
[1] 1991 figures

Source: Irish Timber Growers Association, 1997; COFORD, 1994.

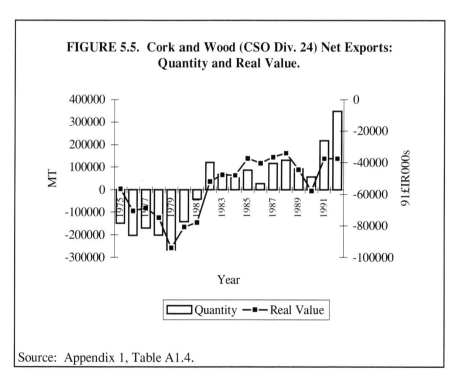

FIGURE 5.5. Cork and Wood (CSO Div. 24) Net Exports: Quantity and Real Value.

Source: Appendix 1, Table A1.4.

Table 5.20 shows the destination of various categories of forest products exported from Ireland. Eighty six percent (in terms of value) of cork and wood products, 80 percent of pulp and waste paper and 74 percent of wood manufactures (excluding furniture) are exported to the UK.

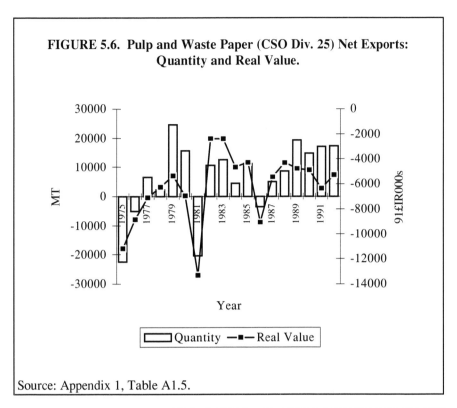

FIGURE 5.6. Pulp and Waste Paper (CSO Div. 25) Net Exports: Quantity and Real Value.

Source: Appendix 1, Table A1.5.

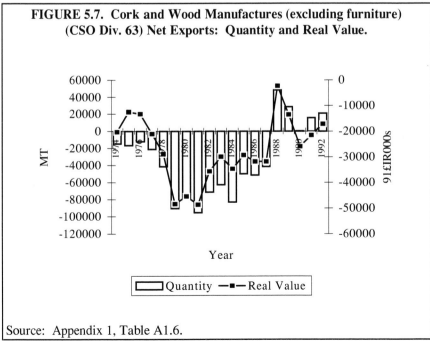

FIGURE 5.7. Cork and Wood Manufactures (excluding furniture) (CSO Div. 63) Net Exports: Quantity and Real Value.

Source: Appendix 1, Table A1.6.

More specific data are shown in Table 5.21. The value of non coniferous exports may seem rather high. However, it is important to note that the unit value of non coniferous wood is much greater than that of coniferous timber e.g. the 1992 unit value of class 24740 is £25 per mt as opposed to £184 per mt for the non coniferous equivalent (class 24750). The unit value of class 24821 is £154 per mt as opposed to £211 per mt for the non coniferous equivalent (class 24840).

TABLE 5.20. Cork and Wood (Div. 24), Pulp and Waste Paper (Div. 25), Cork and Wood Manufactures (ex. furnit.) (Div. 63) Exports, 1992 (£000s).

	Div. 24	*Div. 25*	*Div. 63*
EU	33,969	3,165	49,002
UK	29,291	2,544	36,074
Great Britain	19,316	1,279	30,125
Northern Ireland	9,975	1,265	5,949
France	468	0	2,110
Belgium & Luxembourg	1,416	0	2,614
Netherlands	650	0	3,560
Germany	467	0	1,288
Denmark	0	0	1,138
Spain	1,615	0	136
Norway	51	0	0
Sweden	41	0	1,444
Finland	2,713	0	142
Greece	0	0	665
Italy	0	0	1,352
USA	39	1	932
Canada	0	0	156
Portugal	0	0	65
Malaysia	0	0	28
Austria	0	0	58
Other	61	635	886
TOTAL	36,813	3,179	52,649

Source: CSO, 1973-1993

Future Demand for Irish Produce
Ireland's largest export market, the UK, has a growing gap between consumption and domestic production of roundwood. However, forecasts suggest that the UK will become more self sufficient in conifer sawnwood which may squeeze out Irish exports. Changes in domestic demand as a result of the development of Medite and the foundation of Louisiana-Pacific will soak up increases in pulpwood production from an enlarged forest estate. Timber quality from the predominant *Sitka spruce* is lower than that from the large exporting countries, e.g. Canada and Sweden (duQuesne, 1993), but is suitable for pulpwood production in particular and for the manufacture of engineered woods for which demand is on the rise. However, opportunities for import

substitution will eventually dry up after the initial demand surge from the aforementioned mill expansions when timber yields from the enlarged private forest estate come on stream in 15 or 20 years time.

TABLE 5.21. Value and Percentages of Selected Irish Timber Exports to EU, Great Britain, Northern Ireland and Total.

Classif.	Product Type	Destination	1989	1991	1993
24730	Wood in the	Total £000s	2,579	3,645	2,092
	rough, treated.	EU £000s	2,579	3,479	2,048
		GB £000s	2,099	2,453	819
		NI £000s	na	972	1,229
		% to GB	81	67	39
		% to NI	na	27	59
24740	Wood of	Total £000s	2,737	4,567	4,861
	coniferous	EU £000s	2,442	3,321	4,502
	species	GB £000s	na	na	1,427
	not treated.	NI £000s	2,148	2,186	3,051
		% to GB	na	na	29
		% to NI	78	48	63
24750	Wood of non-	Total £000s	2,428	2,490	1,061
	coniferous	EU £000s	2,424	2,490	885
	species, in the	GB £000s	1,953	2,013	867
	rough, not	NI £000s	na	na	179
	treated.	% to GB	80	81	82
		% to NI	na	na	17
24821	Conifer wood,	Total £000s	7,830	7,013	20,685
	sawn,	EU £000s	7,830	7,013	20,643
	over 6 mm.	GB £000s	4,081	4,731	15,159
		NI £000s	3,745	2,254	5,397
		% to GB	52	67	73
		% to NI	48	32	26
24840	Non-conifer	Total £000s	8,382	6,969	6,062
	wood, sawn,	EU £000s	8,382	6,969	5,948
	over 6 mm.	GB £000s	5,533	4,074	3,079
		NI £000s	2,826	2,069	2,848
		% to GB	66	58	51
		% to NI	34	30	47
	TOTAL	£000s	23,956	24,684	34,761

Source: Irish Timber Growers Association, 1995.

Softwood lumber consumption in Ireland is relatively static while production has increased 3.5 times in ten years (Simons, 1991) stressing the country's reliance on overseas markets for future sales. The long term position of supply-demand equilibrium for standing timber is uncertain. Over the next 25 years or more it has been predicted that the growth in demand will not outstrip that of supply on a global basis and the forests of the former USSR are likely to act as a backstop, thereby restricting any significant increase in timber prices in the long run. Indeed, successful structural adjustment in Eastern Europe could possibly increase timber supply from that region and put downward pressure on real prices. A shrinking UK market is of even greater concern. This outlook would suggest that it would be unwise to expect any long term increase in the real price of Irish standing timber. Prices are discussed in greater detail below.

Timber Prices
This section studies past timber and timber product prices. Making inferences is difficult due to lack of data. There is no reliable long term time series of prices for standing timber in Ireland and no comprehensive study of Irish prices for standing timber has been published. However, Coillte does provide standing timber prices from 1976 to date. Comparable data prior to 1976 are unavailable. The Irish Central Statistics Office has two timber wholesale price indices but these only go back as far as 1975. The British Forestry Commission publishes price data twice yearly and also publishes a number of price indices. The Northern Ireland Forest Service publishes price data in its annual report.

Categories and definitions differ in the three jurisdictions making exact comparison difficult. For this reason, price trends rather than absolute values are examined. Some output indices were obtained from the UK CSO. Due to the poor quality of the data no attempt was made to show causality by applying econometric techniques but correlation coefficients were calculated to examine relative trends. The correlation coefficient between x and y is represented by r_{xy}^2.

Three export price indices for Ireland (trade divisions 24, 25 and 63) were calculated by dividing total value of exports by total quantity.

Selection of Appropriate Deflators
For Irish figures the choice of an appropriate index to convert from nominal to real prices rests between the Consumer Price Index (CPI), the general Wholesale Price Index (WPI) and the Gross Domestic Product (GDP) deflator. The CPI was considered inappropriate because it is calculated from a basket of consumer goods. A more general index than the WPI was desirable in order to compare prices of forest products from the raw material stage to finished products. The GDP deflator was chosen for these reasons and for the additional purpose of comparison with the general performance of the economy. In any case, there is a particularly high correlation ($r^2=0.998$) between the CPI and the GDP deflator. A unit price index of exports for all products (EPI) was used to calculate real prices of timber exports.

For UK prices the choice rested between the Retail Price Index (RPI), the Producer Price Index (PPI) and the GDP deflator. For similar reasons to the above and for ease of comparison the GDP deflator was chosen. Again, the indices are highly correlated (r^2=0.977 or greater). An Import Price Index (IPI) was used to deflate import prices.

Global Softwood Prices since 1900

Figure 5.8 shows global softwood timber real prices to have grown at about one percent per annum on average during the twentieth century. However, it must be borne in mind that comparisons made over a long period are suspect due to inconsistencies in the data as a result of differing methods of collection etc. Softwood real prices rose after the first world war but levelled out again in the 1920s. They jumped dramatically in the 1940s, as might be expected after the Second World War. However, the average price from that time has remained at a much higher level. Taking the period 1950 to date, real prices, on average, have shown negligible growth despite large fluctuations and a peak in the late 1970s.

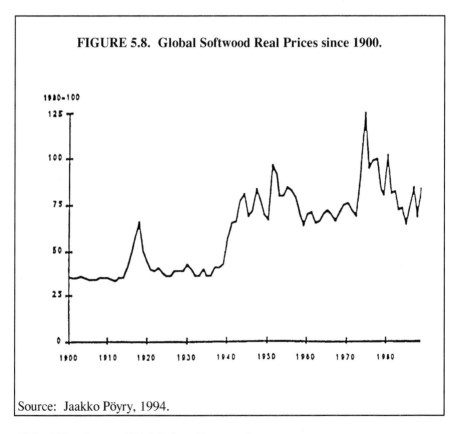

FIGURE 5.8. Global Softwood Real Prices since 1900.

Source: Jaakko Pöyry, 1994.

United Kingdom and Irish Prices Compared

The best indication of standing timber prices in Ireland is given by prices received by Coillte. A study of standing timber prices between 1976 and 1996 shows that prices peaked in the late 1970s and took a sharp fall to a low in 1983. Prices had recovered somewhat by the late 1980s but took a small downturn in the early 1990s. They have recovered over the last four years.

Over the entire period standing prices have shown an average annual growth rate of 0.9 percent.

British Forestry Commission prices and Northern Ireland Forest Service prices follow a similar pattern but return slightly negative average annual growth rates of -1.1 percent and -0.3 percent respectively.

Price indices were derived using the raw price data for Ireland (ROI), Northern Ireland (NI) and Britain. Figure 5.9 shows that Irish prices move in tandem with UK and Northern Irish prices with high positive correlations being reported.

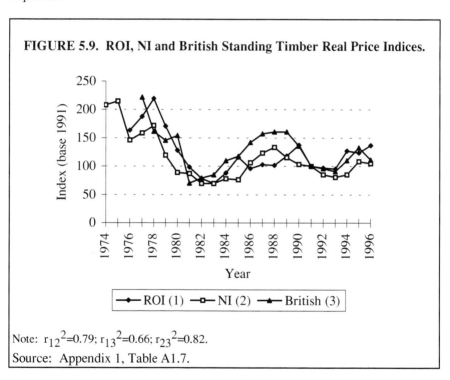

FIGURE 5.9. ROI, NI and British Standing Timber Real Price Indices.

Note: r_{12}^2=0.79; r_{13}^2=0.66; r_{23}^2=0.82.
Source: Appendix 1, Table A1.7.

The Irish CSO has two WPIs for "Rough Timber" and "Other Timber" dating from 1975 which are remarkably stable apart from a dip in the 1980s (Figure 5.10) with average annual growth rates of 0.3 percent and 0.1 percent respectively. A comparison with Figure 5.9 suggests that standing timber prices are subject to greater fluctuations than those of sawn timber and timber products.

Selected UK forest products price indices (Figure 5.11) show a marked fall from the mid 1970s and, as is the case in Ireland, standing timber displays the largest variation in price.

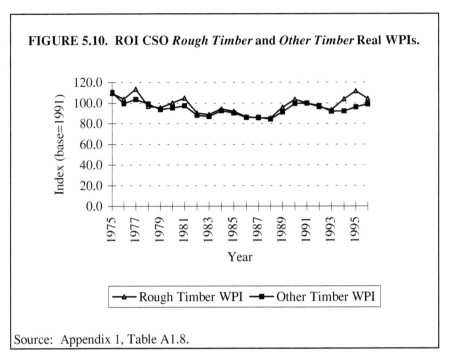

FIGURE 5.10. ROI CSO *Rough Timber* and *Other Timber* Real WPIs.

Source: Appendix 1, Table A1.8.

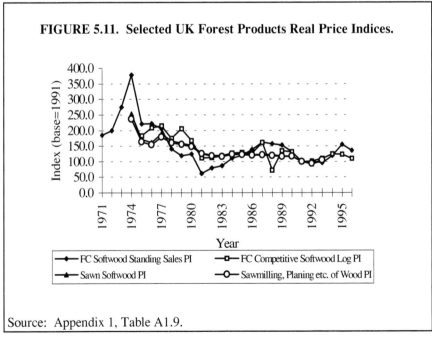

FIGURE 5.11. Selected UK Forest Products Real Price Indices.

Source: Appendix 1, Table A1.9.

Selected export price indices were calculated from Irish trade statistics (Figure 5.12) for the years 1975 to 1992. Comparable data for 1993 onwards are not available. Indices for divisions 24 and 25 show a fall from the mid 1970s to a low in the early 1980s, remaining stable on average over the last 12 years. Division 63 shows a remarkable increase in the real price in the early 1980s falling back thereafter. However, this is in conflict with all other price trends and remains an unexplained aberration.

UK imported cork and wood and softwood lumber prices have remained relatively stable as shown in Figure 5.13.

Thus, for most classes of wood products, the 1970s peak is clearly visible but, on average, real prices have fallen since.

Future Price Trends

Projections for global real prices vary between 0.2 percent and 1.2 percent per annum growth for roundwood prices. Hardwood prices are forecast to rise by between 35 percent and 40 percent in the next 15 years. While prices of high quality sawlogs may rise there are unlikely to be any real price increases for pulpwood and chips. There is no shortage of softwood and so coniferous wood prices are unlikely to rise and a supply shock from the former USSR could precipitate a fall in prices. Forest product prices are not expected to grow in real terms and the availability of wood substitutes will put a ceiling on timber price increases.

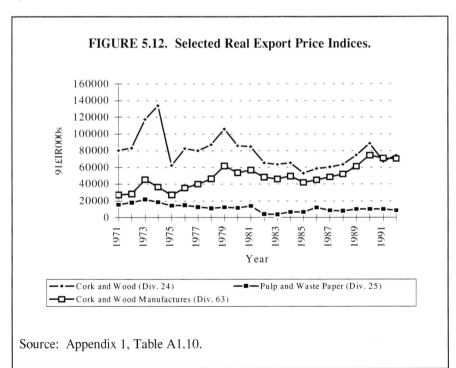

FIGURE 5.12. Selected Real Export Price Indices.

Source: Appendix 1, Table A1.10.

The demand from Medite's expansion and the new Louisiana-Pacific mill may possibly cause a slight rise in standing prices but this will be compensated for by the supply from private harvests by around the year 2004. It is recognised that wood prices are cyclical and fluctuations will occur. While it is perilous to predict so far into the future, the conclusions regarding supply and demand in the previous section suggest that, while timber prices may fluctuate over the next 50 years, it would be unwise to expect them to rise in real terms above average historical prices in the long term.

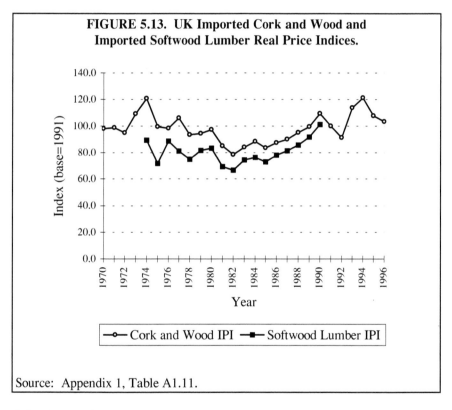

FIGURE 5.13. UK Imported Cork and Wood and Imported Softwood Lumber Real Price Indices.

Source: Appendix 1, Table A1.11.

Price Assumptions

The Forestry Commission also tends to assume that there will be no long run upward or downward trend in timber prices. This assumption is based on an analysis of a time series of prices from 1870 to 1990. The analysis showed that, in any one year, product prices could be up to 25 percent above or below the long run average (Whiteman and Sinclair, 1994). Thus, depending on the year in which the timber is sold its value may be higher or lower than average prices but it is *not* reasonable to predict long run growth in timber prices.

The conclusions of the analysis of markets and prices above suggests that this is a reasonable conclusion and, therefore, for the purposes of this analysis, it is assumed that the most likely prices to prevail are average historical prices.

However, timber values under high and low prices scenarios of historical prices plus and minus 10 percent are also calculated for illustrative purposes.

Shadow Pricing Timber
There is some controversy over whether Coillte exercises market power in the supply of timber to sawmills. If this is the case and market prices are thereby distorted, they would be invalid as measures of the social value of timber.

While there has been some research on market power in the product market and its impact on the forest rotation there has been little written on the impact of a monopoly supplier. Hanley *et al.* (1997) provide a succinct summary of this, relatively sparse, literature. A straightforward economic analysis would suggest that a monopoly supplier will shorten the rotation to restrict output and thereby increase price. However, if there is a fixed forest area, a uniform forest and a constant regeneration cost, Crabbe and Long (1989) suggest that both monopoly and competitive market structures result in the same output and price. Hanley *et al.* (1997) conclude that in most cases where there is potential monopoly power, the monopoly is owned by the state and, rather than being a profit maximiser, the monopoly endeavours to replicate the socially optimal rotation.

However, it is clear that this is not so in the case of Coillte. While the Forestry Act of 1988 does include as one of the company's statutory general duties the rather vague duty of having "due regard to the environmental and amenity consequences of its operations", the four statutory objectives[23] make it clear that Coillte is to be run as a commercial company.

Thus, Coillte is expected to be a profit maximiser. Therefore, economic theory would suggest that there is the *potential* for Coillte to exercise monopoly power and this potential exists partially because competition from imported timber is restricted since timber may not be imported unless de-barked.

The Joint Committee on State-Sponsored Bodies report on Coillte (Seventh Joint Committee on State-Sponsored Bodies, 1997) outlines the controversy surrounding Coillte's pricing of timber in detail. The Irish Timber Council (which represents Irish sawmillers) put forward a number of complaints to the Committee regarding Coillte's pricing policy. It presented evidence that Irish sawmills paid the highest log prices in Europe over the 1994/95 period. This is supported by a consultant's report on the Irish sawmilling industry (Simons,

---

[23] - to carry on the business of forestry and related activities on a commercial basis and in accordance with efficient silvicultural practice;
- to establish and carry on woodland industries;
- to participate with others in forestry and related activities consistent with its objectives, designed to enhance the effective and profitable operation of the Company;
- to utilise and manage the resources available to it in a manner consistent with the above projects.

1991) which states that the main cost competitive disadvantage of the Irish sawmillers is the relatively high stumpage cost of Irish timber.

The Council showed that timber prices charged by Coillte were £9 million higher than UK prices in 1995 and alleged that Coillte has a secret reserve price which, if not met, would result in timber being held back and the price being driven up. It presented evidence that, on the 9th July 1996, as much as 40 percent of timber put out to tender by Coillte was not sold and was re-tendered two weeks later.

Coillte disputed the 40 percent figure. In addition, it claimed that the comparison of UK and Irish prices was invalid due to the variation in tree quality, tree size and species mix. Coillte also point out that they are obliged to supply and adhere to forecasts of production to the Forest Service. The Joint Committee concluded that it would be impossible, without a detailed study, to compare Coillte's prices with UK prices and that imminent changes in Coillte's sales and pricing systems, which will be based on an electronic bidding system, will make such a study unjustified.

While the evidence as to whether market power was exercised in the past is inconclusive, it is clear that there was the potential for such. Thus, it is possible that Irish prices have been distorted. Given this possibility, and given that the only Irish price data available is published by Coillte, it was considered appropriate to use UK prices as a measure of the social value of timber. While the Forestry Commission is the dominant supplier in the UK, the market is highly competitive given the high level of timber imports and the market prices are generally regarded as effectively undistorted (Price, forthcoming). It is therefore unlikely that UK prices are distorted. For this reason, Forestry Commission price size curves for conifers and broadleaves, which give average prices over the 1956 to 1995 period for each category of timber, were used in the timber value calculations below.

ECONOMIC SECURITY

It is often suggested that it is important that there be a domestic supply of wood for an indigenous sawmilling industry rather than relying upon imports. Thus, there is a rationale for subsidising domestic afforestation since the market fails to reflect the importance of substituting for imports in its valuation of the timber benefits of afforestation. Pearce (1991) outlines two arguments which support the view that timber produced domestically is of higher value that imported timber:

1.   The market fails to account for the import substitution argument whereby the value of an avoided import is believed to be higher than the market price of that import;

2.   The market may not anticipate supply interruptions from trade embargoes and other possible interruptions in supply.

The first point is not legitimate. Pearce (1991) points out that, so long as the country in question is a price taker in world markets and no other country has monopoly power in the supply of wood (and ignoring argument 2 for the moment), the law of comparative advantage tells us that the product should be produced where the production process is most efficient, i.e. where the opportunity cost of producing the good is at its lowest such that resources are allocated so that the maximum net benefit is achieved. Subsidising forestry merely to encourage import substitution would divert scarce funds from other sectors where it would be better used.

The second argument is legitimate in certain cases. If the country is heavily dependent on imports of timber, if a trade embargo or some other interruption in supply occurs, this would impose a cost on the nation. For the UK, Markandya, Pearce and Knight (1988) and Markandya and Pearce (1990) evaluate the chances of timber supply interruptions and the consequent benefits of supplying timber domestically in the UK and propose that an increment in prices of 0.2 to 1.8 percent to reflect the shadow value of economic security is justified. Pearce (1991) settles on a premium of 1 percent in his cost benefit study of UK forestry.

The UK figure is inappropriate for Irish timber given that Ireland is more self sufficient in forest products. A crude calculation of the economic security value of Irish timber can be made by comparing the ratio of the value of the production of forest products to the value of consumption in each nation. The figures are 1:3.57 for the UK (i.e. for every £1 of forest products produced there are £3.57 worth consumed) and 1:2.78 for Ireland. This would suggest a premium of 0.78 on prices to reflect the economic security value of Irish timber. However, Price's (forthcoming) suggestion that the self sufficiency of the enlarged EU (due to the accession of Sweden and Finland) renders strategic considerations less relevant seems correct. If the probability of the break-up of the EU and a consequent trade war ensuing is low, so will be the economic security value of Irish timber. For this reason, the operating assumption is that the economic security value of timber is zero.

TIMBER VALUE PROJECTIONS

A perpetual rotation is assumed[24] when calculating the timber benefits of the Forest Strategy. A trial version of PC-FIAP for Microsoft Excel was kindly provided by the Forest Enterprise in the UK. This financial appraisal package

---

[24] In practice, any benefits accruing after 300 years can be ignored. In the case of a zero discount rate, timber values would be infinite so, for purposes of calculation, a 300 year life is arbitrarily chosen.

for forestry enabled timber output and value for various species to be calculated. The present value of timber output over one rotation at the five test discount rates was firstly calculated. A spreadsheet model was then created to simulate a perpetual rotation and to calculate its net present value at the five test discount rates. The timber value under varying price and discount rate assumptions is presented in Table 5.22.

TABLE 5.22. Timber Value of Strategy under Various Assumptions.

Discount Rate (%)	Low Prices (£m)	Average Prices (£m)	High Prices (£m)
0	80,855	89,839	98,823
3	2,759	3,065	3,372
5	798	887	976
8	184	204	224
10	76	84	92

As explained above, the economic security value of Irish timber is assumed to zero. However, for purposes of illustration, a "possible" economic security value is calculated using a premium of 0.78 percent of the timber value. The results under varying assumptions are presented in Table 5.23.

TABLE 5.23. Possible Economic Security Value of Strategy under Various Assumptions.

Discount Rate (%)	Low Prices (£m)	Average Prices (£m)	High Prices (£m)
0	631.0	701.0	771.0
3	22.0	24.0	26.0
5	6.0	7.0	8.0
8	1.4	1.6	1.8
10	0.6	0.7	0.7

If 5 percent is taken to be the social rate of discount and average historical prices are expected to prevail, it is reasonable to conclude that the (discounted) timber value of the Forest Strategy is £887 m. If the timber is believed to have economic security value, this would add £7 m to its value. As expected, the rate of discount used has a major effect on the result due to the bulk of the timber benefits arising at the and of the forest rotation. A 10 percent rate gives a value of just £84 m compared with a value of over £3 billion at a 3 percent discount rate.

CONCLUSIONS

There has been no secular tendency for real timber prices to increase over time in Ireland and the UK. Improvements and increased acceptance by the public of non wood substitutes and reconstituted wood products are likely to limit the potential for increases in timber prices. The predominant species in Ireland is *Sitka spruce*. It has been predicted that there are unlikely to be real increases in global prices for the products made from this type of tree. Competition from British producers will intensify in the UK market and while global prices of high quality hardwood sawlogs are forecast to rise, most Irish standing timber is coniferous. With this evidence it would seem unwise to predict a rise in the real price of Irish standing coniferous timber in the long term and it is a distinct possibility that there may be downward pressure on prices.

The potential does exist for Coillte to act as monopoly supplier and thereby inflate prices. However, the evidence is unclear as to whether Coillte exploits this potential. Given that price distortion may occur, price series provided by Coillte are not reliable as indicators of the social value of Irish timber.

The value of the timber which will be produced under the Forest Strategy is estimated to be worth £887 m in present value terms. The expansion of the EU from 12 to 15 member states and the consequent shrinking of the timber deficit renders the economic security value of Irish timber close to zero.

CHAPTER 6

INPUTS

INTRODUCTION

Chapter 3 explained the importance of using shadow prices where it is considered that market prices are distorted such that they are no longer appropriate as indicators of social opportunity costs. This chapter calculates the input costs of planting forests by, in the first instance, analysing the appropriateness of using market prices and, where it is considered inappropriate, using shadow prices. The usual assumption that is made is that inputs will be used in the same ratios as at present. However, while this is the most reasonable approach, it is clear that, over the long time horizon being assumed, technology is likely to change considerably such that the capital to labour ratio may change and the actual composition of capital may also change. This should be borne in mind when interpreting the results. As is the norm, all data are expressed in real (net of inflation) terms.

LAND

Shadow Price of Land

Under the EU Common Agricultural Policy, farming in Ireland has been heavily subsidised. Similarly, afforestation has been in receipt of major subsidies under the Operational Programmes for forestry. Since land is in relatively fixed supply, this has resulted in the distortion of the price of land such that it no longer provides an adequate measure of the opportunity cost of its use in the absence of subsidies. Since subsidies increase the returns to land use, this drives up the price of land and thus, the shadow price of land will be some fraction of the market price.

With CAP reform, subsidies to agriculture are declining, thus it would be expected that there would be less upward pressure on the price of land. However, there will be an off-setting effect from the increase in forestry subsidies.

Calculating the Shadow Price of Land

For the purposes of this study, the shadow price of land is estimated by calculating the opportunity cost of afforesting the land. Since the majority of the land on which afforestation will take place would be suitable for grazing, this opportunity cost is estimated to be the value of agricultural output forgone. However, due to the existence of subsidies and trade restrictions, when calculating the value of the agricultural output lost, shadow pricing must be used.

Fitz Gerald and Johnson (1996) have recently estimated the shadow price of land for biomass. They estimate that, at present, the price paid for beef is 53 percent above the price which would prevail in the absence of subsidies. They therefore suggest that the returns to cattle farming would be approximately half the existing returns in a free market. They take the returns to cattle rearing on a site suitable for afforestation and then subtract agricultural subsidies. Thereby, they estimate the social value of agricultural output on the site to be approximately £79 per ha.

This figure is then capitalised[25] at the test discount rates to give estimates of the opportunity cost of keeping land under forestry. This figure is, therefore, the shadow price of forestry land. The results are presented in Table 6.1. At the 5 percent discount rate, the shadow price of land is £1,580 per ha. It is interesting to note that, if a zero discount rate is assumed, the shadow price of land is very large in magnitude since agricultural returns in 300 years time have the same weighting of returns in the present.

TABLE 6.1. Shadow Price of Land.

Discount Rate (%)	Shadow Price of Land per ha (£)
0[26]	23,700
3	2,633
5	1,580
8	988
10	790

Land Value
The Forest Strategy projects that 25,000 ha of land will be afforested each year to the year 2000 and 20,000 ha of land will be afforested each year thereafter until 2030.   The value of the land planted for each of the 35 years of afforestation was entered into a spreadsheet and then discounted at each of the test discount rates. Table 6.2 shows the present value of the land required for the afforestation programme under the five test discount rates.

TABLE 6.2. Land Costs of the Strategy at Test Discount Rates.

Discount Rate (%)	Present Value (£m)
0	17,183
3	1,193
5	552
8	250
10	167

---

[25] Using 300 years - beyond this, the discount factor does not change significantly for a positive discount rate.
[26] For the purposes of calculation a rate of 0.000000001 is used.

LABOUR

Shadow Wage Rate

If labour markets clear, the shadow price of labour will equal the market wage. Any increase in employment in one sector of the economy will merely reduce the availability of labour to another sector. However, in a country with a high unemployment rate, it could be argued that an increase in the demand for labour in one sector of the economy will not necessarily displace a job in another sector, i.e. there may be employment additionality whereby if the new job is filled by a person who was previously unemployed, no cost in terms of output forgone is imposed upon society[27]. In this case, the shadow price of labour would equal zero.

The difference between the shadow price of labour and the market wage depends on the degree of displacement. If the new job requires specific skills for which there is great demand in other sectors, it is likely that the market wage will reflect the true opportunity cost of employing an individual in the new job. However, if the job requires skills for which there is an excess supply of labour and the employee was previously under-employed, then the shadow price of labour will be less than the market wage.

It has been the practice of government cost benefit analyses to assume a shadow price of labour of zero. Indeed, many studies carried out for government departments, including the Forest Strategy (Department of Agriculture, Food and Forestry, 1996) treat labour as a benefit rather than a cost. However, this is against the international practice of setting the shadow price of labour at most a fraction below the market wage e.g. in Canada the shadow wage is 95 percent of the market wage and in the UK the shadow wage is set equal to the market wage (Honohan, 1995).

Honohan (1995) argues that "it is hard to justify a shadow wage far below the going market wage" in Ireland. He bases his conclusions on the recognition that migration responds so readily to job creation such that when the economy is in recession, there is net emigration as people travel abroad (mostly to the UK) in search of employment. The exodus of thousands of Irish people in the 1980s demonstrated this quite clearly. The present boom in the economy has resulted in net immigration resulting in a rate of growth of the labour force much more rapid than the rate of decline of unemployment.

Honohan (1995) shows that the key variable required to calculate the shadow wage is the sensitivity of the unemployment rate to job creation which should be measured over an "appreciable" time interval and reduced to present value terms. He estimates the rate of job loss as 0.10 per annum, the rate of convergence of unemployment rates as 0.2 per quarter, and a 5 percent discount

---

[27] For this to be the case involuntary leisure time must have no value.

rate. Using these figures, he calculates the shadow wage[28] to be approximately 0.80 of the market wage. Therefore, he suggests that a reduction of the shadow wage to as low as 80 percent of the market wage "could" be justified. It is important to note that the estimation of shadow wages tends not to take account of the opportunity cost of working in terms of leisure time forgone. This is another argument against a low shadow wage.

If the shadow price of labour is assumed to be 0.8 of the average market wage of a forest worker and the average market forest workers wage net of tax[29] is £7,800 per annum, this gives a shadow per annum wage of £6,240.

In the present economic climate it would seem that it is not justified to use a shadow wage of less than the market wage given that the economy is close to full employment. It is unlikely that the emergence of forests on the landscape will reduce the stock of long-term unemployed. Forestry is not labour intensive and forestry contractors carry out most private planting. However, if there is a downturn in the economy, this could change and therefore, for the purposes of calculation, the cost of labour of the Forest Strategy is estimated using both the market wage and a shadow wage of 80 percent of the market wage. These can be considered to be upper and lower bounds on the cost of labour.

Labour Costs
Employment figures in person years per 1,000 ha of *Sitka spruce* and of Oak were provided by Coillte. The figures were provided on a yearly basis to ensure precision when discounting (assuming rotations of 42 and 80 years for *Sitka spruce* and Oak respectively) but are presented in intervals in Tables 6.3, 6.4, 6.5 and 6.6 to save space.

TABLE 6.3. Labour Costs per 1000 ha of *Sitka spruce* Afforestation.

Years	Mean Person Years Per Annum	Market Wage Bill (£)	Shadow Wage Bill (£)
1-5	6.2	241,800	193,440
6-10	1	39,000	31,200
11-15	1.4	55,160	44,128
16-20	2	77,800	62,240
21-25	1.2	47,280	37,824
26-30	1.2	47,280	37,824
31-35	1.4	55,160	44,128
36-40	1.6	62,240	49,792
41-42	1	15,760	12,608

Source: O'Brien, 1997.

---

[28] Calculated to be 1 minus the present value of the reduction in unemployment expressed as a fraction of the present value of an increase in employment when the unemployed are assigned a zero opportunity cost.
[29] In Cost Benefit Analysis, transfers are omitted.

The figures exclude harvesting because the timber value is calculated in Chapter 5 using standing timber prices. The fourth column of the tables shows the wage bill based on a shadow wage of 80 percent of the market wage as derived above. Employment figures differ slightly for afforestation and reforestation.

TABLE 6.4. Labour Costs per 1000 ha of Oak Afforestation.

Years	Mean Person Years Per Annum	Market Wage Bill	Shadow Wage Bill
1-5	6	236,400	189,120
6-10	0.2	7880	6304
11-15	0.2	7880	6304
16-20	0.8	31,520	25,216
21-25	0.2	7,880	6304
26-30	1.6	63,040	50,432
31-35	0.8	31,520	25,216
36-40	0.8	31,520	25,216
41-45	0.8	31,520	25,216
46-50	0.8	31,520	25,216
51-55	0.8	31,520	25,216
56-60	0.8	31,520	25,216
61-65	0.8	31,520	25,216
66-70	0.8	31,520	25,216
71-75	0.8	31,520	25,216
76-80	0.6	31,520	25,216

Source: O'Brien, 1997.

TABLE 6.5. Labour Costs per 1000 ha of *Sitka spruce* Reforestation.

Years	Mean Person Years Per Annum	Market Wage Bill	Shadow Wage Bill
1-5	8.6	338,840	271,072
6-10	1	39,400	31,520
11-15	1.4	55,160	44,128
16-20	1.2	47,280	37,824
21-25	1.2	47,280	37,824
26-30	1.2	47,280	37,824
31-35	1.4	55,160	44,128
36-40	1.6	63,040	50,432
41-42	1	15,760	12,608

Source: O'Brien, 1997.

The present values of both market and shadow wages for perpetual rotations (afforestation and reforestation) of broadleaf and conifer forest were calculated at all five test discount rates and included in a spreadsheet for afforestation over the 35 years of the Strategy. Labour input for reforestation is slightly different and, thus, the present value of figures in Tables 6.5 and 6.6 were included for reforestation of the sites. The total streams of labour costs were then discounted at the five test discount rates to give the total wage bill at market and shadow prices as shown in Table 6.7. At a 5 percent discount rate, the total wage bill of Forest Strategy is £136 m in present value terms. If a shadow price of labour is taken to be 80 percent of the market, the true social cost of the labour is £109 m.

TABLE 6.6. Labour Costs per 1000 ha of Oak Reforestation.

Years	Mean Person Years Per Annum	Market Wage Bill	Shadow Wage Bill
1-5	9	354,600	283,680
6-10	0.2	12,000	9,600
11-15	0.2	7880	6304
16-20	0.8	31,520	25,216
21-25	0.2	7880	6304
26-30	0.8	31,520	25,216
31-35	0.8	31,520	25,216
36-40	0.8	31,520	25,216
41-45	0.8	31,520	25,216
46-50	0.8	31,520	25,216
51-55	0.8	31,520	25,216
56-60	0.8	31,520	25,216
61-65	0.8	31,520	25,216
66-70	0.8	31,520	25,216
71-75	0.8	31,520	25,216
76-80	0.6	31,520	25,216

Source: O'Brien, 1997.

TABLE 6.7. Labour Costs of the Strategy at Test Discount Rates.

Discount Rate (%)	Present Value at Market Wage (£m)	Present Value at Shadow Wage (£m)
0	3,105	2,484
3	258	206
5	136	109
8	74	59
10	55	44

TABLE 6.8. Non-Labour and Land Costs per ha of
Sitka spruce Afforestation and Reforestation.

Years	Mean Cost Per Annum Afforestation (£)	Mean Cost Per Annum Reforestation (£)
1-5	67.60	72.20
6-10	0.40	0.40
11-15	2.00	1.60
16-20	8.80	7.20
21-25	1.20	1.80
26-30	1.00	1.60
31-35	1.00	1.60
36-40	2.20	3.40
41-42	1.00	1.00

Source: O'Brien, 1997.

OTHER INPUTS

Input costs other than labour and land include costs associated with cultivation and drainage, plants and planting, fertilisation and weeding, fencing, brashing, roads and roads repair, and marking and measuring.

TABLE 6.9. Non-Labour and Land Costs per ha of
Oak Afforestation and Reforestation.

Years	Mean Cost Per Annum Afforestation (£)	Mean Cost Per Annum Reforestation (£)
1-5	177.80	812.00
6-10	0.40	0.40
11-15	0.40	0.40
16-20	2.60	2.20
21-25	0	0
26-30	8.80	7.00
31-35	1.20	1.20
36-40	1.60	1.20
41-45	0.80	1.20
46-50	1.20	1.20
51-55	1.20	1.20
56-60	1.20	1.20
61-65	1.20	1.20
66-70	1.20	1.20
71-75	1.20	1.20
76-80	1.20	1.20

Source: O'Brien, 1997.

Coillte provided estimates of these costs for both afforestation and reforestation by year. The precise year was included in the spreadsheet to ensure precision when discounting. However, in order to save space, total costs are presented in intervals in Tables 6.8 and 6.9.

The discounted non labour and land costs per ha of afforestation and reforestation at each of the five discount rates was firstly calculated. Afforestation costs were included in a spreadsheet for the 35 years of afforestation. Reforestation figures were used subsequently. These figures were then discounted at each of the five test discount rates. The results are presented in Table 6.10 At a five percent discount rate, non labour and land input costs of the Forest Strategy amount to £169 m.

**TABLE 6.10. Non Labour and Land Costs of the Strategy
at Test Discount Rates.**

Discount Rate (%)	Present Value (£m)
0	2,690
3	326
5	169
8	136
10	97

CONCLUSIONS

Taking a five percent as equal the social rate of time preference, the opportunity cost of the land to be afforested under the Forest Strategy amounts to £552 m in present value terms. The shadow price of labour is considered to be equal to the market price of labour giving a total labour cost of £136 m. If the shadow price was 80 percent of the market wage, this cost would be reduced to £109 m. The cost of other inputs amounts to £169 m. The total cost of inputs into the Forest Strategy therefore amounts to £857 m.

CHAPTER 7

CARBON SEQUESTRATION[30]

Perhaps the most widely recognised external benefit of the global forest endowment is carbon storage. Trees absorb (sequester) carbon dioxide (CO_2) and store it in the wood. This carbon is released when the wood, or the products that have been made from the wood, decay. In this way forests delay the release of CO_2 to the atmosphere. This chapter outlines the process by which forests sequester carbon, examines suitable methods to value this process, and finally provides estimates of the carbon sequestration benefits of the expansion of the forest estate under the Forest Strategy.

MEASURING CARBON SEQUESTRATION AND STORAGE

The Greenhouse Effect

The greenhouse phenomenon was noticed as far back as 1824 by a French scientist named Fourier. He recognised the existence of a 'natural' greenhouse effect which provides the temperature necessary to sustain life on earth (Fankhauser, 1995). Certain atmospheric gases combine with short-wave radiation from the sun to warm the earth giving a mean surface temperature of 15 degrees Celsius. In the absence of these gases, the surface temperature would be, on average, minus 18 degrees Celsius. Ignoring water vapour, CO_2 accounts for 50 percent of the warming effect while methane, nitrous oxide, ozone and chlorofluorocarbons (CFCs) account for the remainder. The concentration of greenhouse gases in the atmosphere is therefore a key determinant of the surface temperature of the earth (Cannell and Cape, 1991).

In the late 1800s, Swedish scientists recognised that an artificial greenhouse effect may occur through the burning of coal, a phenomenon they saw as desirable. This global warming effect remained the concern of scientists until President Johnson's Scientific Advisory Committee published the first US report on the problem of global warming resulting from CO_2 emissions. Since then there have been more than 10 international meetings which have sought to control the emission on greenhouse gases (Fankhauser, 1995). This is because global warming is expected to result in climatic changes in both temperature and precipitation which are predicted to cause widespread damage both as a direct result of the temperature increases and indirectly through the redistribution of water supplies and the rise in sea levels resulting from the

---

[30] Note: this study was prepared prior to the Kyoto global warming conference. Therefore, by time of publication the results may be somewhat inaccurate. However, as can be seen in Chapter 15, the carbon sequestration benefits are relatively small when compared to other costs and benefits. Therefore, the overall conclusions of this book are unlikely to be compromised.

thermal expansion of sea water and the melting of glacial ice. While it is thought that some countries may be beneficiaries, the overall effect on well-being is expected to be negative.

As the global economy expands, so does the emission of greenhouse gases. The concentration of methane is expected to double in the next 50 years while the concentration of nitrous oxide is increasing by 0.3 percent per annum. While there have been agreements on the use of CFCs, they are not global and, since CFCs have atmospheric lifespans of between 80 and 120 years, it is expected that emissions are likely to remain at current values. CO_2 emissions result from the burning of fossil fuels, the destruction of tropical forests and the disturbance of soils that store carbon. Less than half of the carbon released remains in the atmosphere, most of the rest is sequestered by the oceans (through photosynthesis by plankton) and some by forests. The extent of the increase in CO_2 concentrations in the atmosphere depends mainly on the extent of fossil fuel burning and the mix of fossil fuels being burned (Cannell and Cape, 1991).

The combined effect of increases in CO_2 and other greenhouse gasses is expected to result in a warming effect equivalent to a doubling of CO_2 by the middle of the twenty first century. Table 7.1 shows the (equilibrium) increases in temperature and precipitation that would result from such a scenario as predicted by five General Circulation Models.

TABLE 7.1. Predictions of General Circulation Models of the Climate Effects of a Doubling of the Atmospheric Levels of CO_2.

	Temperature (^0C)	Precipitation (%)
UK Met Office	+5.2	+15.0
Goddard Institute of Space Studies	+4.2	+11.0
Geophysical Fluid Dynamic Laboratory	+3.5	+7.1
National Centre for Atomic Research	+4.0	+8.7
Oregon State University	+2.8	--

Source: Hulme and Jones, 1991 (quoted in Cannell and Cape, 1991).

There is a considerable body of research which endeavours to predict the net damage that will result from global warming and, in addition, there is a body of research which puts a value on this predicted damage. An in-depth assessment has been carried out by the Intergovernmental Panel on Climate Change (1995). It has produced three volumes on the science of climate change (Houghton *et al.*, 1996), the impacts, adaptation and mitigation of climate change (Watson *et al.*, 1996) and the economic and social dimensions of climate change (Bruce *et al.*, 1996). For industrialised countries it is expected that the damage will amount to 1 to 2 percent of GNP on average (Fankhauser, 1995). Therefore, any process which removes CO_2 from the atmosphere is beneficial from a global point of view.

Carbon Sequestration and Storage by Trees

Through the process of photosynthesis, a tree absorbs CO_2 and stores it in perennial tissue. The storage capacity is a positive function of the age of the tree and the higher is the yield class (and thus the faster is the growth rate), the greater is the storage capacity, all else equal. The storage capacity over time for different yield classes and species can be calculated e.g. for conifer stands of yield class 18, Cannell and Cape (1991) estimate the mean annual carbon storage in stem wood to be 2.5 tonnes of carbon per ha.

CO_2 is released back into the atmosphere when the timber decays or is burned. Thus, the carbon dynamics depend upon the uses to which timber is put. If, after clearfelling of the first rotation, the timber is burned, then the carbon will be released immediately. If, on the other hand, it is put into other uses there will be an overlap with the second rotation. If timber from a *Sitka spruce* plantation is converted to packaging, it will take four years on average for almost all of the carbon to be released to the atmosphere whereas if it is used in construction it will take, on average, about 150 years (Cannell and Cape, 1991). Thus, afforestation has the potential to delay carbon emission to the atmosphere, the exact delay depending upon the species type, the yield class, the rotation length and the uses to which the timber is put.

The Net Effect and Soil Type

When forests are planted on peatland, the peat is firstly drained and then is subsequently dried by the forests themselves. This causes a release of CO_2 from afforested peatland areas. Peatlands are net sources of methane and net sinks of CO_2. Each greenhouse gas absorbs infrared radiation at particular wavelengths. Since CO_2 already absorbs much of the infrared radiation within its particular wavelength but methane does not, the relative temperature increase per molecule increase in CO_2 is less than for methane (Cannell and Cape, 1991). Thus, while the net CO_2 sink on peatland is several times greater than the methane source, the direct global warming potential of a molecule of methane is several times that of a molecule of CO_2 (four times over 500 years and 11 times over 100 years) (Cannell *et al.*, 1993).

Cannell *et al.* (1993) examine whether when afforestation takes place on peatland, there is a net gain or loss of carbon. Drainage of peatland increases aeration and decreases water levels. While increased oxygenation reduces methane release, it increases oxidation thereby increasing the rate of CO_2 loss. However, the oxygenation enhances microbial mineralisation of nitrogen which can increase the net primary productivity of peatland vegetation resulting in an increased input of litter to the peat above and below ground. This can result in either a net loss or a net gain in the amount of carbon stored by the ecosystem.

The authors suggest that if the natural vegetation is replaced by trees it is likely that there will be a gain of carbon in the whole system at least in the short term especially if fertilisers are added. They show that the 16.7 kg C m^{-2} that is estimated to be stored by growing *Sitka spruce* of yield class 12 is equivalent to the carbon stored in 35.5 cm of deep peat and 20.9 cm of shallow peat, i.e. if more than 20 cm of deep peat or 12 cm of shallow peat is lost by decomposition, the carbon loss will exceed the amount of carbon that can ever be added to the soil by growing conifer plantations of yield class 12. If more than 36 cm of deep peat or 21 cm of shallow peat is lost by decomposition, the loss will exceed the maximum additional carbon that can ever be stored in forest soil, litter, trees and wood products.

The length of time before there is a net loss of carbon from the system is dependent on the rate of loss of carbon from drained peat. However, there is considerable uncertainty as to this rate. Taking *Sitka spruce* of yield class 12 on deep peat, if the average sustained loss of peat is 50 g C m^{-2} then a net loss of carbon will not occur until after about 400 years. If the loss is 100 g C m^{-2} a net loss will occur after 175 years and if the loss if 200 g C m^{-2} then the net loss will occur after 100 years. Thus, if it can be assumed that the rate of oxidation of peat is slow then there will be a net release of CO_2 only after hundreds of years. However, if it is fast, afforestation on peat may not provide any net carbon sequestration gain. Thus far, the rate of oxidation of peat has not been ascertained.

VALUING CARBON SEQUESTRATION AND STORAGE

Valuation Techniques
There are three approaches to valuing the carbon sequestration and storage benefits of afforestation:

1.   The Damage Avoided Approach
The Damage Avoided Approach values a tonne of carbon sequestered by the cost of the damage that would have been done by global warming if that tonne of carbon had not been sequestered. Examples of studies which use this approach include Pearce (1991) and Price and Willis (1993).

2.   The Offset Approach
The Offset Approach measures the value of a tonne of carbon sequestered by a forest by the next cheapest alternative method of sequestering the carbon. Since CO_2 reduction technology does not exist, the tonne of carbon sequestered is valued by the cost of substituting a non-carbon fuel for a fossil fuel at the margin (Pearce, 1991). An example of this approach can be found in Anderson (1991).

3.   The Avoided Cost of Compliance Approach
A third approach which is very similar to the Offset Approach measures the value of a tonne of carbon sequestered by the avoided cost of compliance with a global CO_2 emissions reduction policy. In the case of a fixed emissions quota, the measurement is as described in the definition of the Offset Approach above, i.e. by the cost of substituting a non-carbon fuel for a fossil fuel at the margin.

In the case of a carbon tax, the cost of a tonne of carbon sequestered is measured by the tax which would have been paid if the tonne had not been sequestered. In the case of a system of tradeable carbon emissions permits, the value of a tonne of carbon sequestered is measured by the cost of the permits which would have been purchased if the tonne of carbon had not been sequestered or by the income received from the selling of permits due to the tonne of carbon sequestered, i.e. the value of a tonne of carbon sequestered equals the market price of a permit to emit one tonne of carbon.

The Damage Avoided Approach
The Damage Avoided Approach is the most appropriate valuation method for calculating the global external benefit of carbon sequestration by forests since it is the most direct valuation measure.   However, this approach requires information on the damage costs of global warming.   This quality of this literature varies almost as much as the damage estimates it has produced (Table 7.2).

Fankhauser (1995) provides an excellent summary of this research.   Nordhaus (1991) calculated a mid-range value for the social costs of a doubling of CO_2 emissions of \$7.30 per ton of carbon emitted (£4.60 per tonne) thereby suggesting that abatement should only be undertaken so long as the marginal cost does not exceed this amount.   However, his assumption of a resource steady state would require a constant level of CO_2 emissions over time.   This incorrect assumption also implies that marginal damage costs will remain constant throughout.   Ayres and Walter (1991) based their study upon the Nordhaus' methodology and, in addition, they assumed commodity prices to be identical in all countries.   These assumptions make their damage estimates unreliable.

Nordhaus attempted to rectify his earlier mistake using a Dynamic Integrated Climate Economy (DICE) model which included a climate model and a damage sector which feed back to the economy.   The results do not differ much from those in his 1991 study but they rise over time.   Cline used the same model but disputed Nordhaus' assumptions regarding parameter values.   His suggested much larger damage estimates but his results are very sensitive to his assumption of a 2 percent discount rate[31].   Peck and Teisberg (1992) assumed a discount rate of 3 percent and, using a Carbon Emission Trajectory Model, they estimated the marginal social damage of a tonne of carbon emitted to be \$10 in 1990 rising to \$22 by 2030.

One of the most recent and detailed studies of the marginal social damage of CO_2 emission was undertaken by Fankhauser (1995).   By allowing emissions to be exogenously determined, he estimated the marginal damage costs of emissions at the actual emissions level observed rather than at the point where marginal damage equals marginal abatement costs (the result produced by

---

[31] Readers interested in exploring this further should consult Cline (1992), Cline (1993) and Birdsall and Steer (1993).

optimisation models). Having produced a range of possible values depending on the emissions level assumed, he then assigned probabilities to these outcomes. Uncertainty was taken into account by modelling all key parameters as random. The results show a rise in the damage costs of emissions over time as a result of income and population growth. He recommends the use of $20 per tonne of carbon emitted between 1990 and 2000 rising to $23 per tonne, $25 per tonne and $28 per tonne in the subsequent decades (Table 7.2).

TABLE 7.2. Estimates of CO_2 Emission Costs (£ per tonne carbon)

Study	1991-2000	2001-10	2011-20	2021-30
Nordhaus (1991)		4.6		
Nordhaus (1993)	3.2	4.2	5.3	6.1
Ayres and Walter (1991)		18.9-22		
Peck and Teisberg (1992)	6.1-7.3	7.30-8.5	8.5-11	11-13.4
Cline (1992)	3.5-75.6	4.6-93.9	6-113.5	7.2-134.8
Fankhauser (1995)	12.4	13.9	15.4	17

Source: Fankhauser, 1995 and individual papers.

The Avoided Cost of Compliance Approach

The Damage Avoided Approach is the appropriate measure of global carbon sequestration benefits. However, it is not clear that this measurement method is appropriate for measuring the carbon sequestration value to the nation of afforestation in Ireland. In terms of global emissions, Ireland, being a small economy, is a relatively small polluter. All else equal, if Ireland was to reduce its emissions of CO_2 by, e.g. 10 percent, the total impact on the total damage of global warming to Ireland would be insignificant[32]. Therefore, if Ireland acts in its own self interest, it will not reduce its emissions in the absence of an international agreement. This was the attitude taken by HM Treasury to the cost benefit analysis of the National Forest in England[33]. Carbon sequestration values were omitted from the analysis since the UK had not signed an agreement committing it to reducing CO_2 emissions. It was therefore considered that there was no benefit to the UK from carbon sequestration.

In a short time, however, the sequestration by Irish forests could be of significant value to the nation. As a result of the United Nations Conference on Environment and Development in Rio in 1992, the European Union agreed to stabilise CO_2 emissions by the year 2000 but this agreement had no statutory authority. However, in advance of the next round of negotiations under the United Nations Convention on Climate Change in Kyoto, EU environment ministers agreed to a 15 percent cut in emissions of greenhouse gasses from 1990 levels by 2010 (Smyth, 1997). This will be achieved by "burden sharing" between member states as part of the 'Luxembourg Agreement' e.g. Portugal is

---

[32] Indeed, global warming is predicted to give Ireland a significant competitive advantage in global markets for agricultural produce although it will also impose costs (see McWilliams, 1994).

[33] See London Economics, 1993.

being allowed a 27 percent increase while Germany and Britain must cut their emissions by 21 and 12 percent respectively. Ireland is being allowed to increase its emissions of greenhouse gasses to 13 percent over 1990 levels.

The Irish Government has commissioned a study to ascertain the appropriate mix of instruments to achieve this goal (Department of the Environment, 1997b). The possibilities include the encouragement of energy conservation and the use of renewables. However, it may also be necessary to use an economic instrument such as a carbon tax to achieve this objective. In any case significant costs are likely to be imposed on consumers and producers particularly given that Ireland's emissions are already 10 percent above 1991 levels.

It is now widely expected that, at the UN meeting in Kyoto in December 1997, an agreement will be reached to introduce a system of global tradeable carbon emissions permits. The precedence for the allocation of pollution quotas (permits) can be found in the Montreal Protocol for ozone depleting gases. However, the key addition to this system is that these permits would be tradeable. It is also likely that the calculation of a country's emission will be net of the carbon sequestered by its forests.

<u>Tradeable Permits for Carbon Dioxide Emissions and the Costs of Compliance.</u>
The following example provides a simple explanation of how the system might work. Figure 7.1 shows notional global marginal cost and marginal social benefit curves for CO_2 abatement.

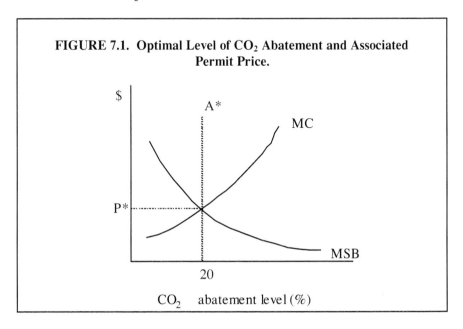

FIGURE 7.1. Optimal Level of CO_2 Abatement and Associated Permit Price.

The intersection point of the two curves indicates an optimal abatement level of 20 percent. In this case, the optimal level of emissions is the present level of emissions minus 20 percent. A number of pollution permits is then issued such that the sum of pollution permitted equals the optimal level of emissions. These permits are then allocated to nations or directly to firms via an auction or they are distributed free of charge ('grandfathering'). Nations or firms are then allowed to trade the permits amongst themselves. In the long run, a market clearing price for permits emerges represented by P* in Figure 7.1. In reality, the abatement level is usually determined by negotiations amongst governments rather than by using estimates of optimal abatement. Supposing that 15 percent is the level of abatement agreed, the market clearing permit price that will emerge is P' (Figure 7.2).

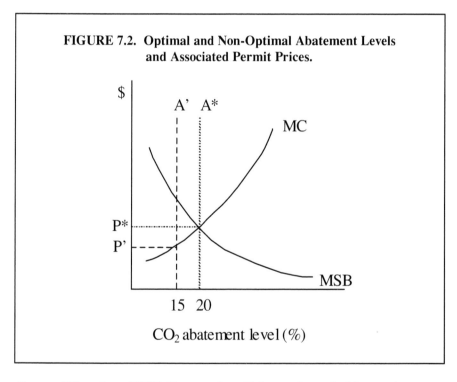

FIGURE 7.2. Optimal and Non-Optimal Abatement Levels and Associated Permit Prices.

Rose and Tietenberg (1993) illustrate the efficiency of a tradeable permit system using an example of a two country world consisting of China and the USA. Figure 7.3 shows that China has a relatively flat marginal cost of abatement curve since it uses relatively older, more polluting technology and relies heavily on coal as an energy source. Thus, the costs of abatement by replacing the old technology with cleaner technology and starting to use less polluting fuels, is relatively low. The USA on the other hand, has already implemented conservation measures and put cleaner technology in place. Any further improvements come at a relatively high cost as shown in Figure 7.4.

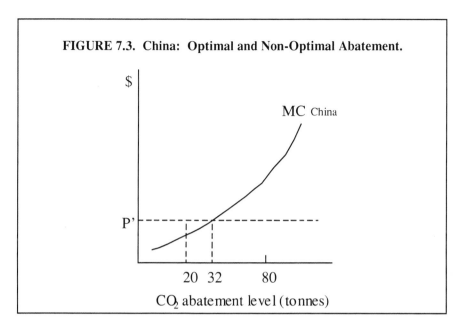

FIGURE 7.3. China: Optimal and Non-Optimal Abatement.

$

MC China

P'

20 32   80

CO₂ abatement level (tonnes)

Supposing CO_2 emissions in China and the USA in 1990 were 70 and 106 million tonnes respectively. Imposing a quota in the year 2010 of 1990 emissions minus 15 percent would allow China and the USA to pollute 60 and 90 million tonnes respectively. Supposing that actual emissions in China and the USA are 80 and 120 million tonnes respectively, this requires China to abate of 20 million tonnes (Figure 7.3) and the USA to abate 30 million tonnes (Figure 7.4).

For economic efficiency the marginal cost of abatement must be equalised across all countries. This will occur if permits may be traded. China will find it beneficial to sell 12 million tonnes equivalent of permits while the USA will find it cheaper to buy 12 million tonnes equivalent of permits. The total reduction is the same but it is achieved at a lower cost. Klaassen (1997) estimates that savings may amount to 1.8 billion ECU (£1.4 billion) per annum for a system of tradeable CO_2 emissions permits based on a 10 percent reduction from 1990 levels.

If a tradeable carbon emissions permits system like the above is introduced, the value of a tonne of carbon sequestered by a forest will be equal to the cost of purchasing, or the revenue from selling, an entitlement to emit one tonne of carbon. Klaassen (1997) estimates that a system based on a 10 percent reduction of emissions from 1990 levels would reduce the marginal cost of abatement from around 23 to 20 ECU/ton (£15 per tonne) of CO_2. The EU agreement is to reduce emissions to 15 percent below 1991 levels, therefore, if this becomes the basis for a global agreement, the long run market price of permits may be slightly higher.

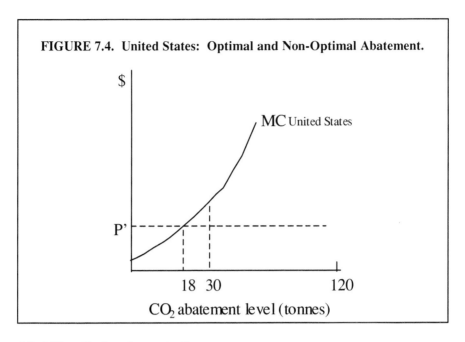

FIGURE 7.4. United States: Optimal and Non-Optimal Abatement.

Modelling Carbon Sequestration
The simplest approach to converting a carbon price into a forest value is to approximate the cycle of carbon sequestration by a simple curve, rising asymptotically to a mean level of carbon fixed. However, this implies that the uptake rate is fastest the beginning of the rotation. Price (1997) points out that, while this formulation gives a reasonable estimate of the carbon sequestered, on average, by a forest and its products, with discounting it is likely to be inaccurate, e.g. using a six percent discount rate, the overestimation of benefits at the beginning of the rotation leads to a three fold over valuation of discounted benefits.

To get around this problem, Colin Price and Rob Willis of the University of Wales at Bangor developed CARBMOD, a computer simulation which models the temporal sequestration of carbon for different yield classes of a range of species of tree based on Forestry Commission yield tables and carbon sequestration figures. For each species type, the model includes assumptions regarding the end uses of the timber to give a complete profile of the carbon dynamics of afforestation. The authors kindly agreed to allow this model to be used for this analysis.

Assumptions

Species and Soil Type
The assumptions regarding species are the same as those used to calculate the timber value in Chapter 5. A perpetual rotation is assumed. Fifteen percent of total planting is assumed to take place on peat soils. Assuming that no broadleaves will be planted on these soils, planting on peat soils will comprise

18.75 percent of all conifer planting. Since the rates of oxidation of peat have not been determined, two possible scenarios are examined. The first is that the rate of oxidation is "fast" such that afforestation on peat soils provides no net carbon sequestration gain. The second is that the rate of oxidation is "slow" such that there will be a net release of CO_2 only after hundreds of years.

Carbon Price
The 'carbon price' used is Klaassen's (1997) estimated equilibrium tradeable emission permit price of £15 per tonne of carbon. However, it is not possible to predict this price with certainty, and past experience of permit markets suggests that there is likely to be some volatility over the first five years before the market settles down. Therefore, results using prices of £10 and £20 are also calculated. For illustrative purposes the global external sequestration benefit of the Forest Strategy is calculated using the marginal damage estimates of Fankhauser (1995)[34].

Growth Rate of the Permit Price
It is sometimes assumed that the carbon price will rise with population growth and/or growth of Gross World Product (GWP) as the pressure on emissions and, consequently, the pressure on the permit price rises. However, in the long run, it is possible that innovation might restrict the growth of the permit price or even reduce it. The inclusion of a positive growth rate effectively reduces the discount rate. The International Monetary Fund forecasts that GWP (adjusted for population growth) will rise by 4.4 percent in 1997. However, this is the fastest rate for more that a decade (Economist, April 26, 1997). An assumption of a long run average growth rate of 3 percent is more reasonable. For the purposes of this analysis, annual permit price increase rates of -3 percent (the rate of innovation outweighing the growth in demand for emissions), 0 percent (the rate of innovation offsetting the growth in demand for emissions), and +3 percent (no innovation) are used.

Discount Rates
Results are calculated for all five discount rates.

RESULTS

Figure 7.5 compares the present value of the carbon sequestration benefit of a ha of *Sitka spruce* of yield class 18 on a 40 year rotation, with the benefits for *Norway spruce* of yield class 14 on a 50 year rotation and Oak of yield class 6 on an 80 year rotation at a range of discount rates (assuming no change in the permit price). It is clear that the speed of growth of *Sitka spruce* gives it the edge from mid to high discount rates but at lower discount rates, oak is of greater value. This is for two reasons: firstly, the slower growth rate is less of a

---

[34] The results will be slightly inaccurate since, strictly speaking, the damage estimates should be calculated at the same rate of discount as is applied to the stream of carbon credits from afforestation.

disadvantage as the future is discounted less heavily and secondly, greater weight is given to the fact that the end uses of the timber will degrade less quickly.

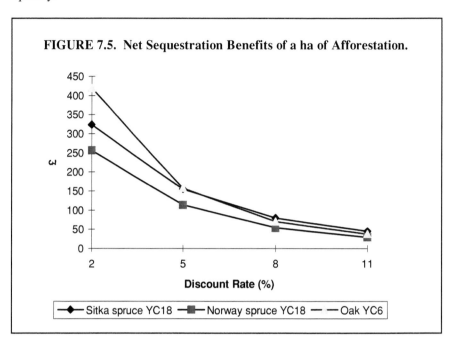

FIGURE 7.5. Net Sequestration Benefits of a ha of Afforestation.

Tables 7.3 to 7.5 present calculations of the sequestration benefits of the Forest Strategy. Each table shows the results for both high and low peat oxidation rates at each growth rate of the permit price (ΔP) at each of the five test discount rates. Table 7.6 presents the global external benefit estimates. By inspection, it can be seen that the key determinants of the magnitude of the benefit estimates are the discount rate and the growth in the permit price. Assuming a "fast" rate of oxidation of peat causes the benefit estimates to be reduced by a relatively small amount. This reflects the assumption that only a small percentage of afforestation will take place on peat soils.

TABLE 7.3. Carbon Sequestration Benefits of the Strategy (£m) with a Permit Price per tonne of Carbon of £15.

			Discount Rate (%)		
	0	*3*	*5*	*8*	*10*
ΔP (%)			Slow Peat Oxidation		
-3	114	36	18	8	5
0	295	114	52	18	10
3	--	295	173	52	25
ΔP (%)			Fast Peat Oxidation		
-3	101	32	16	7	5
0	261	101	46	16	9
3	--	261	152	46	22

TABLE 7.4. Carbon Sequestration Benefits of the Strategy (£m) with a Permit Price per tonne of Carbon of £10.

			Discount Rate (%)		
	0	*3*	*5*	*8*	*10*
ΔP (%)			Slow Peat Oxidation		
-3	76	24	12	5	3
0	197	76	34	12	7
3	--	197	115	34	17
ΔP (%)			Fast Peat Oxidation		
-3	67	21	11	5	3
0	174	67	30	11	6
3	--	174	102	30	15

Assuming that the rate of growth in demand for emissions will be offset by a declining marginal cost of emissions abatement due to technical progress, at a five percent discount rate, the national carbon sequestration benefits of the Forest Strategy range between £30m and £65 m depending on assumptions regarding the equilibrium permit price and the rate of oxidation of peat. Taking Klaassen's (1997) estimate of an equilibrium permit price of £15 and assuming afforestation on peat will produce no net sequestration benefits, this results in a conservative estimate of the carbon sequestration benefits of the Forest Strategy to the nation of £46 m. The global sequestration benefits are estimated to be £40 m.

TABLE 7.5. Carbon Sequestration Benefits of the Strategy (£m) with a Permit Price per tonne of Carbon of £20.

			Discount Rate (%)		
	0	*3*	*5*	*8*	*10*
ΔP (%)			Slow Peat Oxidation		
-3	153	48	25	11	7
0	393	153	65	25	14
3	--	393	230	48	34
ΔP (%)			Fast Peat Oxidation		
-3	135	42	22	9	6
0	348	135	57	22	12
3	--	348	203	57	30

**TABLE 7.6. Global Carbon Sequestration Benefits
of the Strategy (£m)[35]**

	0	*3*	*5*	*8*	*10*
			Discount Rate (%)		
ΔP (%)			Slow Peat Oxidation		
-3	99	31	16	7	4
0	256	99	45	16	9
3	--	256	150	45	22
ΔP (%)			Fast Peat Oxidation		
-3	88	28	14	6	4
0	226	88	40	14	8
3	--	226	132	40	19

CONCLUSIONS

The benefits to the Irish nation as a result of carbon sequestration by forests planted under the Forest Strategy when measured in terms of the avoided damage from global warming may not be very large. However, it seems very likely that a system of tradeable carbon emissions permits will be introduced. If countries' emissions are calculated net of carbon sequestered by forests, it is clear that the carbon sequestered by the forests to be planted under the Forest Strategy will be of considerable value. However, the net sequestration effect is unclear on peat soils. A conservative estimate of sequestration benefits can be calculated by assuming peat oxidation rates are fast such that there are no net sequestration benefits on peat soils. Using a five percent discount rate, this gives a total value of carbon sequestration benefits of the Forest Strategy of £46 m. However, if the carbon price is assumed to grow at the same rate as GWP, this value equals £173 m.

---

[35] The global value will be somewhat higher given that some cattle and sheep will be displaced, therefore emissions of methane will be reduced.

CHAPTER 8

WATER

The chapter evaluates the impact of increased afforestation on water supply and quality. The interaction between forestry and water is examined temporally across the forest rotation from establishment phase to harvesting. Valuation techniques are then examined and the impact on the water supply of the Forest Strategy is valued.

WATER IMPACTS AT ESTABLISHMENT

Ground Preparation
The effect of ploughing, roading and ditching on the environment has been shown to differ depending on soil type, topography and the level and intensity of rainfall. Ploughing removes water, increases aeration and raises soil temperature encouraging mineralisation of organic matter, nutrient availability and root growth. In lowland areas, ploughing may be used to suppress weeds.

Ploughing early in the year will enable spring growth of plants to bind the exposed soil. Ploughing and ditching across slopes helps to prevent rapid runoff and collecting drains level with contours reduce velocity and therefore erosion. However foresters have, in the past, been reluctant to plough at right angles to the slope because furrows can close as upslope turf falls into those below, and because of the need to drain water quickly in order to prevent windthrow. Contour ploughing can be dangerous on steep slopes (Maitland *et al.*, 1990). This should be less of a problem in Ireland, where most of new planting is taking place in lowland areas.

In stable conditions, particularly on porous soils and bogland, water is retained in the soil and released gradually maintaining relatively constant flow rates. Drainage changes the hydrology of a catchment so that runoff is rapid and there is increasing risk of flash flooding. During periods of high rainfall river spates are followed by rapid subsidence to low water flows.

Erosion resulting from increased runoff removes mineral and organic materials, the fine sediments leaving the catchment area over a period of five years or more. Table 8.1 shows the results of experiments which measure increased sediment resulting from ploughing.

Road construction can also cause erosion, but the effects are difficult to separate from the effects of ground preparation, and are extremely variable because of differences in terrain, vegetation cover, and the stage at which the road network is installed. If gravel is removed from stream beds for road construction spawning sites can be damaged or removed (Hickie, 1990).

TABLE 8.1. Suspended Sediments in Streams (kg per ha per annum).

Study Area	Sediment before Plough	Length of Time after Plough	Sediment after Plough
Llanbrynmair area A Mid Wales	37	14 months	90
Llanbrynmair area B Mid Wales	7	6 months	31
Coalburn N.England	30	first 5 years 6 years	240 120
Holmstyes N.England	32	1 year	513

Source: Adapted from Hornung and Adamson (1991).

Streamload studies of coarser sediments have shown effects on channel formation and geometry substrata and on stream biota. This can occur after incision of ditches or road making (Maitland *et al.*, 1990).

Biological Effects of Ground Preparation
Changes in water flow and volume can affect fisheries which may be damaged by increased discharge or excessive drought (Whelan, 1995). Increased turbidity and additional suspended material in stream beds has a marked effect on stream biota. Reduction in the amount of light inhibits photosynthesis and silt smothers algae. Higher plants are also affected by silt and discouraged by shifting sediments. Invertebrates such as mayflies and stoneflies are extremely sensitive to silting and while burrowing worms and midge larvae may increase in numbers, they are less readily available to fish. Gravel spawning beds are clogged by sediment thereby reducing incoming fresh water. Decomposition of organic material brought down from forest waste uses up available oxygen. Several studies have shown that, once ground works have stabilised, recovery may occur after a few years (Maitland *et al.*, 1990).

Kilroy and Murphy (1980) (quoted by Maitland *et al.*, 1990) show that, although increased runoff and erosion may occur in the five years following planting, samples from the Glenamong river, when compared with a survey by Griffiths and Morley in 1961, indicated recovery. There was a greater variety of invertebrates and a similar population of juvenile salmon. However the population of trout was smaller, and of eels much smaller.

In the early years following planting, vegetation growth reduces erosion. However, maintenance of drains can allow increased sediment rates to continue.

Fertilisers
Fertilisers are applied where weather and soil conditions slow the processes which make nutrients available. Table 8.2 contrasts the application rate of fertilisers for forestry with rates for other land uses. The figures suggest that,

while the frequency of application of fertilisers is less frequent on forest land than on lowland grasslands, the amount applied (especially of P and K) in the year of application is greater. Thus, while long term build up of fertilisers in the soil is likely to be greater on lowland grasslands, the potential for fertiliser runoff and therefore the threat of forestry in the establishment phase to fisheries is greater (particularly during rainy periods).

TABLE 8.2. Application Rates of Fertilisers in the UK (kg per ha).

Land Use	N_2	P	K	Method
Lowland Tillage	160	12	47	Annual
Lowland Grass	133	5	23	Annual
Upland Peat Pasture Improvement	50-80	30	80	5 to 7 year intervals
Forestry	150*	60**	100**	*At planting and 6-10 year intervals until closure **6 years after planting and every 3 years until closure

Source: Adapted from Hornung and Adamson, 1991.

Although a buffer strip is normally left, fertilisers may reach streams through furrows or by being washed through soil. The risks are greatest at planting when drains are free from obstruction. Later in the rotation, tree roots may obstruct leakage. Retention is assisted by root uptake by trees and ground vegetation and by microbial action and absorption by soil particles. The slow solubility of some fertilisers helps to prevent rapid loss by leaching. In Scotland studies quoted by Hornung and Adamson (1991) indicate that fertilisers can be detected for up to three and a half years after application but the amounts are unlikely to affect fish stocks and may even be beneficial. Detrimental effects are greatest where water is static. Phosphorus is of concern since it becomes attached to particulate organic matter transported by streams and the bacteria, algae and protozoa attached to it (Maitland *et al.*, 1990). Algal blooms have been reported from salmonid lakes in Connemara where significant changes to the ecology of previously nutrient poor lakes may alter the potential of the lake as a fishery (Hickie, 1990). When deposited as sediment in reservoirs or lakes, the phosphorus may be released over a long periods and may encourage algal bloom. Table 8.3 summarises some studies of the rate of fertiliser loss after application to forestry sites.

In upland agriculture there is little use of fertilisers except for pasture improvement. However, afforestation requires fertilisers on upland acid soils. On lowland sites, rates of fertiliser application for forestry are lower than those for intensive agriculture.

Coillte points out that the application rates in these tables are much higher than that used in Irish forests. Much of the enclosed farmland that transfers from agriculture to forestry will require no fertiliser (approximately 40 to 50 percent of the afforestation area). The poorer areas require one application of P at 350

Kg of Rock phosphate (equal to 50 Kg of P of planting). Nitrogen is applied to poor old red sandstone sites and peat sites that were planted some time ago. These sites may require a number of applications of N for a number of years after planting. With the move away from peat sites the requirement for such a process is less. K is applied to midland sites (O'Brien, 1997).

TABLE 8.3. Losses Following Application of Fertiliser.

Study Area	Source	Fertiliser	Time After Application	Loss as % of Total
Loch Ard and	Harriman	K	3 years	73%
Braes of Angus	(1978)	P	3.5 years	15%
Leadburn	Malcolm and	P	3 years	16%
	Cuttle (1983)	K	3 years	39%
Braes of Angus	Swift (1986)	P	3 years	11%
Glenorchy	Swift (1986)	P	3 years	11%
Glen Orchy	Roberts (1988)	P	3 years	10%

Source: Maitland *et al.*, 1990; Hornung and Adamson, 1991.

Pesticides

Herbicides are used to protect young trees from competition. If applied sparingly with large areas left untreated there is little risk because of attenuation by soil. Glycophosphate, which is used to remove bracken or heather, has low mammalian toxicity, but is harmful to fish. Spraying should be avoided before wet weather. The reduction of vegetation cover by 40 percent or more may affect stream chemistry for five years or more. The use of herbicides is likely to be greater on better soils, however application and frequency are less than in intensive agriculture (Hornung and Adamson, 1991).

Insecticides are generally used only in the case of major infestations. Maitland *et al.* (1990) quote studies which have shown detrimental effects on fish and invertebrates while O'Halloran and Giller (1993) mention that high levels of pesticides have been found in the eggs of Dippers from upland areas.

WATER IMPACTS AT MATURITY

Restriction of Water Flow

Evaporation loss takes place in two ways. Studies have shown that the major difference between forest and non forest evaporation is by means of interception. Interception occurs where rainfall trapped in the canopy is removed by ventilation rather than by transfer to ground water. It is most likely to occur in areas of mist and fog since the fine droplets remain suspended in the canopy. Loss increases with increased amounts of rainfall, windiness, and canopy density. The main reason for the difference in interception loss between trees and grass is the greater surface roughness which increases the evaporation loss, the increase being approximately proportional to the duration of wet conditions (Calder, 1979).

Transpiration is the removal of water from the ground through the root system and elimination via the leaf surface. This is more likely to occur in areas of heavy rainfall because water droplets fall to the ground rather than remaining suspended in the canopy.

Models have been developed for investigation of evaporation from wet heather, grass and forest and in snow conditions. These can be used to predict losses from afforestation on part or all of a catchment. Interception loss is based on an interception loss from forests of 35 percent of annual rainfall. In wet uplands in the UK, afforestation of 75 percent of catchment is expected to result in reduction of runoff of 20 percent (Hornung and Adamson, 1991).

Refinements should be allowed for differences between tree species and between pre-planting vegetation species as well as for dryer uplands. Loss from broadleaved trees is less than that from conifers (Hornung and Adamson 1991). The interception fraction decreases with increasing rainfall.

The simple Calder and Newson (1979) model predictions for planting on the Crinan Canal, West Scotland, where planting began in 1960, suggested that runoff would decrease from 1970 to give a reduction of 26 percent by 2000 remaining the same until 2020, then increasing to 16 percent by 2025 (Hornung and Adamson, 1991).

A report produced for the Institute of Hydrology (Johnson, 1995) presents the findings from a model measuring the response of forest cover ranging from 0 percent to 100 percent. The indications were that, with increasing cover in the two catchments at Balquhidder, the mean flow would decrease, the flow duration curves would shift down and the annual minimum flows would decrease. They show the results from a simple generalised model of annual water use (interception plus transpiration) by individual vegetation types as well as a model for predicting catchment water use which can estimate the probable effects of change in land use. Ideally, such models would be used to assess sites for suitability for afforestation where there is doubt about the effects on the water supply in different catchments.

Table 8.4 summarises the results of various studies on the effect of forestry on hydrology. These results suggest that water flow is reduced by between approximately 20 and 50 percent depending on the former land use, the extent of forest cover, the species type and yield class, and the length of the rotation.

Thinning

Thinning reduces canopy cover. However, the canopy of the remaining trees rapidly fills the spaces, and undergrowth will also provide interception loss. Thinning will cause some of the problems connected with road use and drainage which occurred at preparation so that similar precautions should be taken, (Maitland *et al.*, 1990)

TABLE 8.4. Interception Loss as Percentage of Incoming Rainfall.

Area	Author	Ground cover	Interception
Plynlimon	Newson (1979)	Grassland	17%
Plynlimon	Newson (1979)	60% forest cover	38%
Plynlimon	Smith (1977)	Mature *Sitka spruce*	40%
Plynlimon	Hudson (1988)	Forest age 29 years High rainfall	25%
Greskine	Ford and Deans (1978)	Forest age 14 years	30%
Stocks	Law (1956)	Forest age 25 years	38%
Stocks	Walsh (1980)	80% forest cover	30%
Kielder	Anderson and Pyatt (1986)	Forest age 25 years Forest age 63 years	29% 49%
Kershope	Anderson *et al.* (1990)	Forest age 35 years	38%
Balquhidder	Johnson (1995)	Forest age 50 years High rainfall	28%

Source: Adapted from Hornung and Adamson, 1991 and Johnson, 1995.

Light and Temperature
Reduction of light limits undergrowth beneath trees, and also in stream beds. All else equal, water temperatures are warmer in winter and cooler in summer in the presence of forestry. The diversity of invertebrates appears to be reduced in streams in afforested areas, particularly in acidic streams, but also independently of pH (Maitland *et al.* 1990). Where trees are planted up to stream side, extreme shading can result thereby excluding primary producers. As a consequence, secondary producers and fish are also excluded. The prevention of high temperatures protects salmonid fish from stress but reduces the growth rate of fish and invertebrates (Allott and Brennan, 1993).

Scavenging and Acidification
Effects vary depending on local atmospheric chemistry and frequency of cloud and fog. The presence of fog, mist and cloud cover influence deposition rates. Where low-growing vegetation is replaced by forestry, pollutants and non-pollutants show a net increase. When trees are planted on grasslands there is an increase in dry deposition. The ability of the canopy, particularly in the case of conifers, to intercept dust and aerosols leads to a greater concentration of ions in the throughfall under trees than would be the case in the open.

Gases are absorbed in different ways, some by leaf and stem surfaces (NH_3, HNO, HCl) and are sensitive to surface roughness, therefore changes are seen where smooth grass is replaced by forest. Sulphur dioxide and O_3 are absorbed through stomata and in this case there is little difference in absorption between forest and other vegetation cover. As a result concentrations and fluxes of Na, Mg, NO_3, SO_4 and Cl are greater in drainage waters from forested catchments than from unplanted land on similar bedrock and soil. Soil/water interaction of the increased solutes to acid soil systems and consequent changes in drainage water acidity and aluminium are of concern.

Atmospheric deposition forms an additional source of nitrogen. In areas where there is intensive livestock production, or a high level of air pollution, there is reason for concern.

The components in air causing acidification are SO_2 (sulphur dioxide) from combustion of fossil fuel and NO_x (oxides of nitrogen) from power stations and petroleum combustion. The amounts present in air will depend on proximity to the sources of pollution (Maitland *et al.*, 1990).

Results from Wales suggest that streams from forest areas are more acid and/or have higher aluminium concentrations than from grassland (for similar soil/geology), the difference being greater in high flows. The effect is only seen on acid based soil overlying massive rocks with few readily weathered minerals (silicates/carbonates) in areas of significant levels of atmospheric pollution (Hornung and Adamson, 1991). With Calcium rich soils the acid neutralising capacity is high, so the chemical composition of drainage water is dictated by the soil through which it has passed (Maitland *et al.*, 1990).

Differences in relief, soil, geology and hydrology make comparisons difficult. Some long term studies established around planting time have not shown increases in aluminium/acidity (Hornung and Adamson, 1991) but much depends on the site type examined.

Both native and exotic trees scavenge sulphur dioxide and nitrous oxide from polluted air, and sea salts in coastal areas. However, conifers have a greater ability to scavenge (O'Halloran and Giller, 1993).

The results of an Irish study (Giller *et al.*, 1993) were broadly in line with those from Britain, showing stream acidity and increased aluminium levels in afforested catchments on granite and quartzite while catchments on old red sandstone appeared to be more buffered and were less affected.

Increases in acidity/aluminium have been linked with reduction of salmonids and water invertebrates. The Central and Regional Fisheries Boards suggest that acidification is potentially the most damaging effect of forestry development for fisheries. Increasing acidity leads to mobilisation of aluminium from the soil and increased concentrations in the water. Some forms of aluminium are toxic to fish and other fauna. In Ireland acidification problems in the West have been associated with sea salt scavenged from sea spray during storms and with atmospheric pollutants borne by easterly airflows. Streams in afforested granite catchments in Wicklow and Galway tend to be more acidic and have more aluminium in acidic episodes than those in unafforested catchments. Sea salts and organic acids as well as ammonium sulphate scavenged by the canopy have been reported causes of acidity in these streams (Bowman, 1991; Giller *et al.*, 1993). Streams in Galway have also been shown to have a higher organic content in forest areas. These acidic episodes may be determined by weather conditions. Bowman and Bracken (1993) report a high level of mortality in a sample of brown trout contained for seven days in the acidified Lugduff River which drains an afforested catchment in Wicklow. The fish showed aluminium and mucus coating on the gills. No evidence of stress was found in the adjoining unafforested Glenealo River.

Bowman (1991) found that emissions from the newly commissioned Moneypoint power station had little impact on precipitation. However, deterioration in water quality occurred in some lakes and was most pronounced in the Lugduff River which flows into Glendalough Lake Upper. The catchment of the Lugduff is totally afforested. A neighbouring stream, from a non afforested catchment showed no evidence of acidification and in contrast to the restricted fauna of the Lugduff had an abundant and diverse fauna. The same restricted fauna was seen in inflowing streams from afforested catchments to Loughs Doo and Naminna on the West Coast. Further evidence of acidification associated with forestry was found in studies of Diatoms in sediments which showed two periods of acidification. One, from 150 years ago, associated with mining, which indicated recovery after cessation of mining in the area, the second, and more severe period of acidification, coincided with large areas of the afforested catchment reaching maturity 30 years ago.

In Ireland, areas with acid bedrock overlain by acid soils occur in upland catchments in Wicklow, South Galway, and parts of Mayo, Donegal and Clare (see Appendix 3, Figure A3.3). Most other catchments have soils and rock types which are adequately buffered (Allott and Brennan, 1993).

WATER IMPACTS AT HARVEST

Harvesting usually involves road improvements, felling, extraction, transport and possibly some processing. Little research has been done in the UK or Ireland on the environmental effects of harvesting. However, it is clear that mechanical disturbance increases sediment load and the effects are similar to those which occur at the initial stages of ground preparation and will be greatest where there is heavy rainfall.

Johnson (1995) cites studies undertaken during felling at Kirkton which show that sediment loads from forestry were high in 1986 and 1988, years which were very wet, but low in the very dry year of 1987. This suggests that, even during periods of the most active felling, rainfall is needed for the transportation of sediments. The Salmon Research Agency of Ireland Incorporated (1995) reports a series of serious silt events on the Fiddaun River in Ireland as a result of clearfelling using heavy machinery on steep slopes. Silt loadings have been reduced following the excavation of silt traps.

The removal of the crop removes the nutrients which have been taken from the soil by tree growth. There is an increase in nutrients in drainage waters after felling until regrowth of ground flora provides a sink for nitrates. The amount varies between sites and depends on whether wood is left on the site or removed and the proportion of the site that is felled. If brush is removed, there is a quicker re-growth of ground flora and therefore less nitrate runoff. If brash remains, rotting will return some of the nutrients to the soil. Buffer strips or delayed felling in the riparian zone can reduce loss. On the most acid and least fertile sites, nitrate outputs are small, although they may be long lasting. On fertile sites the output is greater but not as long lasting. The increase in nitrates is not likely to be important except where it diminishes the dilution factor downstream (Hornung and Adamson, 1991). In lowland areas, increased nitrate levels following felling are likely to be similar to those of agriculture, but, as felling only occurs at intervals of 40 to 70 years, pollution will be less. Soil type, water pathways and proportion of catchment felled are important in phosphate output. Phosphate releases from felling debris tends to remain in freely draining soils.

If felling takes place in the riparian zone water temperature rises and solar radiation increases. However, O'Halloran and Giller (1993) report that, in the majority of cases, the increase in water temperature is not sufficient to reach the tolerance limit of resident fish. The increase in solar radiation will, however, increase primary stream production, and consequently changes in stream ecology.

VALUING WATER IMPACTS

Valuation Methods

The Contingent Valuation Method is normally used to assess the value of clean water when the water resource in question is used for recreation when the cost is borne directly by the individual. However, in the case of water pollution from forestry in Ireland, the direct cost would be borne directly by the Central and Regional Fisheries Boards. They are charged with endeavouring to replace damaged fisheries. Similarly, costs of reduced water supply caused by forestry are likely to be borne by local authorities and/or group water schemes. Therefore, Production Function Approaches are the most suitable valuation methods, replacement cost being the most utilised approach. Production Function methods are described in detail in Chapter 3.

Previous Studies

There have relatively few attempts to value the impact of forestry on water quality and quantity. Price (1997) quotes a study by Collet (1970) which established a technique for evaluating runoff loss and the effects of sedimentation on reservoir life in the UK based on the cost of replacement. It is thought that HM Treasury's (1972) study which suggested a cost of £5 per acre afforested (1972£) in North Wales was based upon Collet's method. Barrow *et al.* (1986) surmise from studies in Wales and Scotland that afforestation in upland sites is unlikely to be justifiable given the effect of water loss on hydroelectric power. Stretton (1984) suggested that cultivation of a 100 ha plantation in South Wales imposed extra water treatment costs of £400,000 due to increased sediment while Milner and Varallo (1990) estimate that forestry-induced acidification of waters had a potential cost to Welsh Fisheries of £25 m (Price, 1997). Whiteman (1991) estimates the cost of replacement of the water restricted by forests in East England to be £0.5 m per year. In addition, he estimates the discounted cost of forgoing the use of fertilisers in afforestation to be between £50 and £80 per ha. However, he suggests that the cost of environmental damage is much lower than the cost of abatement and suggests an average figure of £20 per ha.

Stream Flow Reduction
In general, Ireland has a very generous supply of water as a result of a low population density and high rainfall levels. However, the lowest rainfall levels and the highest population levels occur on the East coast, specifically in the Greater Dublin Area. Thus, while increased afforestation in other parts of the Ireland is unlikely to impose a significant cost in terms of reduced water supply, the greater Dublin area is an exception. M. C. O'Sullivan (1996) examines supply and demand for water in this area. Water is supplied from four main treatment works. The Vartry source at Roundwood, the Dodder source at Ballyboden, the upper Liffey source at Ballymore Eustace and the Middle Liffey source at Leixlip. Total reliable production capacity is 442 mega litres per day. Of the four existing abstractions, those on the Vartry and the Dodder are at their maximum hydrological yield. However, the Liffey catchment is much more healthy. Current abstraction at Ballymore Eustace is 235 mega litres per day with a permitted level of 318 mega litres per day. The Leixlip plant has been upgraded to a production capacity of 170 mega litres per day while the abstraction is, at present, only 105 mega litres per day.

Water Demand in the Greater Dublin Area
Current average daily demand is just over 450 mega litres per day (Table 8.5). Present losses are estimated to be 44 percent of the total input, most of which is accounted for by distribution losses.

M. C. O'Sullivan (1996) forecasts future demand for each of these components as follows: Domestic demand is forecast to rise by 0.6 percent per annum due to population growth and by 0.6 percent per annum due to a reduced house occupancy rate and increased appliance use. Metered demand has increased by 4.7 percent per annum over the last 10 years and is forecast to rise by 2.2 percent per annum. Subject to certain recommendations, distribution losses are forecast to be reduced from 44 percent to 16 percent by 2016 and consumer losses from 60 litres to 40 litres per property per day. New supply areas are expected to increase demand by 15 to 20 mega litres per day by 2016. Estimated future demand is shown in Table 8.6.

TABLE 8.5. Current Demand for Water in the Greater Dublin Area.

Components	mega litres per day
Estimated Domestic	164.6
Metered Industrial/Commercial	73.8
Fixed Charge Accounts	7.8
Non-Domestic Unbilled Commercial	9.3
Current Demand	255.5
Customer-side Losses	22.0
Estimated Distribution Losses	160.0
Estimated Suppressed Demand	15.0
Total Demand	452.5

Source: M. C. O'Sullivan, 1996.

TABLE 8.6. Future Demand for Water (Mean mega litres per day).

	1997	1998	1999	2000	2005	2010	2016
Greater Dublin	443.0	423.9	412.9	409.2	420.3	432.2	442.2
Extended Area	443.0	424.9	414.9	412.2	428.3	446.2	462.2

Source: M. C. O'Sullivan, 1996.

Demand-Supply Balance

The average daily demand for water already exceeds the reliable supply; it has proved necessary to choke off supply at certain times of the year. As demand increases the problem will become more acute. Given that almost all of the water supply comes from surface water, if an increase in the forested area were to reduce water supply this would add to the problem. It is difficult to engage in demand-side management because, in the absence of metering, there is little incentive for a consumer to conserve water as it is perceived to be "free". Therefore, for demand and supply to meet, it will be necessary to increase water supply or to ration the supply. Both of these impose a cost, the former would be imposed on the local authority(ies) and the latter on the consumers. The cost to consumers of a reduced water supply is difficult to measure particularly in the case of domestic use. It would probably be necessary to undertake a contingent valuation survey to calculate this cost. It is not politically feasible to restrict water supply so it is likely that supply would be increased. The cost of increasing the water supply via various options is shown in Table 8.7.

TABLE 8.7. Possible Approaches to Increasing Dublin's Water Supply

Method	Increase in Supply (mega litres per day)	Cost (£m)
Repair Leaks	88	5.5
Upgrade Ballymore Eustace	83	36.7
New Bog of the Ring treatment works	5	2.5

Source: adapted from M. C. O'Sullivan, 1996.

Using Whiteman's (1991) method, it is possible to calculate the cost of reduced water supply from the existing forest estate. Most of the water supply comes from sources in Wicklow, Kildare and Dublin. These counties combined have an average forest cover of 8.33 percent such that the non-afforested area is 91.67 percent. Total water supply in the Greater Dublin Area is 442 mega litres per day. Where x is the percentage by which the evapotranspiration rate is above normal due to forestry, the relationship between potential water supply (PS) and actual water supply can be written as follows,

Actual water supply = Potential supply in non-afforested area + Potential supply in forested area reduced by x percent

Actual supply = 0.9167PS + {[PS(1-x)]0.0833} = 442 mega litres per day

$$\text{Potential supply} = \frac{442 \text{mega litres per day}}{0.9167 + [0.0833(1-x)]}$$

Table 8.8 gives the potential water supply and the probable loss due to afforestation for five possible rates by which evapotranspiration is above normal (x).

TABLE 8.8. Potential Water Supply in the Greater Dublin Area and the Probable Loss due to Afforestation.

Evapotranspiration Above Normal (%)	Potential Water Supply (mega litres per day)	Probable Loss due to Afforestation (mega litres per day)
10	446	4
20	450	8
30	453	11
40	457	15
50	461	19

Taking the most recent study on interception loss due to forestry by Johnson (1995) which suggests the loss is 28 percent, this suggests that the probable loss in the Greater Dublin Area is approximately 11 mega litres per day.

If we assume that the forest estate of the three counties from which water is supplied doubles in line with the Strategy, this would suggest a further reduction in the water supply of 11 mega litres per day when the forest matures. According to the figures in Table 8.8, the cheapest way of replacing this water would be to repair leaks at a cost of £5.5 m. Table 8.9 gives the external cost of water loss as a result of the Forest Strategy at the five test discount rates. At a five percent discount rate, the cost amounts to approximately £2 m[36].

---

[36] There may be an external benefit from afforestation where it reduces flooding. There has been no assessment of this benefit to date.

TABLE 8.9. **Water Restriction Cost of the Strategy.**

Discount Rate (%)	Present Value (£m)
0	6
3	3
5	2
8	1
10	0.8

Water Pollution

Due to the site specific nature of the effects of forestry on water it extremely difficult to predict the likely costs of future afforestation. This is particularly the case in relation to water quality. The magnitude of the cost will depend in a large part on the effectiveness of the forestry guidelines with regard to fisheries.

In 1992 the Forest Service published Forestry and Fisheries Guidelines (Forest Service, 1992b). In areas which are designated as "sensitive", i.e. those areas with important fisheries and low buffering capacity (low levels of calcium), applicants for grant-aid who propose to plant an area in excess of 5 ha are expected to consult the Regional Fisheries Board prior to establishment of the plantation, while those in non-designated areas who plant in excess of 40 ha are expected to do the same.

Applicants in designated areas are limited as to how closely they can plant to streams, and when they can carry out work and use pesticides and fertilisers. They are not allowed to interfere with the stream (building fords, or removal of gravel) and silt traps and interceptors must be provided as appropriate.

The Central Fisheries Board and the Forest Service are at present formalising the identification of Designated Sensitive Areas which are vulnerable to acidification. Areas are designated as sensitive if the aquatic zone is part of a recognised salmonid fishery and is a spawning, nursery or angling area, the geology base is poor and, in water samples taken regularly between 1st February and 31st May, the pH readings are greater than or equal to 5.5 or water hardness measures less that 12 milligrams of calcium carbonate per litre or water alkalinity measures less than are equal to 10 milligrams of calcium carbonate per litre. The Regional Fisheries Board will serve notice of designation on landowners and details will be published in *Iris Oifigiuil* and newspapers. These designations are to be reviewed every 5 years.

Acidification

According to Allot and Brennan (1993), the guidelines will be unable to prevent acidification in poorly buffered catchments exposed to an atmosphere charged with acidifying acids (pollutant or otherwise) nor will they protect the soil from organic acids resulting from the drainage and afforestation of peats.

The Forest Strategy restricts grant aid to areas of yield class 14 and above. In addition, it is expected that conventional afforestation will not be permitted in Natural Heritage Areas. From the inspection of the maps in Appendix 3 (Figures 3.1 to 3.3) it can be seen that there is a high correlation between areas designated by the EPA as sensitive to acidification, areas of below yield class 14 and the new Natural Heritage Areas. It seems reasonable to assume, therefore, that *if* it is certain that the rules regarding minimum yield class are upheld and planting is forbidden in Natural Heritage Areas, then the cost imposed by acidification from forests planted under the Forest Strategy will be minimal. The "if" which is italicised above cannot be stressed enough. For the purposes of the overall cost benefit analysis in Chapter 15, the acidification cost of the Strategy will be assumed to equal zero but this will only be a reasonable assumption if the conditions described above are enforced.

The designation by local authorities of areas as sensitive to afforestation as requested by the Minister for the Environment in April 1996 (see Chapter 4) will assist matters. Once these designations have been made, the Forest Service will notify the local authorities of all proposals for afforestation in these designated areas regardless of size. However, the Forest Service will remain responsible for the final decision on the application.

Eutrophication
The extent of eutrophication from fertilisers and pollution from biocides will depend upon the extent to which forestry contractors comply with the guidelines and the extent of consultation with the fisheries boards. Aerial fertilising which is sometimes carries out on Coillte sites was of particular concern but the potential for damage has been reduced due to consultation between the EPA and Coillte prior to fertilising (Bowman, 1997).

It is most difficult to value the likely cost of pollution from an increase in the forest estate. The actual cost can depend very much on particular events e.g. there may be only one or two pollution incidents in a year involving forestry but the costs would be very high if they happened to occur, for example, in areas of great value to angling. While the EPA provides figures for pollution incidents involving agriculture and forestry combined it proved impossible to obtain figures for forestry alone.

While it is not possible to predict the cost of pollution very accurately, Whiteman's (1991) figure of an average net (of the cost imposed by the former land use[37]) discounted cost of £20 per ha gives an indication of the likely order of magnitude of this cost. Table 8.10 gives the net present value at the five test discount rates of the water pollution costs of afforestation under the Forest Strategy assuming a perpetual rotation. At a five percent discount rate, total water pollution costs (assuming an acidification cost of zero) amount to £8 m.

---

[37] The cost imposed by alternative land uses can be very high such as river pollution caused by overgrazing in upland areas. In this case, afforestation results in a net benefit.

TABLE 8.10. Water Pollution Cost of the Strategy.

Discount Rate (%)	Present Value (£m)
0	89
3	12
5	8
8	5
10	4

The total costs imposed by the effect of the Forest Strategy on the water supply at the five test discount rates are given in Table 8.11. At a five percent discount rate, the total cost amounts to £10 m.

TABLE 8.11. Total Cost of Water Supply Effects of the Strategy.

Discount Rate (%)	Present Value (£m)
0	95
3	15
5	10
8	6
10	5

CONCLUSIONS

The effect of afforestation on the water supply is one of the most difficult externalities to value. What has been presented in this chapter is by no means a complete approach. However, it does give an indication of the likely order of magnitude of the cost. At a five percent discount rate, the costs of the effects of afforestation on the water supply amount to £10 m. This shows that, in comparison with the timber value results presented in Chapter 5, the external costs of the Strategy with regard to water are relatively small. However, it is important to stress once more that these figures assume an acidification cost of zero. This assumption is only reasonable if grant aid is supplied to areas of yield class 14 or above only and if afforestation is prohibited in Natural Heritage Areas. This should be borne in mind when interpreting the results of the full cost benefit analysis in Chapter 15.

CHAPTER 9

RECREATION AND TOURISM

This Chapter examines the value of forests for recreation. The uses of forests for recreation is outlined. Existing data on the level of forest recreation is then assessed and the gaps highlighted. New data on forest visits are derived using two surveys. The first estimates annual visits by Irish nationals and gives details of the profile of forest visitors. The second estimates the number of visits by foreign nationals. The supply of forest recreation and the (dis)incentives to supply forests for recreation are then examined. Methods for valuing forest recreation are outlined and estimates of the value of the existing estate are examined. Finally, the methodology for the calculation of the recreational value of an expansion in the forest estate is outlined.

FOREST RECREATION TYPES

Walking
Forests in Ireland are used for walking, enjoying the scenery, camping, pony trekking, horse riding, mountain biking, motorcycling, hunting and orienteering. Waymarked trail walking is a relatively new pursuit in Ireland with the first trail being opened in 1982. In Ireland there are twenty trails and almost all of them have some portion in woodland. The Mountaineering Council has over 3500 members but sales of walking guides are well in excess of this figure (Lynam, 1994). There are an increasing number of accommodation providers who are offering forest walks as a core part of their attraction (Convery *et al*, 1992).

Orienteering
Orienteering is reliant on forests for its survival and its growth and success in Sweden sprang from the right of every citizen to free access to forests. Results are distorted when competitions takes place on open land since it allows competitors to see other runners. In 1993, 153 orienteering competitions were organised under the auspices of the Irish Orienteering Association (IOA) with the number of runners varying between 150 and 600. Assuming an average of only 200, this means that more than 30,000 runs were made last year. Club membership is about 2,100 with an estimated 1,000 others also involved.

Hunting
Forests also have the potential to provide a habitat for game. The National Association of Regional Game Councils (NARGC) has 21,500 members who benefit indirectly from the habitats provided by certain forest types (see Chapter 10). Plantation forestry, however, is of relatively low value for game.

Tourism
Walking is deemed to be the third most important special interest product in Ireland with 230,000 overseas participants in 1991 of which 40,000 had their choice of holiday destination influenced by the provision of this facility. Bord Fáilte's target is to raise these numbers to 350,000 and 70,000 respectively by 1997 (Bord Fáilte, 1992, 1993). In 1991 7,000 overseas visitors participated in adventure sports of which 3,000 were influenced in their choice of holiday destination by the facilities provided and the intention is to increase these numbers by 1,500 and 1,000 respectively by 1997 (Bord Fáilte, 1992, 1993).

EXISTING LEVELS AND TRENDS OF FOREST RECREATION

Existing Data
Published data on forest visits in Ireland is extremely limited. Convery (1979) provided data on forest visits as shown in Table 9.1.

TABLE 9.1. Number of Visits to Forest Parks, 1972 to 1976.

Park		Year		Mean Annual
	1972	*1973*	*1976*	*Growth Rate (%)*
Ards	-	27,845	51,708	23
Avondale	-	18,000	36,000	26
Dún a Rí	38,460	52,475	60,742	12
Gougan Barra	71,000	56,000	58,000	-5
Lough Key	125,000	147,000	264,000	21
JFK	115,300	90,000	80,000	-9
Total	349,760	392,156	550,450	12

Note: Growth rate computed from the widest spread of data available, except for the total, where the rate is computed from 1973 to 1976.

Source: Convery, 1979.

These data show an overall compound annual rate of growth of 12 percent, with considerable variation within this total.

It is necessary to draw together a variety of published and unpublished data in order to assess what has happened since 1976. While there are figures for charged day visits to Coillte's forest parks (Table 9.2) these data are not comparable with those in Table 9.1 since they do not capture the number of visitors who enter on days when no charge is levied. However, aggregate data are provided in Table 9.3.

TABLE 9.2. Day Visits to Coillte Forest Parks for which a Charge[1] is Levied, 1993.

Name	County	Visits[3]
Ards	Donegal	15,000
Portumna	Galway	4,000
Rossmore	Monaghan	1,000
Dún a Rí	Cavan	20,000
Lough Key	Roscommon	60,000
Currahchase	Limerick	6,000
Farran	Cork	15,000
Gougan Barra	Cork	13,000
Killykeen	Cavan	4,000
Donadee	Kildare	4,000[3]
TOTAL		142,000

Notes:

[1] A Charge is levied when it is considered economical to do so e.g. weekends, high season etc.

[2] to nearest thousand.

[3] Excluding caravan park.

Source: Brennan, 1994.

TABLE 9.3. Forest Usage.

Category	Numbers (000s)
All Forest Use[1]	1475
Forest and Other Parks[2]	587
Specialist Groups:	
Orienteers[3]	30
Walkers[4]	230

Notes and Sources:

[1] Figures include visits to Forest Parks, and all other forest visits (walking, orienteering etc.) in Coillte's forests. Source: Brennan, 1994.

[2] Includes National Parks (under jurisdiction of OPW) as well as Forest Parks. Source: Tourism International, 1994.

3 Source: Cunanne, 1994.

4 'Tourist' walkers.

Source: Bord Fáilte, 1992.

These data indicate a reasonably high level of visitation to State-owned forests but negligible growth and a possible drop in visits to Forest Parks since 1976. This lack of growth stands in contrast to the pattern of rapid growth recorded in the case of the 37 National Monuments under the control of the Office of Public Works, where visitor numbers rose from 835,962 in 1989 to 1,481,529 in 1993, an average annual growth rate of 15 per cent; this exaggerates the growth rate slightly, because the 1993 number includes some new sites, notably Céide Fields and Hill of Tara, which have come on stream since 1989 (Scully, 1994).

New Data

It is clear that the data on forest recreation is far from adequate. For this reason, one of the objectives of this chapter is to provide more accurate figures for the current level of forest recreation. In order to do this, two surveys were carried out. The first surveyed a random sample of households in the State in order to estimate the number of domestic visitors to forests in the past year. The second surveyed a random sample of overseas tourists in order to assess the annual number of visits to Irish forests by tourists.

Domestic Visits

As part of the mixed-mode survey outlined in Chapter 13, questions were asked of a random sample of Irish households regarding their visits to forests in the past year. A response rate of 76 percent was achieved giving an effective sample of 2,895 households.

Respondents were asked if any members of their household had visited a forest within the last twelve months. If they replied in the affirmative, they were then asked for the total number of household visits to a forest. The respondents were then asked to give an estimate of the number of household members who were present on each visit. If the total number of visits was six or fewer, the number of household members on each visit was summed to give the total number of "person visits" by that household. If the number of visits was greater than six, the mean number of household members on the first six visits was taken as an estimate of the mean number on all visits. This mean number was then multiplied by the total number of visits to give the total "person visits" for this household. By inspecting the data it could be seen that this approach is likely to be quite accurate since, in virtually all cases, those visiting more than once or twice a year had a similar number of household members on each of the visits.

The results are weighted to ensure that the sample results are representative of the population. The average number of "person visits" when multiplied by the total number of households in the State gives total annual visits to Irish forests. The results are shown in Table 9.4. Forty two percent of households had visited a forest in the last year. Thus, since the majority of households did not visit a forest, the mean number of forest visits for all households is substantially lower than the mean for visiting households. This shows that those who visit forests tend to do so regularly. This is as expected given that number of visits is likely to be a function of proximity to a forest and taste. It was considered appropriate to use a trimmed mean when calculating total visits in order to exclude outliers[38]. This gives an estimate of total forest visits by domestic residents of 7.7 million per annum. This is much higher than would have been expected given Coillte's estimate of visitor numbers to State forests of 1.5 million per annum. However, as can be seen later in the Chapter, it seems that the majority of forest visits are to sites that are not 'manned' and this may explain the inaccuracy of Coillte's figures.

It is possible that the figures are exaggerated since the term "forest" was not defined due to space restrictions on the questionnaire. However, preliminary survey work carried out in the West of Ireland suggests that Irish people have a good understanding of the term (van der Sleesen, 1997) (e.g. they do not consider a public park to be a forest nor do they count searching for a ball in the rough of a golf course as a forest visit!).

TABLE 9.4. Annual Domestic Forest Visitor Estimates.

Mean visits for all households	10.9 (9.5-12.3)[1]
Mean visits for 'visiting households'	24.8 (21.7-27.8)[1]
Trimmed mean (5%)	6.7
Total domestic visits (untrimmed)[2]	12,589,500
Total domestic visits (trimmed)[2]	7,738,500

Notes:
[1] 95 percent confidence interval.
[2] 1,155,000 households.

Profile of Domestic Forest Visitors
As part of the survey, socio-economic information on each respondent was collected. This allowed for the analysis of the profile of forest visitors. The results show that those households with children are much more likely to visit a forest. Half of those households with children had visited a forest in the last year compared with just 37 percent of those without. Older members of society are less likely to visit a forest. Only twenty five percent of households where the respondent was retired had visited a forest in the last year compared with an average of 43 percent. Better off households with a higher level of education are more likely to be forest visitors. Only 23 percent of those households where the respondent was educated to primary level had visited a forest in the past 12 months compared with 65 percent in those households where the respondent had completed third level education. Twenty four percent of those households with a net income of less than £130 per week had visited a forest compared with 58 percent of those with incomes greater than £360 per week. Urban dwellers are more likely to visit forests with 45 percent having visited in the last year compared with 39 percent of rural dwellers.

---

[38] This was to exclude, for example, forest workers.

Visits by Tourists

In July 1996, a survey of overseas tourists was undertaken in conjunction with Tomás O'Leary and Art McCormack of the Department of Forestry in University College Dublin. The overall objective of the survey was to assess the attitudes of tourists to the Irish landscape and, in particular, their attitudes to forestry on the landscape. One thousand tourists were interviewed outside the Dublin Tourist office in Suffolk Street, Dublin. A comparison of the age profile, sex, nationality and frequency of visits of the respondents to the survey with results from Bord Fáilte's visitor surveys shows the sample to be relatively representative of foreign tourists. While not the main objective of the survey, an estimate of the total number of forest visits by tourists can be calculated from the results.

Thirty one percent of tourists visited a forest or forest park during their stay in Ireland. This is quite high given that forests cover only 8 percent of the land area and given that the results of the rest of the survey showed that forests rank well down the list of tourists' preconceived images of Ireland. When comparing responses to a question which asked respondents to rank forested landscapes with other landscape types in order of preference with a question on whether the respondent visited a forest, a chi-square test rejects the hypothesis that the preference for forest and visiting a forest are independent at (p value $<$ 0.00000). The hypothesis that the extent to which the respondent thinks that forestry improves the environment and the respondent's attitude to the level of forest cover (too much or too little) are independent is also rejected (p value $<$ 0.00000). These results suggest the data are quite robust.

It would be unreasonable to assume that such a high percentage would visit forests in the winter. Therefore, for the purposes of calculation, it is assumed no visits take place outside of May to September, but, during these months the rate of 31 percent can be applied to total visitor numbers. The results are given in Table 9.5.

TABLE 9.5. Annual Forest Visits by Overseas Tourists.

Total overseas visitors between May and September inclusive[1]	2,496,290
Total forest visits by overseas tourists[2]	773,850

Notes and Sources:
[1] Source: Bord Fáilte (1995).
[2] At 31 percent.

TABLE 9.6. Total Annual Visits to Irish Forests.

Category of Visitor	*Visits*
Irish Resident	7,738,500
Overseas Tourist	773,850
Total	8,512,350

Combining the results in Tables 9.4 and 9.5 gives an estimate of total annual visits to Irish forests of 8.5 million (Table 9.6).

THE SUPPLY OF FOREST RECREATION IN IRELAND.

While the majority of the forested area is owned by Coillte it is important to note that annual planting by private investors has increased dramatically over the last ten years and this must be taken into account when assessing the future supply of forest recreation. Some of this forestry will not be suitable for recreational use and not all is available for such a purpose.

Forests are increasing in importance for outdoor recreation as public access to farming land becomes increasingly limited. In the UK, the government's "Forestry Review Group" examined the costs and benefits of selling off portions of the Forestry Commission's estate. The Review Group received submissions from some 300 organisations and 3,000 individuals and faced a strong anti-privatisation lobby led by the Ramblers Association which is concerned about the loss of public access. While woodland has been sold to private companies with an agreement to allow public access, this agreement cannot be continued to a second purchaser (*Economist*, February 5th-11th 1994).

The first official way marked trail, the Wicklow Way, opened in 1982 and there are now 20 ways covering 1700 km of walking (Cospoir, 1994). The routes are established in co-operation with Bord Fáilte, Coillte, private landowners and local authorities. Bord Fáilte (1992) estimate that an extra 20 nature trails will be required by 1997 in order to accommodate the increased number of walkers.

Incentives to Provide Forest Recreation in Ireland

Coillte
Coillte estimates that the cost of providing forest recreation in 1993 was £527,496 or £0.36 per visitor (Table 9.7). It is important to note that the figure for total cost is comprised of variable cost and depreciation, i.e. it constitutes the cost of the upkeep of the forests (the maintenance cost) but does not include the fixed cost of establishing the plantation (Brennan, 1994). It also does not include any modification of timber management required to accommodate the recreation use in question.

There is a disincentive to allow access to existing forests for recreational purposes because of fears about damage. However, the greatest disincentive would seem to be public liability insurance. Forest owners are liable for possible large payouts to those who injure themselves while in the woodland (even to trespassers). Coillte (and its predecessor) has paid out over £100,000 in damages to visitors to its forests since 1986 including a single payout of £80,000 for an ankle injury. It faces a possible further £130,000 payout in unsettled cases (Brennan, 1994). The Irish Orienteering Association has its own public liability insurance which indemnifies Coillte and the Minister against claims which arise from orienteering activities. However, other groups do not have their own insurance and there is, therefore, a dispute over who is liable.

Annual revenue generated by Coillte from forest recreation is estimated to be £267,000 or £0.18 per person. Thus net revenue to Coillte is minus £260,496 (Table 9.7), to which must be added the cost of meeting public liability costs. This amounts to Coillte subsidising each visitor by 50 percent (£0.18). It is interesting to compare this with the position in Northern Ireland where revenue from forest recreation is estimated to be £419,000 giving a net revenue of minus £710,000 (Table 9.8).

TABLE 9.7. Coillte Costs and Revenues from Forest Recreation.

Category	Amount (000s£)	Per Visit (£)[1]
Cost[2]	528	0.36
Revenue	267	0.18
Net Revenue[3]	(261)	(0.18)

Notes:
[1]Based on number of Visits of 1.475 million.
[2]Not including costs of public liability claims.
[3]Brackets indicate a deficit.

Source: Brennan, 1994.

TABLE 9.8. NI Forest Service Costs and Revenues from Forest Recreation.

Category	Commercial Recreation[1] (000s£)	Non-Commercial Recreation[2] (000s£)	Total (000s£)
Cost	108	499	607
Admin. Cost	179	343	522
Revenue	190	229	419
Net Revenue	-97	-613	-710

Notes:
[1]Cost of operating camping and caravan sites at forest parks plus services involving the rearing, selling and shooting of game.
[2]Cost of providing amenities at forest parks for day visitors.

Source: Hunter Blair, 1994.

TABLE 9.9. Entrance Fees Charged at Coillte Forest Parks.

Category	Entrance Fee (£)
Adults	1
Car/Family	3
Season Ticket	15 (access to all forest parks)
Coach	16
Minibus	8

Source: Brennan, 1994.

The entrance fees charged at Coillte's forest parks are shown in Table 9.9. A survey calculated the average admission charge to parks (forests and otherwise) in 1994 to be £1.66 with 63 percent of those surveyed rating value for money to be "very good" (TDI, 1994). The parks are also used by a wide variety of groups who apply on an individual basis for permits to carry out certain activities such as orienteering and pony trekking.

Grants for planned recreational forestry are payable from the *Rural Development Operational Programme*. However, grants contribute to establishment costs but not to Coillte's maintenance cost.

From the above it would seem that there is no incentive for Coillte to provide forest recreation under the pricing and other conditions prevailing.

Under Section 12 of the Forestry Act, 1988, the duties of the company are laid out: They emphasise the financial and commercial dimension, including:

The need to ensure that revenues are sufficient to meet all charges (including depreciation); to generate a reasonable proportion of capital needs; to remunerate capital and repay borrowings; to conduct business in a cost effective and efficient manner.

The only oblique reference to recreation is the duty: *to have due regard to the environmental and amenity consequences of its operations.*

Defining "due regard" given the other pressures on the company is a challenge. Under Section 38, the Minister may issue directions in writing to the company requiring the company to, *inter alia, provide or maintain specified services or facilities, to maintain or use specified land or premises in the company's possession for a particular purpose.*

If the company satisfies the Minister that......it has sustained a loss in complying with a direction under the relevant subsection, it shall be entitled to recover the loss from the Minister.

There is an implicit, if rather weak, recognition here that cross subsidising may be inhibiting the achievement of commercial objectives.

Private Investors

Grant Support for Forest Recreation and Amenity Provision
Grants are available for the planned recreational forestry and the improvement of existing woodland under the Operational Programme for Agriculture, Rural Development and Forestry 1994-1999[39].

---

[39] The following details of the amenity grant schemes can be found in Forest Service (undated).

Woodland improvement grants, woodland establishment grants, and facilities grants are available. An existing woodland of over 20 years in age and greater than 1 ha of conifers or 0.1 ha of broadleaves is eligible for a grant to assist with planting, thinning and pruning and the provision of firebreaks, water points and reservoirs. The following are the improvement grant rates:

	£/ha
Conifers	1,100
Broadleaves	2,000

To qualify for an establishment grant, the woodland must be capable of producing a crop of trees of sawlog dimensions and the minimum planting area is 1 ha for conifers and 0.1 ha for broadleaves. The planting may include open space as follows:

Total Project Area	Maximum Open Space
less than 5 ha	30 percent
5 to 10 ha	20 percent
over 10 ha	10 percent

Amenity woodland establishment grant rates are the same as for regular plantation forestry (see Chapter 4) which range from £1,300 to £3000 per ha depending on species types.

The Facilities grants provide assistance for the provision of recreational and amenity facilities such as for walking, rambling, orienteering, equestrian activities and various activity sports and for supporting infrastructure such as signs and car parking. The maximum facilities grant is determined by the total area of the project as follows:

Total Project Area	£/ha
less than 5 ha	1,100
5 to 10 ha	750
over 10 ha	500

Access to a grant-aided forest must be permitted on at least 90 days per year during the period May to September unless otherwise agreed with the Minister. The relevant tourist authority must be notified of, and kept up to date on, the location of the project, its facilities, attractions and opening hours.

The grant rates for the amenity schemes have become more generous and the restrictions fewer under the present Operational Programme. This is probably due to the rather poor progress made by old scheme as shown in Table 9.10.

TABLE 9.10. **Progress of Planned Recreational Forestry Scheme**

Year	Number of Schemes	Area (ha)
1992	4	172
1993	10	253

Source: Forest Service, personal communication.

It is clear that the involvement in Ireland in grant aided amenity/recreational forestry is extremely modest at present. However, it is growing, and if one takes the view that there is a greater demand for recreation in broadleaf forests, then this could tip the revenue streams in favour of broadleaves and increase their rate of planting. However, the long time span required for the development of a forest (particularly broadleaf) capable of providing a recreational secondary use may be seen as prohibitive. For this reason incentives to convert derelict forest (particularly broadleaf or mixed forest) seem most appropriate.

VALUING FOREST RECREATION

Valuation Methods

Recreation is probably the most frequently valued external effect. The principal method that has been used to measure the recreational value of forests is the Travel Cost Method. This uses the cost of travel to the site as a proxy for willingness to pay for a forest visit. In more recent times, the Contingent Valuation Method has been used to assess the willingness to pay a site entry charge. This can then be combined with the estimate of travel cost to give the total willingness to pay for a forest visit. Results from a study by Benson and Willis (1990) which valued the British forest estate using the Travel Cost Method are provided in Table 9.11. Further reference to the study of the recreational value of forests in the UK can be found in Chapter 2 and a more detailed explanation of the Travel Cost Method is contained in Chapter 3.

TABLE 9.11. **Estimates of British Forestry Recreation Values using the Travel Cost Method (Benson and Willis, 1990).**

	Lowest Value Forest (1988£)	Highest Value Forest (1988£)	Mean Value Forest (1988£)
Individual recreation value (per visit)	1.34	3.31	2.00
Recreation value per ha	1.00	428.00	47.00
Total annual recreation value of Forestry Commission Estate (1988£)		53m	

Source: Bateman, 1992.

Valuing the Recreational Benefits of the Forest Estate

Total Value Estimates
Prior to the work in this book, the only piece of non-market valuation research on Irish forestry was undertaken by Hutchinson and Chilton (1994). They examined forest recreation in Ireland and Scotland using Contingent Valuation and multi-site Travel Cost. Thirteen sites were chosen in Ireland comprising 0.7 percent of the forested area. Willingness to Pay (WTP) a site entry charge for a single day visit to a forest varied from approximately £0.80 to £2.18, with an average WTP of approximately £1.50. Some of the most frequently visited sites received a lower average WTP. Since many of these sites are urban forests, WTP is reduced by frequent return visits.

Aesthetic assessments of the sites were undertaken and the authors report a positive correlation between site quality and WTP. Total recreational benefit for the sites studied was £7 m. They estimate total recreational benefit by adding declared travel and other visit related expenditures to average WTP site entry charges which are then raised by estimated visitor numbers. The study finds no relationship between site size and total recreational benefits.

The authors suggest that the generally high value of urban forestry combined with the small geographical size of their market area provides a "strong argument" for more resources to be devoted to this form of land use. The study estimates that over 50 percent of recreational visits took place on sites covering 0.7 percent of the forested area. This would suggest that the majority of subsidies for the provision of forest recreation should go to a small geographical area rather than to all forest owners.

Value for Tourism
As part of the survey of tourists described earlier, questions were included on the questionnaire to provide a crude estimate of the value of Irish forests to tourism. The 31 percent who visited forest parks were asked whether they paid a site entry charge and, if so, the magnitude of the charge. Only 22 percent paid a site entry fee. Such a low figure suggests that many visits take place in areas that do not have 'manned' gates. This may explain the large divergence between Coillte's figures for forest visits and the estimate of total visits in Table 9.6. The admission charges paid are given in Table 9.12. The mean admission charge was £2.41.

Multiplying the mean admission charge by the estimated annual number of tourists who visit Irish forests and were charged a site entry fee [773,850x0.22)] gives an estimated total annual revenue from forest visits by overseas tourists of over £410,295. This figure is low, reflecting the fact that an estimated 78 percent of overseas visitors to forests did not pay a site entry charge.

The 31 percent who visited forests were asked what they would have been willing to pay to enter the forest which they visited. The results are shown in Table 9.13. The mean willingness to pay a site entry charge was £2.05. Multiplying this figure by the total number of overseas visitors to Irish forests (773,850) gives an estimated total willingness to pay for forest recreation on the part of overseas tourists of £1.6 million. This might be used as a crude estimate of the economic value of forest recreation for tourism. However, it does not measure consumer surplus. Rather, the figure represents the potential revenue to forest owners should they be able to capture it.

TABLE 9.12. Admission Charges Respondents Paid to Irish Forests.

£	%
1.00	28
2.50	38
3.00	27
5.00	7

Note:
Mean admission charge excluding zeros: £2.41; 95% confidence interval: £2.15-£2.66

In order to estimate the economic value of forest recreation for tourism it would be necessary to add travel costs. It was not possible in the survey to elicit these costs. However, if, when setting out on a journey, the principal aim was not to visit a forest but the forest was on the way to some other destination, the willingness to pay to enter the forest would accurately measure consumer surplus. However, if a long trip was made for the express purpose of visiting the forest this figure would underestimate consumer surplus.

Table 9.14 shows the difference between the estimated total willingness to pay a site entry charge and the estimated actual payment made. The difference is a clear example of an external benefit.

TABLE 9.13. Admission Charge Respondents would have been Willing to Pay.

£	%
0	13
0.50	12
1.00	28
3.00	34
5.00	13
more than 5	1

Note:
Mean willingness to pay including zeros: £2.05, 95% confidence interval: £1.87-£2.23.

TABLE 9.14. Actual and Potential Revenue from Foreign Tourist Recreational Visits to the Forest Estate and the Partial[1] External Benefit.

	£
Actual Revenue	410,295
Potential Revenue	1,586,393
Partial External Benefit	1,176,098
Note:	
[1]Partial since travel costs not included.	

Value of Future Planting for Recreation

The recreational value of future afforestation is difficult to calculate. The first problem is that data from travel cost studies tend to be very site specific. This is shown in the results of Hutchinson and Chilton (1994) which suggest that there is no relationship between the area of a site and the total value. Indeed some of the smallest sites in their study were the most valuable. It is clear that a large forest in an area of low population density will be of less Use value for recreation than will a small site next to a large town. Benson and Willis (1990) study returned figures for the per ha recreational value of forests of between £1 and £428. This range demonstrates the danger of applying values from one area to another area.

The second problem relates to the danger of applying an average figure where a marginal figure is required. The (albeit poor) data on trends in forest park recreation in Ireland suggest that forest visits are stable (it is unclear as to whether the high visitation rate implied by the results of the household survey suggests that there has been growth or whether previous measures were simply inaccurate). It is unlikely that the relationship between recreational value and forest area is linear. Rather, if it rises at all, it is likely to be at a diminishing rate.

The other problems with the Travel Cost Method are that the benefits measured are gross in that they fail to reflect the value of the former land use for recreation, and the technique is incapable of measuring option value (including bequest value and vicarious value). Therefore, the results of travel cost may not measure consumer surplus correctly. In addition, by using benefit transfer one would not be comparing like with like, i.e. the value of forest parks designed specifically for recreation use will have a much higher value per ha than will the mostly coniferous short rotation plantation forests to be planted under the Forest Strategy.

For the reasons outlined above it was not considered appropriate to use the travel cost method to estimate the recreational value of afforestation under the Forest Strategy. The only technique that can measure option value and measures the net value of recreational benefits is the Contingent Valuation Method. This allows the respondent to 'purchase' the future option of using the forest for recreation either for themselves, for their children or for others. However, this method also is not ideal since it is not possible to give exact details of the location of planting to the respondents. The respondents are therefore buying while uncertain of the product they will receive in the future. It can be thought of as equivalent to buying something by mail order but without the luxury of having a 30 day money back guarantee! This approach can be justified, however, by thinking of the process as being similar to voting. If asked to vote on whether they think the Forest Strategy should go ahead they would also be uncertain of the outcome if the project were to be approved.

Chapter 14 outlines a contingent valuation experiment which assesses the wildlife, recreation and landscape value of the doubling of the forest estate under the Forest Strategy. These three issues are addressed together because of the difficulty of disaggregation. In order to facilitate the valuation of the net benefit of forest recreation, it was necessary to facilitate bids to preserve the present land use for recreation as well as bids for the recreational value of afforesting the land. As can be seen in Chapter 14, this is partially achieved by giving the respondents two opposing views regarding the effect of increased afforestation on recreation, i.e. that some people argue that more forestry will improve opportunities for recreation while others argue it will reduce available areas for recreation. The valuation of recreation is therefore addressed Chapter 14.

CONCLUSIONS

It is clear that there has been a serious deficiency in data on forest use. However, the figures available prior to this study suggested that there has been little growth in forest park patronage. This study has supplemented the available data by the use of two surveys. The first, a household survey, resulted in an estimate for annual visits by Irish residents to forests of 7.7 million. This figure is much higher than expected given that only 42 percent of households visit forests but seems to be explained by a high frequency of visits probably as a result of location and tastes. A tourist survey resulted in an estimate for total visits to forests by overseas tourists of just under 744 thousand giving a total annual number of forest visits of 8.5 million. Age is negatively correlated, and household income and the presence of children, are positively correlated with forest visits. Urban households are more likely to visit forests than are rural households. It is unclear as to whether this result implies that there has been rapid growth in forest visits or whether previous measures were simply inaccurate.

The limited fee revenues generated by forest recreation do not cover the costs of provision. In addition, costs are tending to increase driven by public liability costs. The difficulty of 'capturing' the benefits of forest recreation are demonstrated by the fact that, out of the 31 percent of overseas tourists who visit forests, only 22 percent are charged admission such that the 'uncaptured' benefit amounts to £1.6 million annually.

Benefit transfer using results from the travel cost method is inappropriate for estimating the recreational value of future afforestation. Rather, the contingent valuation method is the most appropriate technique. Therefore, the estimation of the recreational value of the Forest Strategy is addressed in Chapter 14.

CHAPTER 10

BIODIVERSITY

This Chapter examines the biodiversity value of an expansion in the forest estate. Definitions of biodiversity are presented first and the assessment and measurement of diversity is discussed. The scientific literature on diversity in forest types is examined in detail with a particular focus on plantation forestry. Techniques for assessing habitat value and the reasons for conservation of biodiversity are then presented. Methods for assessing the economic value of biodiversity are discussed. The likely effect of future afforestation on biodiversity is then assessed. Finally, the rationale for the valuation method used in this study is outlined.

WHAT IS BIODIVERSITY?

In 1987 the US Government Office of Technology defined "biodiversity" as "the viability and variability of organisms and the ecological complexes in which they occur. "Diversity" is defined as the number of different items and their relative frequency .... organised at many levels from complete ecosystems to molecular structures that are the basis for heredity....".

At the United Nations Rio Summit in 1992 the Convention on Biological Diversity was signed by 154 nations. For this purpose, biodiversity was defined as: "The variability among living organisms from all sources ...... and the ecological complexes of which these are part: this includes diversity within species, between species, and of ecosystems (UNEP, 1993).

ASSESSING BIODIVERSITY

In order to assess biodiversity within a forest it is necessary to obtain figures for the numbers of species within the forest. It is relatively easy to obtain these figures for birds and wild flowers, fungi etc. in which specialist groups take an interest. It is more difficult to obtain accurate figures for less attractive species. The numbers and variety of vascular plants, bryophytes and lichens, shrubs and dwarf shrubs can be assessed relatively easily and accurately. The same applies to most vertebrates. Invertebrates, however, provide by far the greatest number of species and numbers within species, but quantification is very time consuming and the results vary depending on the methods applied (Peterken, 1996).

Indicators for monitoring and assessment include richness, abundance and identity of elements at several levels of biological organisation. For example genetic, species/population, community/ecosystem and landscape. Kangas and

Kuusipalo (1993) estimate biological diversity using three components: species richness (the number of species in a habitat or community), habitat diversity (the number and abundance of different kinds of forest stand assessed by age structure, abundance of dead trees, snags etc., and abundance of edge habitats) and vulnerability (the number of endangered species).

There are two broad approaches to the measurement of biodiversity (Environmental Resources Ltd., 1993).

1   Measurement of numbers of species and populations.
The degree to which species share dominance, or whether one or two species are dominant. Diversity of age, size and vigour. Levels of decomposition. Structure of canopy and foliage distribution. The problem is that it is difficult to compare one set of diversity with another.

2   Use of indicators from which the degree of diversity can be measured. This method is being used in the UK. Based on the theory of succession, i.e. that diversity changes over time in a broadly predictable way. The Environment and Monitoring Assessment Program (EMAP) in the USA has developed a set of indicators based on ecosystem health comprised of:

a)   Response indicators, such as relative abundance of animals, tree growth, foliage condition, Nitrogen export, understory vegetation etc.
b)   Exposure-habitat indicators, such as nutrients and chemical contaminants in foliage, soil productivity, abundance and density of key physical structures, landscape pattern, stable isotopes and mosses and lichens.

Further information of the measurement of biodiversity can be found in Noss *et al.* (1992).

DIVERSITY IN A FOREST

The variety of habitats and diversity of ecosystems within the forest depend on the following factors.

- The age, class and variety of tree species;
- The availability of open spaces;
- The number of large trees, variety of debris and structural diversity;
- The depth of organic accumulations;
- Whether the conditions are moist or dry;
- Opportunities for colonisation from neighbouring habitats.

Diversity in Irish Forest Types
Roughly speaking there are four broad categories of forest in Ireland:

1.   Native Irish forest: This includes stone age pine, hazel, elm and oak which grew when the temperature was 5 degrees higher than today, but as the temperature cooled the lowlands were covered by alder, oak and elm, with pine/brush in the upland areas. The Neolithic people cleared the forests for grazing and crop growing, and the elm died out (Bellamy, 1986; Mitchell, 1990). Little of true native Irish oak woodland is left apart from the remnant sessile oak woods in Killarney, Glenbeigh and Glengarriff. All of these have been invaded by rhododendrons (Hickie, 1990).

2.   Old broadleaf plantations: Many of these were planted in the 18th and 19th centuries. Most are in private ownership (33,000 ha) and many are "neglected". Coillte owns about 12,000 hectares, some of which are in nature reserves (Hickie, 1990).

3.   Scrub Woodland: This includes a variety of native trees such as birch and alder.

4.   Plantation Forest: These forests have been planted this century and most have been established since 1980. Their primary function is timber production and they are mainly comprised of coniferous monoculture (see Chapter 1).

Diversity in Native and Semi-Native Broadleaved Woodlands

Woodlands are dynamic entities, changing with time (Good *et al.*, 1991). Wild animals and plants living within them generally depend on the trees for food and shelter. Some thrive in shade or take refuge within the forest, others find that there is less competition than in the open. There are animals which prey on others and plants and animals which exist on products of decomposition. Some species require a unique combination of vegetation types or certain successional stages or particular breeding locations. Others are more versatile and use a wide range of habitats.

Among the variety of species of plants and animals living in a particular forest attention tends to be focused on particular species of birds and flowers, or visible insects such as butterflies. However, in order for any of these to exist there is a web of supporting species, perhaps of less interest to the casual observer e.g. insects, lichens and fungi.

A natural forest supplies a wide range of habitats. The forest has grown in a series of stages from early colonisation to maturity. The flora and fauna of the original open space will survive to some extent at the forest edges and clearings. Deciduous trees allow penetration of light in season allowing survival of a field layer, typically vigorous and colourful in spring but sparse in winter.

Within an ancient native forest or a neglected old plantation woodland the soil will tend to be rich in nutrients and the microclimate relatively warm and moist. The distribution of the plants will depend on the mixture of tree species, the variety of canopy structure, the position of gaps in the canopy and the shrub layer. The nutrient needs of different species of trees may produce particular plant associations. Mounds and hollows will provide dry and wet micro-habitats, respectively.

Mature woodlands contain large trees and much rotting wood, providing habitats for decomposers such as fungi and for epiphytic lichens. A variety of such species inhabit wood at different stages of decay. Species also vary depending on whether the dead or rotting wood remains on the tree, or has fallen (Good *et al.*, 1991). Bryophyte mats form on fallen logs allowing herbs and seedlings to take root. Rotting trees contain holes for nesting birds, bats and invertebrates. Snags decay and are easier to excavate. Bark beetles and wood-boring insects are plentiful.

Open spaces within and around such woodland will contain cliffs, rivers, pools and mires providing a wide variety of habitats. From the margins and scrublands, colonisers will move into open spaces within the woodland. The woodland will provide shelter for animals grazing on the open ground and birds of prey will feed on the occupants of the open land. Deer will appear at the entrance of the forest, grazing on the vegetation and using the trees for shelter. Bats will use the snags for roosting and feed on the insect life. Birds use the canopy mainly for structural reasons when nesting rather than for food. Butterflies and moths from the open spaces may depend on the underlayer for food for caterpillar stages.

These old semi-native broadleaved woodlands thus provide a wide range of habitats. 40 percent of the European population of badgers exist in Ireland (Hayden, 1995). Bats roost, and feed on the insects which occur in large numbers in forests. Although many forest birds have adapted to life in hedgerows, gardens and farmland, some, such as Woodpecker, Flycatcher and Redstart, which are hole nesters, remain only in older forests where there are decaying trees. These species are regarded as indicator species for ancient forest as are certain lichens and flatworms which are slow colonisers, unable to adapt to farmland or managed forest (Peterken, 1996).

In Ireland about 20 percent of plant species, 20 percent of breeding bird species, and 50 percent of invertebrates are dependent on semi-natural woodland habitats (Hickie, 1990).

Diversity in Upland and Scrub Woodland

These include forest types such as pine and birch. They are more prone to disturbance from wind, grazing and fire. On uplands grazing animals will maintain spaces containing grassland, some tall herb growth, marsh and heathland because tree generation will be limited. There is therefore less canopy cover and more open space. The woodlands can regenerate in open areas and therefore ground cover can merge with species from the neighbouring habitats and there tends to be an interchange of species with areas of woodland fluctuating with grazing habitats. There may be a high proportion of open space because of rough ground, cliffs etc. These areas contain rich assemblages of wildlife of open spaces but a variety of species associated with shady conditions disappear (Peterken, 1996).

<u>Diversity in Plantation Woodland</u>

The effects of a plantation
Plantation forests disturb the existing ecosystem. In the case of commercial plantations, existing vegetation is eliminated and ploughing breaks up pans. On blanket bogs the existing ecosystem is irreversibly destroyed (Hickie, 1990). Improved drainage disturbs the path of small natural streams and soils become dryer. On coarse textured poorly buffered soils conifer plantations may promote soil acidification and slow decomposition leads to deep accumulation of humus in which Nitrogen is trapped[40] (Peterken, 1996).

As in the case of agriculture, gains in productivity have been assured by the use of machinery, herbicides and fertilisers. Pesticides reduce insect populations, and there is a corresponding reduction in the numbers of insectivores. Herbivores may be affected by residues (Hayden 1995). Monoculture plantations provide high yields. However, being less resistant to disease or disturbance, they are fragile.

Grasses, sedges and other flora will grow until heather or other shrubs replace them. Wet or damp habitats dry out leading to the disappearance of plants such as Butterworts, Bladderworts, Bogworts and Sundew. Wading birds and those birds which depend on large tracts of open land for nesting also disappear. However, Golden Plover, Dunlin, Snipe, Curlew and Red Grouse will remain until displaced by the growth of trees. As the trees grow, the number of songbirds will increase. Ground predators (Fox) and aerial predators (Crows, Magpies) will feed on eggs and nestlings but fencing excludes grazing animals. With the richer growth, Stonechat, Whinchat and Meadow Pipit appear. Food and shelter will increase the population of small mammals such as Shrews and Woodmice (Hickie, 1990). Between planting and canopy closure on upland sheepwalks, the increase in ground vegetation promotes a hundred fold increase in the Vole population (Good *et al.*, 1991). Hen Harriers avail of the nesting sites and birds of prey such as Short Eared Owls and Kestrels come to prey on the small mammals. These changes occur over a period of 10 years, the changes being due almost entirely to the exclusion of grazing (Hickie, 1990).

As the canopy closes, the open ecosystems are destroyed and true woodland habitats are established. The need for access to plantations by road or ride

---

[40] See Chapter 8 for further details.

generates a number of different habitats allowing colonisation by edge species where there is sufficient light. However, if these are placed geometrically, they may not be related in such a way as to allow easy colonisation. Cuttings expose soil and rock outcrops. If roadstone is imported alkaline soil may develop in acid areas (Peterken, 1996).

Managed broadleaved or coniferous woodlands differ from natural woodlands in that they contain less dead wood, there is little soil turnover, and open space tends to be more permanent. Single or limited tree species and even aged stands will also reduce the variety of habitats.

The species of tree and the manner of planting will influence the nature and variety of habitat provided in a mature plantation. Plantation size is of importance, 100 hectares is necessary to support a typical woodland bird community. Outside effects penetrate 600 m, therefore a circular forest with 70 hectares may contain no true forest (Hayden 1995). For woodland specialist invertebrates, which require dark, moist and stable conditions, the minimum distance from the edge is about 50 metres (Tickell, 1994).

If modelled on natural native woodland, plantations can produce a variety of habitats. This is especially the case when mixed species and native trees are planted in uneven-aged stands, some of which are allowed to mature and senesce. The benefits may, however, be less than expected. In Britain, new woods established within farmland over the past 300 years have preserved some grassland etc., which might have been "ploughed out" but the woods themselves have not developed into rich habitats. However on upland moors an appreciable woodland fauna can develop within 30 years (Peterken, 1996). This is because upland species are used to disturbance rather than to stable conditions over long periods of time.

Given similar soils, sources of seed for colonisation and availability of light non native tree species will have similar ground vegetation to that of native broadleaf woodland (this is much the same for thinned conifer plantations). Forest structure and macro and micro climatic conditions have an effect on the distribution of epiphytic algae, lichens and bryophytes. High rainfall and humidity produce a wider range of species and greater density of cover than low. There is some evidence that the non-native broadleaves support fewer species of invertebrates. Introduced species related to native species are likely to be colonised more quickly than those which are not closely related (Good *et al.*, 1991).

Mixed woodlands contain a wide variety of habitats especially if native broadleaves are dominant, and if they are planted in uneven age stands, with retention of some mature trees. Native hardwoods may be planted in blocks among conifers. In Finland, Birch has been reported to improve stand stability, stand fertility, stem quality and soil structure as well as to reduce butt rot (Hickie, 1990).

Bird species may be grouped according to breeding and feeding habits. They may need a combination of vegetation types, or certain successional stages, or particular breeding locations. Versatile species use a wide range of niches, specialist species use a narrow range. Not all use trees - they can use the spaces between the trees. Species diversity is lowest at the pole sapling stage. The number of species using each successional stage increases with age. Specialisation is greatest in young stands or mature stands. Middle aged stands generally include many generalist species. Specialists in the early stages tend to be open space species. In the late stages with thicker branches and more rotten wood, they tend to be hole-breeding species (Peterken, 1996). Birds such as siskin and common crossbill require conifers, whereas blackcap wood warbler and green woodpecker need broadleaves (Good *et al.*, 1991).

Conifer Plantations in Particular
Since 80 percent of future afforestation will be conifers, it is worth investigating the level of diversity which is likely to emerge in these plantations.

Conifer plantations differ from broadleaf at the canopy closure stage. Thinning may be reduced in order to prevent wind damage, so that canopy closure can occur at the thicket stage such that ground vegetation may be excluded because of lack of light. This is particularly the case with *Sitka spruce* which generates heavy shade. Even shade loving ferns, mosses and lungworts will disappear. In unthinned plantations the rotation period may be 30 years or less, and the time available for development of ecosystems is reduced. Scots pine and larch allow more light to penetrate and a richer ground layer survives.

Thinning usually takes place at 15 plus years and although bracken and brambles may appear the ground layer remains very limited. Sparrow hawks, long-eared owls and woodcock are attracted, but since there is no woody shrub layer and little dead wood the variety of habitat available means that there is a reduced number of plant, bird and invertebrate species (Hickie, 1990). In the early phases of the forest cycle this increase in diversity can be seen as valuable provided the afforestation is not on too large a scale in comparison with the ecosystems displaced (Good *et al.*, 1991). Decomposers such as fungi are absent unless some rotting wood is available. Red squirrels thrive in conifer plantations, and although the rare pine marten may avail of shelter, if prey is not abundant, it may have to forage outside the forest where it is vulnerable (Hickie, 1990).

After the first felling some dormant bryophytes and herbs may regenerate. On subsequent rotations these will diminish except along roadways etc. Vascular plants tend to vanish and bryophytes increase. On extreme sites (e.g. high altitude or peat) changes will be greatest and a limited range of ecological communities remain (Peterken, 1996). Bird diversity is greater in conifer forests containing broadleaves; the proportions need only be small, and they may be scattered or in groups (Good *et al.*, 1991). The effect on invertebrates is more uncertain. Mature thinned Norway spruce has a richer population than unthinned. Clearfelling can produce diverse and abundant populations if the previous habitat was rich. When dormant deeds remain in the soil, species dependent on wet conditions die out, so that variety is reduced. Rosebay, Willow Herb, Foxglove, Bracken and Bramble will appear. On replanting the cycle will repeat itself (Hickie, 1990).

The number of invertebrate species depends on the tree species. Lodgepole pine hosts 18 while *Sitka spruce* hosts 32. *Sitka spruce* also hosts ninety phytophaginous (vegetable eating) species (Good *et al.*, 1991).

Tickell (1994) quotes work which shows that in even age conifer woods, spiders occurred in comparable numbers to those of oakwoods. The work also shows that the numbers of invertebrates at canopy and ground level increase away from woodland edges. This suggests that substantial areas more than 50 metres from edges (including those of paths, rides etc.) are needed in order to preserve diversity of woodland core species. Conifer canopies support a very high density of arthropods, much higher than broadleaves, perhaps reflecting the higher density and greater longevity of foliage.

Invertebrate communities are dominated by insects feeding on fungi, algae and lichens. Mites, which may be herbivorous or predators, are also abundant. Arthropod groups are comparable to those on broadleaves They are often dependent on structure rather than on particular tree species, thus native species can survive on exotics. Some species are specialist herbivores, requiring a particular species for survival. For example some Lepidoptera and aphids are more species rich on willow and oak, although some are becoming adapted to conifers (Ozanne, 1996).

ASSESSING HABITAT VALUE FOR BIODIVERSITY

The assessment of the value of habitat is extremely difficult. The Nature Conservation Review of 1977 suggests ten criteria for site evaluation for conservation purposes. Size, diversity, naturalness, rarity, typicalness, fragility, recorded history, position in ecological or geographical unit, potential value and intrinsic appeal (Good *et al.*, 1991).

Some of these criteria are difficult to assess and will depend upon who is carrying out the assessment e.g. bird watchers as opposed to game hunters.

1. Size: one large area may be better than several smaller areas. Large areas support more individuals than small. Populations are bigger and rare species less vulnerable to extinction. Isolated gene pools need a connection with the outside and there is a need for exchange of individuals in order to prevent inbreeding.

2. Diversity: while large areas are likely to provide more diverse habitats, variability of aspect, relation to surrounding areas and connection to other similar but separated habitats are all important. Diversity of habitats would generally indicate diversity of species. In using the term "diversity" in defining habitat value it is necessary to differentiate between habitats which are appropriate to the area, or "natural", and those introduced. For example introduction of a Spruce plantation into a moorland area will provide a new habitat, and new species will be introduced. Strictly speaking the diversity is greater, but the value of the new habitat will have to be balanced against any loss of value caused by reduction of the original habitat. The conservationist argues that the increase will not compensate for the natural or semi-natural habitats lost. This argument holds for birds as shown by the relative paucity of woodland as opposed to moorland bird species protected in the British Wild Birds Directive. However, it does not hold for mammals and is doubtful for plants (Good *et al.*, 1991). Many woodland species have become adapted to living in gardens and farmland, while moorland species require large areas of open habitat and would therefore be more likely to require protection.

3. Naturalness: this means different things to different people e.g. grazing and prevalence of fire have denuded upland forests so that heather moorland which, developed, might be considered "unnatural" in the strict sense (although not to be compared with obviously unnatural monoculture plantations which are really "farmed trees"). New plantations can be assessed for naturalness by comparison with natural or semi-natural woodlands, i.e. by looking at the dominant species, structure, range of plants and animals and the variety of niches. The concept of "naturalness" depends on the context. For example, in a rural community, naturalness might be associated with wildness or with communities of native species under the influence of human and environmental factors. Unnaturalness might include "artificial" plantations and other sown crops. In an urban context, natural might include parkland (Peterken, 1996).

4. Rarity: recognition the importance of areas of blanket bog or unmanaged grassland on limestone, dune systems etc. should ensure their protection in the future. A habitat which is common locally may in fact be rare internationally.

5. Typicalness: fragility, recorded history and position in ecological and geographical unit could be taken into consideration by using expert knowledge.

6. Intrinsic Value: Intrinsic value can defined as the value which exists independent of the value of the object to the valuer or to someone other than the valuer (Hanley, Spash and Walker, 1995). Despite the efforts of some, it is clear that, by definition, it is impossible for human's to be able to assess intrinsic value.

7. Potential Value: see 'Option Value' below.

Reasons for Conserving Biodiversity

1. Genetic capital: the greater variety of genetic material the greater the variety of organisms that exist or will exist Loss of biodiversity means loss of options for the future. The variety of plants and animals of use to man which have been recently discovered illustrates the potential value of the undiscovered (see 'Option Value' below). The value of such resources is reflected in the value of patents sought by firms involved in research and development in biotechnology (Aylward, 1992).

2. Resistance to exogenous shocks. crops and animals under threat from disease are in danger when monoculture systems exist. Diverse strains may provide resistance. In the United States introduction of wild relatives of domestic wheat provided annual disease protection valued (1985 prices) at between $50 million and $160 million (Swanson, 1992).

3. The provision or preservation of means to mutate and evolve: the evolution of species and their attributes is a function of diverse ecosystems. The preservation of ecosystems may be of more importance than the preservation of individual species.

There may be a conflict of interest between species and/or habitats e.g. planting of forests on bogland will favour forest flora and fauna and diminish bogland fauna. There are many species which will be maintained because of their apparent economic value. Trees for wood products, plants (corn, potatoes) and animals (sheep, cattle) for food. There are, however, many species which might be considered unimportant by the average person but which play an important part in the ecosystems within which the trees, plants or animals might live. These will include the little known or less visible forms such as invertebrates and soil micro-organisms. Only 1 to 2 percent of the earth's species are higher plants, and less than 0.25 percent are vertebrates (Environmental Resources Ltd., 1993).

Ideally conservation of biodiversity would maintain ecological and evolutionary processes and entire ecosystems, their flora and fauna, before individual species become critically rare (Reed at al, 1992). The argument that every species is invaluable and that minimum levels of species and habitats must be maintained at all costs is not always practical. It may however be considered essential to maintain a current stock of natural capital. This might invoke the safe minimum standard rule which states that a sufficient area should be preserved to ensure the survival of each species or ecosystems unless the costs are intolerable (Randall 1993). This puts biodiversity beyond the reach of routine trade-offs while avoiding giving it trump status. The problem lies in defining intolerable, as opposed to substantial, costs (Randall, 1993).

Conservation of biodiversity will depend on the maintenance of a number of ecological niches appropriate to the site. Conservation of a species is not always compatible with the maintenance of biodiversity. One species may require a habitat less diverse than another in order to survive. For example, the Red Squirrel will survive quite happily in monoculture spruce and therefore conservation of the species would not depend on the maintenance of a diverse habitat. Coniferous forest is in fact the only habitat in which the red squirrel competes successfully against the grey squirrel. While increasing biodiversity, the introduction of broadleaves gives the grey squirrel a competitive advantage by providing survival habitats where the greys exist at higher densities and from which the grey squirrel population expands into the conifer stands depending on the food supply (Gurnell and Pepper, 1991).

VALUING BIODIVERSITY

The external benefit of biodiversity within temperate forests is comprised of:

- Use values: Since wildlife live in forests, hunting/food gathering and bird/animal watching could be considered to be an *indirect use value* but is usually classified as recreation. *Option value* is the value of preserving the forest biodiversity in order to keep the option of benefiting from such uses in the future e.g. the Western Yew in the US has recently been discovered to provide Taxol, an anti-cancer compound (Environmental Resources Ltd., 1993). This shows that it may be of some value to preserve a forest if it might yield other benefits in the future. *Bequest Value* is the value to present generations of preserving the biodiversity within forests for future generations. *Vicarious value* is the value from knowing others are benefiting from biodiversity within forests.

- Non-Use/Existence value: The value attributed simply because forest biodiversity is there.

The external cost in terms of biodiversity of plantation forests is comprised of:

- The destruction of the use and non-use value of the biodiversity provided by the former land use;

- The conflicts of interest between humans and animals such as: predation on domestic stock or harvested wild species by animals living in forests (e.g. foxes on domestic stock); wildlife in forests as a reservoir for diseases (e.g. badgers as a possible reservoir of Tuberculosis and foxes as potential reservoir for Rabies); structural damage to biodiversity through forest recreation (e.g. damage by hunters and walkers) (Hayden, 1995).

Valuation Methods

Pearce and Moran (1994) and Navrud (1993) both explain methods for valuing biodiversity in some detail. Production function approaches tend to be more applicable in cases where forest biodiversity produces some goods which have market value e.g. plants from tropical forests used in the manufacturing of pharmaceuticals. It is much less useful in the case of plantation forestry. The Travel Cost and Hedonic Price Methods are the most popular valuation techniques. However, as explained in Chapter 3, neither of these techniques can calculate the existence value of biodiversity in forests and the travel cost method is also unable to calculate option value. In general, these methods are only suitable for site specific valuations.

The only method which can capture existence value is the Contingent Valuation Method (CVM). This is also the only suitable method for calculating a nation-wide (i.e. non site-specific) expansion in the forest estate. However, the following difficulties arise when using the CVM to value biodiversity[41]:

- Information provision: in the first case, the natural scientists must be able to ascertain the exact effect of an expansion in the forest estate on biodiversity. The second problem is the extent to which the interviewer can convey this, usually complicated, information to the general public in a concise fashion. Lastly, there is the problem that the general public may not be able to comprehend such an explanation.

Spash and Hanley (1994) surveyed a sample of students and the general public about the meaning of biodiversity. In the case of students, the most commonly used word in response to the question were "species", "different" and "biological". In the case of the public the words were "don't", "know", "haven't" and "clue". Respondents were also presented with three possible definitions of biodiversity and asked if they agreed or disagreed with each statement. Less than half of the students and the public agreed with the statements although they were true. When shown the World Resources Institute's definition and asked to score their familiarity with the meaning of biodiversity on a scale from 1 (totally unfamiliar) to 5 (totally familiar), the average score for students was 2.09 and for the general public 1.49. Environmental Resources Ltd (1993) state: "It is likely that biodiversity is 'undervalued' because it is ill understood. Increasing this understanding and making it more widely understood is therefore necessary in order that the full potential or actual value can be assessed in an informed way".

- The "Bambi Syndrome": the general public tends to be willing to pay to preserve "fluffy" or attractive animals such as Whales and Pandas. However, these animals will also depend on an ecosystem which contains less beautiful or less visible plants and animals;

---

[41] Interested readers should consult Hanley, Spash and Walker (1995) for a full treatment of the problems.

- Lexicographic Preferences: the general public may refuse on ethical grounds to trade-off animals and/or plants for money. A contingent valuation survey carried out by Spash and Hanley (1994) showed that about one quarter of respondents had lexicographic preferences whereby they refused to state their willingness to pay and stated that animals, plants or ecosystems had the right to be protected irrespective of the costs to society.

- Disaggregation of values: the CVM in common with most other non-market valuation methods suffers from the difficulty of separating values such as the isolation of the value of biodiversity within forests from other forest values (an example of one attempt using the CVM can be found in Kriström, 1989).

Apart from efforts to value human life, the valuation of biodiversity is probably the most controversial area of environmental economics. This is because we are unable to calculate the intrinsic value of nature. Thus, just as individuals' valuations of market products differ, so will their valuations of nature. As Pearce and Moran (1994) point out, many people feel it quite wrong to allow economic values to play any role in determining that which should and should not be saved by conservation. They believe it is purely a moral question. This is shown in the World Charter for Nature of the UN General Assembly (1982) which states: "every form of life is unique, warranting respect regardless of its use to man, and to accord other organisms such recognition, man must be guided by a moral code of action". However, the economic view *is* a moral view in that it takes a utilitarian approach to conservation (Pearce and Moran, 1994). While this approach may not be acceptable to some it is hard to think of an alternative guide to decision making if one accepts the democratic system.[42]

Alan Randall (1991) states that a sound argument can be made that human preference and satisfaction counts morally but "real and considerable difficulties exist in obtaining reliable empirical estimates of the benefits and costs of preserving biodiversity". He believes that estimates are likely to be volatile because the information base is small, and new information may change perceptions. He concludes: "nevertheless the effort should be made and the results should be taken seriously".

Future Planting and the Value of Biodiversity

Sensitive Areas
In any discussion of the importance or value of forest wildlife, comparison must be made with the habitats which might be replaced by the forest areas. Peatlands and natural grasslands host the greatest diversity of species.

---

[42] Readers interested in investigating this debate further should consult Randall, 1993.

The arrival of man resulted in forest clearance which, combined with climate change, produced the great peatlands. Raised bogs and blanket bogs are now regarded as of international importance, providing rich and varied habitats for a variety of plants which are rare, vulnerable or endangered. These include Bog Hair Grass, Marsh Saxifrages, Bog Orchid, etc. and three species of bird, the Golden Plover, Merlin and Greenland White-fronted Goose (Hickie, 1990). Forest clearance and fragmentation allowed the flora and fauna inhabiting forest glades and other open spaces to combine with vigorous or adaptable forest species to form many of the plant communities which now exist. Natural and semi-natural grasslands, particularly unimproved grasslands on limestone harbour a wide variety of plants, birds and insects. There are 49 endangered vulnerable and extinct flowering plants and ferns on Irish grassland (Temple-Lang and Hickie, 1996).

Designation designed to protect sensitive areas were outlined in Chapter 4. There are three categories of sites designated as environmentally sensitive which will be ineligible for grant aid for afforestation:

Natural Heritage Areas (NHAs) have been designated with the objective of conserving plants, animals and wildlife habitats under the forthcoming Wildlife Act (Amendment Bill). NHAs encompass all other designations. The Forestry Operational Programme (Government of Ireland, 1991) specifically excluded areas of ecological importance (now identified as NHAs) and therefore, the Forest Service has generally refused to give grants for afforestation in these areas (Hickie, 1990).

Special Areas of Conservation (SACs) which cover 2 to 3 percent of the land area have been designated with the intention of conserving plants, animals and wildlife habitats of EU importance under EU Directive 92/42/EEC (Habitats Directive) with responsibility resting with the National Parks and Wildlife Service, the Department of Arts, Culture and the Gaeltacht and the Commission of the European Communities. SACs will effectively result in land owners having to apply to the EU if they wish to engage in any potentially damaging land use activity. It would therefore be expected that afforestation would be ruled out in all of these areas. In addition, the Habitats Directive prohibits activities which take place outside SACs but which may damage them (Hickie, 1990).

Special Protection Areas (SPAs) are designated under the Birds Directive. The habitat requirements of listed bird species must be taken into account in development activities, including development in areas outside designated sites (Hickie, 1990).

Net Effects of Future Afforestation
Broadleaves require mineral soils to grow properly and will therefore be located on mineral soils rather than on peats. In addition, the minimum yield class of conifers which is eligible for grant aid is 14 and deep peat generally returns a

lower yield than this. This restriction alone will limit grant-aided afforestation on bogland. Inspection of the maps in Appendix 3 shows a high correlation between areas with soils of below yield class 14 and Natural Heritage Areas. On the assumption that afforestation will be refused grant aid in NHAs and on soils of below yield class 14, afforestation under the Forest Strategy will not pose a major threat to biodiversity in Ireland. Given that most afforestation will take place on lowland areas formerly used for poor quality grazing, it is likely that afforestation will merely cause one rather limited diversity of species to be replaced by another limited diversity. It is therefore a matter of opinion (and some disagreement) as to whether or not the Forest Strategy is likely to be beneficial from the point of view of biodiversity and will very much depend on the interests of the individual.

Valuation of these Effects
The only method capable of assessing the biodiversity value of future afforestation is the Contingent Valuation Method. Chapter 14 outlines a contingent valuation experiment which assesses the wildlife, recreation and landscape value of a doubling of the forest estate. These three issues are addressed together due to the difficulty of disaggregation discussed above.

It was decided that it would be inappropriate to use the term "biodiversity" given the results of Spash and Hanley (1994) referred to above. Rather, the term "wildlife" was used despite its inadequacies. It was considered that the scientific information regarding the effect of increased afforestation on wildlife was not sufficiently clear to allow an unbiased summary of the wildlife effects of an expansion in the forest estate to be given to respondents. In any case, it would not have been possible to give a concise and easily understood explanation. It was therefore decided that the respondents would be given two opinions regarding the likely net impact of an expansion in the forest estate on wildlife, i.e. the respondents were told that, on balance, some people believe that an expansion in the estate will create better wildlife habitats while others feel it will destroy wildlife habitats. While this could not be considered the ideal approach, it was considered the best possible approach in the circumstances and the most appropriate given the conclusion above that the net effects of habitat replacement are likely to be a matter of opinion. The biodiversity issue is therefore addressed in Chapter 14.

CONCLUSIONS

The afforestation that is planned under the Forest Strategy has the potential to destroy valuable habitats if planting takes place in 'sensitive' areas. However, if planting is kept out of NHAs and sensitive areas to be designated by local authorities, the threat to biodiversity is low such that one rather limited diversity will be replaced by another limited diversity. The valuation of biodiversity is extremely difficult when existence values are thought to be significant. This is because there is often a lack of knowledge of the precise effects a proposed development will have on an ecosystem and there is also the difficulty of describing these effects in a contingent valuation questionnaire. In addition, there are a number of other difficulties with contingent valuation. Nevertheless it is the only method which can calculate existence value. Therefore, the estimation of the biodiversity value of the Forest Strategy is addressed in Chapter 14.

CHAPTER 11

LANDSCAPE

Landscape effects are probably the most controversial externalities of forestry. This chapter examines the landscape value of the expansion of the forest estate under the Forest Strategy. The impact of afforestation on the landscape is first examined. Assessment methods are then outlined. Landscape Valuation methods are explored. The rationale for the valuation method used in this book is outlined. Finally, an example of a valuation procedure is summarised.

LANDSCAPE IMPACTS

Ireland is unusual in that the majority of the present forest estate has been planted this century. In the nineteenth century most forestry was confined to large estates, behind walls and on low lying land. Some authors suggest that this created considerable bad feeling amongst the local population, the forests being associated with the oppressive landlord class. Ireland entered this century with most of its indigenous forest having been destroyed. However, as outlined in Chapter 1, in the 1980s and 90s afforestation was revived and the visual impact of the rapid land use change that is ensuing has become an issue of concern.

This concern arises for a number of reasons. Over 80 percent of the forest area planted each year is covered with conifers. The species planted has been predominantly *Sitka spruce*. This is an evergreen coniferous species native to the coastal belt of North America. This species was chosen as it thrives in areas of high rainfall and humidity and is particularly productive on Irish land. It therefore became the basis for the drive by the State Forest Service to achieve commercial viability. In addition, this species was chosen for the secondary reason that it could grow on relatively unproductive upland sites. State planting in the twentieth century took place on these upland sites as the place of the forest was perceived to be confined to land unsuitable for agriculture. The consequent coniferous monoculture plantations that have been developed have a major impact on the landscape particularly in upland areas which are more visible to the human eye.

The introduction of the first EU Forestry Operational Programme in 1989 resulted in increased returns from afforestation just as the returns from traditional agriculture began to fall. This has had the beneficial effect of changing the type of land being afforested. Afforestation has moved "down the hill" onto highly productive lowland areas, where forestry is less obtrusive. This has helped to ameliorate some of the negative visual impacts. However, there is still pressure, mainly from farming organisations, to confine forestry to "bad land". This does not make sense commercially or environmentally.

Broadleaves are not an option on poor quality sites and thus, this type of policy accentuates the monoculture problem and increases the negative visual impact further by pushing forestry onto higher land.

The visual impact of forestry is probably the largest and most immediate effect upon the human environment. Depending upon one's opinion, forestry can be seen to enhance the landscape or to destroy it. Some see pleasant views as a positive side-effect of afforestation and forests can provide the backdrop to a large range of recreational activities (see Chapter 9) and consequently can have a beneficial effect on the tourist industry and on local inhabitants. However, there is a potentially negative implication for the local population and for tourism where forests are perceived to be blocking views, causing claustrophobia, creating angular shapes on the landscape, and providing a dense single species and colour effect. In terms of the forest rotation, the most serious negative landscape impact occurs at clearfelling.

Prior to this study, no research had been undertaken to assess the attitude of the public regarding the effect of afforestation on the landscape. Anecdotal evidence, in the form of newspaper articles and letters to the newspapers suggests that the landscape impact of the present planting programme is negative. However, the results of the public preference survey in Chapter 13 suggest that this is not the case. The results of a tourist survey carried out in conjunction with Art McCormack and Tomás O'Leary of the Department of Forestry in UCD (referred to in Chapter 9) shows the existing forest estate to be beneficial for tourism. Seventy seven percent of tourists are of the opinion that forests improve the Irish landscape while just over half believe there is "too little" forestry in Ireland.

Regulations

Forest Service Guidelines
The Forest Service provides landscape guidelines (Forest Service, 1992c) which have the objective of emphasising "diversity in planting and a forest outline and pattern which are visually acceptable, while recognising the constraints of the forest as a productive system and those imposed by silvicultural and economic considerations". "Approval of forestry development in any area is dependent, *inter alia*, on all *reasonable* (italics added) steps being taken to avoid adverse effects on the environment". The Guidelines see the most important considerations as 'shape', 'diversity' and 'scale'. Shape refers to forest outline and species pattern relative to the overall pattern of the landscape. Straight lines and geometric shapes "should be avoided". Suggestions are also provided for the use of open spaces and the inclusion of pockets of broadleaves. "Broadleaved trees and species such as larch... should comprise at least 10 percent of the area planted". Existing scrub areas "might" be left intact. It is suggested that upland areas are normally more suitable for large forest areas while regular shaped small areas may fit better on lowlands. Guidelines are also provided for public roads and for felling. It is also suggested that, 10 years

prior to clearfelling, an irregular strip be placed at the edge of the plantation. While these guidelines have good intentions, the recurrence of the words "should" and "might" make clear the fact that they are guidelines rather than regulations. They therefore lack the necessary 'teeth' to ensure that best practice is observed.

Planning Regulations

Chapter 4 outlines planning regulations in detail. These have been strengthened in 1997. The use of land for forestry is exempt from the need for planning permission except in the case of forestry developments which require an Environmental Impact Assessment (EIA). Sites requiring an EIA include those where the area involved, either on its own or taken together with any adjacent area planted within the previous three years, would result in a total area planted exceeding 70 hectares, and any site where broadleaved high forest is being replaced by conifers and the area involved is greater than 10 ha. In addition, local authorities have been asked to designate areas as sensitive to afforestation with regard to a number of environmental aspects including landscape. Once these designations have been made, the Forest Service will notify the local authorities of all proposals for afforestation in these designated areas regardless of size.

The Forest Strategy (Department of Agriculture, Food and Forestry, 1996) has amended the minimum distance between grant assisted afforestation and dwellings, buildings and roads (see Chapter 4).

As outlined in Chapter 4, Natural Heritage Areas (NHAs) have been designated with the objective of conserving plants, animals and wildlife habitats under the forthcoming Wildlife Act (Amendment Bill) but they encompass most of the inventory of outstanding landscapes (compiled by An Foras Forbartha in 1977) which identify areas of particular landscape and amenity importance. It is expected that the Forest Service will refuse to give grants to afforestation in these areas. However, the emergence of afforestation in areas of Killarney indicates that such designations are not always effective.

ASSESSING LANDSCAPE IMPACTS

Willis and Garrod (1993) give four categories of landscape assessment:

1. Intuitive assessment, entirely subjective by the appraiser;
2. Database surveys of landscape features, to aid judgement by the appraiser;
3. Subjective scoring of landscape components by the general public;
4. Other public preference techniques such as landscape ranking.

An example of a possible assessment technique suitable for Ireland has been presented by McCormack and O'Leary (1993). They attempt to develop a systematic and thorough procedure for analysing what they see as the landscape issue of greatest overall significance in Ireland, i.e. the visual impact of forestry. They suggest that a national land use policy should include aesthetic controls based on visual sensitivity levels which would indicate the extent and nature of development suitable for each area. When a site is located in an area which is deemed to be sufficiently sensitive a Visual Impact Assessment (VIA) of the planned development will be required before grant eligibility is assessed. This plan can either be accepted, rejected or altered on the basis of this assessment.

Three possible categories of landscape and the appropriate requirements for approval are suggested:

1.   *Very high visual sensitivity*: afforestation application refused;
2.   *High visual sensitivity*: afforestation schemes acceptable subject to the approval of a VIA;
3.   *Moderate or low visual sensitivity*: afforestation schemes acceptable when accompanied with detailed plans of the site. The sites would normally be low lying in areas with a relatively low population density.

Visual sensitivity of the landscape with regard to forestry is measured by examining:

Landscape Susceptibility
This measurement reflects the function, location and character of a landscape which are in turn dependent on the intensity of use of an area and the public interest in or attitude towards the landscape. They suggest that road and Ordinance Survey maps provide some indication of intensity and nature of use but further analysis should take the form of ground investigation.

Key Viewpoint Distance
Key viewpoints are areas where significant numbers of the public gather which are in view of the proposed forest site and there is a positive relationship between landscape sensitivity and its proximity to key viewpoints.

Landscape Quality
The landscape's aesthetic quality is assessed and ranked according to a number of criteria and is then assigned to the high, moderate or low quality category.

Aesthetic Experience
Surveys are undertaken to assess aesthetic experience and the respondent is asked to rank the experience according to a number of factors and the cumulative score is then allocated to one of three categories of aesthetic experience: high, medium or low.

Alternative non-monetary assessment methods and their comparison with monetary assessment can be seen in Price (1991a and b).

VALUING LANDSCAPE IMPACTS

The principal non-market valuation methods used to value landscape externalities are the Travel Cost Method, the Hedonic Price Method and the Contingent Valuation Method. These techniques are outlined in Chapter 3 and an entire edition of Landscape Research (Price, 1994) is devoted to a discussion of landscape valuation methods and their effectiveness.

When using the travel cost method it is difficult to distinguish between recreational and scenic value. In addition, it is more useful for valuing site specific landscape effects. The latter point is also true of the hedonic price method. Neither of these methods are suitable for valuing future landscape costs and benefits. Therefore, the only suitable technique for measuring the net landscape benefits of the Forest Strategy is the Contingent Valuation Method.

The CVM when used for this purpose allows the respondent to 'purchase' future landscape benefits (or pay to avoid the costs) for themselves or for others. As explained in Chapter 9, this method is not ideal since it is not possible to give precise details of the location and visual impact of planting to the respondents. The respondents are therefore buying while uncertain of the product they will receive in the future. In addition, the external cost imposed by the land use change will be a function of location and it is clear that if care is not taken to avoid afforesting areas of "natural" landscape of high value to tourism, the costs could be very high. However, for the purposes of the overall cost benefit analysis the method is appropriate for calculating the total net benefit but it would be inappropriate to break down this results to a per ha value.

Price (1997) points out that very few practical attempts have been made to incorporate landscape valuation techniques into cost benefit analysis of forestry. This book attempts to do just that. Chapter 14 outlines a contingent valuation experiment which assesses the wildlife, recreation and landscape value of the doubling of the forest estate under the Forest Strategy. These three issues are addressed together due to the difficulty of disaggregation. In order to facilitate the valuation of the net landscape benefits of the Forest Strategy, it was necessary to facilitate bids to preserve the present land use for its aesthetic value as well as bids for the aesthetic value of afforesting the land. As can be seen in Chapter 14, this is partially achieved by giving the respondents two opposing views with regard to the effect of increased afforestation on landscape, i.e. that some people argue that more forestry will improve the landscape while others argue that more forestry will destroy the landscape. For the purposes of the overall calculation of the Total Economic Value of the Strategy, the valuation of landscape benefits is left to Chapter 14.

An Experiment

An ongoing research project with O'Leary and McCormack of the Department of Forestry in UCD examines public preferences regarding the landscape effects of forestry using a survey containing photographic simulations. Ultimately it is expected that the results of this survey will assist in the development of new landscape guidelines. However, for the purposes of this study, the survey provided an opportunity to shed some light on a number of issues which could not be addressed in the national public preference and contingent valuation surveys (see Chapters 13 and 14) due to a restriction on space. These issues are:

- The extent of awareness of the Forest Strategy;
- The extent of approval of the Forest Strategy;
- The difference in the value of broadleaf afforestation and conifer afforestation;
- Regional differences in the above;
- Whether contingent valuation surveys using taxation as the payment vehicle underestimate true willingness to pay due to distrust of the exchequer.

A small survey has been undertaken. The counties of Wicklow and Leitrim were chosen for comparison. The former has a long tradition of forestry and has one of the highest levels of forest cover in Ireland. Meanwhile, Leitrim has been pinpointed as having a large area of land which is very suitable for afforestation and it is expected that the level of forest cover will rise dramatically over the life of the Forest Strategy. It was also believed prior to the survey that the population of each county strongly differed in their opinions of afforestation although no survey had been undertaken to establish whether this was so.

Survey Implementation

A random sample of the population of each county was selected from the electoral register. Between the months of March and June, face-to-face interviews were carried out in the households of the individuals selected. The total effective sample size was 795 consisting of 403 respondents in Leitrim and 392 in Wicklow. Thus, using the full sample the margin of error when using a 95 percent confidence level is, at worst, plus or minus 3.5 percent, i.e. differences greater than 7 percent are significant. Using the results from Leitrim or Wicklow alone gives a margin of error of plus or minus 5 percent.

Questionnaire Design

Prior to asking questions which address the issues raised above, respondents were asked about their attitudes to forest recreation and their opinions regarding the extent of coniferous, broadleaf and mixed forest in their county. In addition, photographic simulations were used to assess whether the respondents could correctly identify conifers and broadleaves and to elicit their preferences regarding different shapes of forest and different harvesting techniques. The results of these questions will be reported in future co-authored work.

For the purposes of this study, the respondents' awareness and approval of the Forest Strategy were firstly assessed. The respondents were then shown a photograph of a conifer forest at maturity which was presented as the type of forestry to be planted under the Strategy. The respondents were also shown a photograph of a broadleaf forest (see Appendix 5) and it was suggested to them that this was an alternative forest type which could be planted instead of conifers[43]. The respondents were then asked to indicate their preferred forest type. Those who selected broadleaves were told that they cost more to plant and they take much longer to grow, therefore, the grants would have to be much higher to compensate investors for the extra cost. This provided the platform for a contingent valuation question to assess the difference between the value of broadleaved afforestation and coniferous afforestation.

The respondents were then asked a series of questions to elicit the utility gain they would achieve should broadleaved afforestation replace coniferous afforestation. The first payment vehicle used was a rise in taxation. The respondents were presented with a payment card and asked to choose the amount they would be willingness to pay each year for ten years to finance the doubling of the forest area over the next 35 years using broadleaves rather than conifers. Although binary choice valuation questions are recommended by the NOAA guidelines (see Chapter 3), this was prohibited by the small sample size and, since the ultimate objective was to assess relative rather than absolute magnitudes of willingness to pay, the method of elicitation of bids was not considered to be important.

The final questions tested whether the use of taxation as a payment vehicle underestimates true willingness to pay due to distrust of the exchequer. This may occur due to an unwillingness to pay on the part of some respondents due to an inadequate guarantee that the taxes raised would not be spent on something else. The respondents were presented with an alternative method of collecting the necessary funds, i.e. by voluntary donations to a fund called "Forestry Ireland". They were then asked whether they would prefer such a method of funding the broadleaf scheme. Those who preferred this method were then asked their willingness to donate to such a scheme.

Results

Awareness and Approval of the Forest Strategy
Table 11.1 shows that approximately two thirds of the population of each county is unaware of the Forest Strategy. There is not a significant difference in the level of awareness in each of the two counties.

---

[43] While 10 percent of afforestation under the Strategy will consist of broadleaves, it was necessary to create a clear-cut scenario in order to obtain accurate measurements of preferences and values. At the end of the survey it was made clear to respondents that the forestry schemes discussed were purely hypothetical.

TABLE 11.1. Awareness of the Forest Strategy (%).

	Leitrim	Wicklow
Aware	27	35
Unaware	73	65

The difference in attitudes towards the Forest Strategy is highly significant. Seventy two percent of the Wicklow population approves of the Forest Strategy compared with just 18 percent of the Leitrim population (Table 11.2). The principal reasons for disapproval of the Forest Strategy in Leitrim were: "there is too much forestry" (40 percent), "the land should be used for agriculture" (24 percent), "forestry removes people from the countryside" (18 percent), and "forestry destroys the landscape" (8 percent).

TABLE 11.2. Approval of the Forest Strategy (%).

	Leitrim	Wicklow
Approve	18	72
Disapprove	80	24
Don't Know	2	4

Species Preference

Those who stated their approval of the Strategy and those who disapproved only because of the predominance of conifers were presented with photographic simulations of broadleaved and coniferous forests as described above. Table 11.3 shows that just over 71 percent prefer broadleaves. The principal reasons given for this preference were: "it looks the best" (54 percent) and "not enough broadleaves are being planted at present" (12 percent). Only 7.5 percent explicitly mentioned wildlife or species diversity as the explanation of their preference for broadleaves.

TABLE 11.3. Preferred Species Type.

	%
Conifer	17.3
Broadleaf	71.1
Indifferent	11.6

Willingness to Pay for Broadleaves

For the total sample, the mean willingness to pay to finance the forest area being doubled over the next 35 years with broadleaves rather than conifers is £10.44 each year for 10 years. Mean willingness to pay in Wicklow is £18.79

which is significantly[44] higher than the mean figure of £2.33 for Leitrim. This reflects the substantially lower proportion of respondents in Leitrim who approve of an increase in afforestation no matter what species would be planted.

Chi-square tests suggest that WTP is positively related to income and education but is unrelated to age, gender and watching/listening to nature programmes.

Testing Alternative Payment Vehicles
Fifty six percent would prefer broadleaved afforestation to be funded by voluntary contributions to a fund rather than via increased taxation. Those who do not approve of the Fund give their principal reasons as "people would not pay" and "the Fund is not transparent". Despite the majority preferring the Fund, mean willingness to pay under the fund is not significantly higher than under taxation[45] (Table 11.4).

TABLE 11.4. Mean WTP for Broadleaf Afforestation on the Part of Those Preferring the "Fund" under Different Scenarios.

	Mean WTP (£ per annum for 10 years)
Via Taxes	26.34
Via Fund	30.36

CONCLUSIONS

The extent of awareness of the Government's plans to double the forest estate is low. Given that it will involve a significant change in the character of the landscape, it would seem that the Strategy should receive greater publicity. It appears that large regional variations in attitudes to afforestation exist. This suggests that the distribution of costs and benefits of the Strategy will be rather uneven. Broadleaves are of greater value than conifers mainly due to their landscape value. Awareness of biodiversity arguments for broadleaves is minimal. While most Irish people find voluntary contributions to a fund the most acceptable payment vehicle in a contingent valuation survey, their willingness to pay is not reduced significantly by the use of taxation. The significance of this result is examined in Chapter 14. A national contingent valuation survey is the most appropriate method of valuing the landscape effects of an expansion in the forest estate. Therefore, the estimation of the landscape value of the Forest Strategy is addressed in Chapter 14.

---

[44] The null hypothesis of equality of population means was rejected at a 1 percent significance level.
[45] n=156.

CHAPTER 12

OTHER CONSIDERATIONS

This chapter addresses some further issues which must be examined prior to the undertaking of a cost benefit analysis. The question as to whether land price inflation is a true externality of forestry subsidisation is addressed. The Community Integrity value of forestry is then examined. Finally, the external cost of forestry as a result of damage to archaeology is analysed.

LAND PRICE INFLATION

Traditionally in Ireland afforestation was considered suitable only on land that was of no use to traditional agriculture. Farrell (1983) has shown that up until the early 1980s forestry was not allowed to 'intrude' on agricultural land by constraints placed by the Government on land purchase by the Forest Service. Thus, forestry was concentrated mainly on relatively high-elevation and poor-nutrient sites (mostly in the Western counties) which were not perceived as being of value for farming. However, with the fall in returns to farming from CAP reform and the provision of generous subsides to forestry, trees have moved onto better quality, low-lying land formerly used for agriculture.

The most vocal concerns about the increase in afforestation have come from farming organisations. Their principal complaint is that the availability of subsidies for afforestation has driven up the price of land. There is no doubt that forestry subsidies have been capitalised in the land price. O'Connor and Conlon (1993) estimate that an increase of 10 percent in grants and compensatory payments to forestry is positively associated with a 9.2 percent increase in the average nominal price of forestry land. Farmers argue that, when endeavouring to purchase land for traditional agriculture, they cannot compete with those bidding for land for afforestation.

From a methodological point of view, it is not valid to include this as a cost in a cost benefit analysis. The rise in land prices is not a true externality, rather it closer to what is called a pecuniary externality[46]. A rise in the price of land resulting from an increased demand for land for afforestation does not change the efficiency of the productive process to transform inputs into utility levels of members of the economy. Thus, while there is movement along the production possibilities curve, the frontier is not shifted. A pecuniary externality still leaves agents in the economy at their initial utility level if all inputs are used as before and there is an appropriate redistribution of income (Baumol and Oates, 1988). However, as this analysis utilises the Kaldor-Hicks efficiency criterion, there need only be the *potential* for compensation.

---

[46] Pecuniary externalities are defined in Appendix 2.

It is clear that the subsidisation of afforestation and the consequent increase in the price of land suitable for forestry will result in a lower utility for those farmers who wished to expand their land under traditional agriculture. However, it is also true that the land they already own will become more valuable. Annual subsidies to agriculture amounted to £1.15 billion in 1995 (Lucey, 1996) whereas subsidises to forestry over the lifetime of the Forest Strategy will amount to an average of £100 m per annum. While agricultural subsidies will decline in the future due to reform of the CAP, it is likely that they will have a much more significant effect on land prices than will forestry subsidies for a considerable period. With subsidies to agriculture declining, if no subsides were to be provided to an alternative land use such as forestry, the value of farmers' holdings would actually decline. It is also worth noting that over 75 percent of private sector afforestation is actually undertaken by farmers (Irish Timber Growers Association, 1995). In conclusion, it can be said that the benefits to farmers from the subvention of forestry are likely to outweigh the costs.

COMMUNITY INTEGRITY

A potential benefit of the Forest Strategy that has not been considered in the preceding chapters is what is known as 'Community Integrity'. Community Integrity relates to the value that society puts on the conservation of rural communities (Pearce, 1991)[47]. The contribution of forestry to Community Integrity is measured by the extra utility to society which results from the conservation of rural communities as a direct consequence of an expansion in the forest estate.

One aspect of Community Integrity is captured by the willingness to pay on the part of individuals, in terms of reduced salaries, to return from a job in a foreign location to their home town. Theoretically, this could be measured using contingent valuation by eliciting the maximum salary reduction that individuals would be willing to accept in order to take a forestry job in their home town. Those who, it is adjudged, would be forced to migrate in the absence of employment created by forestry could be asked for the minimum salary increase they would be willingness to accept in order to move away from their home town.

However, it would also be necessary to measure the extra utility that relatives and friends gain by the presence of these individuals in their home town. It is likely that the assessment of these values using contingent valuation would prove to be the most difficult and controversial use of the method to date!

---

[47] Pearce (1991) also notes that this should not be confused with the benefits of creating rural employment which, if they are adjudged to exist, are adjusted for using a shadow price.

To complete the valuation of Community Integrity it would be necessary to measure the increase in the utility of the rest of society from the contribution that forestry makes to conserving rural communities. This would also prove to be difficult in practice.

If the Forest Strategy does not create more rural jobs than it displaces the Community Integrity Value will be zero. If it displaces more than it creates it will have a negative effect. While the Forest Strategy document (Department of Agriculture, Food and Forestry, 1996) states that "young people are much more likely to remain in rural areas to take up a job in forestry, which would be on a par with alternative jobs in urban areas, than to take over a farm" it provides no evidence to support this claim. While the Strategy may make some contribution to Community Integrity, it may also be the case that an employment subsidy to existing industries or a direct transfer to rural communities would be more efficient way of promoting Community Stability.

One study which is relevant to this section is a study of the Community Stability value of forestry by Boyd and Hyde (1989). They evaluate the US Forest Service's efforts to maintain the integrity of small communities scattered throughout the Western US, which are dependent on public timber harvests. The Service attempts to do this by trying to ensure a stable flow of timber in the presence of an externally generated instability. Boyd and Hyde model this approach and their results show that, while a constant harvest policy improves employment and total wage income in the wood products sector, these benefits are offset by foregone gains in the rest of the economy and it involves large public management costs.

Community Integrity as defined in this chapter is different from the concept of Community Stability as presented by Boyd and Hyde. It is also more difficult to value as has been explained above. It has, therefore, not been possible to assess the value of the contribution which the Forest Strategy will make to Community Integrity.

ARCHAEOLOGY

Cooney (1994) provides an excellent summary of the impact of forestry on archaeology from which most of this section is taken. Ireland is fortunate to be endowed with a rich archaeological resource which is of value in terms of its direct use for tourism, both domestic and overseas, and for education and research. In addition it is likely to have both option and existence value. However, none of these values has been assessed.

There are estimated to be approximately 200,000 archaeological sites representing human settlement patterns over the last ten thousand years or so throughout the entire country but the exact number is uncertain since many features may yet be discovered. These sites range from the temporary base camps of Mesolithic hunters through to the industrial archaeological remains of the nineteenth century[48]. While some sites are clearly visible, such as standing monuments, a large number of sites are only partially visible or are completely buried in soil. Buried sites tend to be located in upland areas and survive as integrated landscapes rather than isolated monuments. These are very important in terms of understanding past settlement and economic activity (Cooney, 1994).

The difficulty with most archaeological sites is that their recognition requires specialised archaeological techniques and skills. Thus, two potential problems arise: First, an individual may recognise a feature on their land to be of archaeological importance but may destroy it to avoid interference with his or her desired activity (an individual is not compensated for the external benefit of preservation) and second, the individual may not recognise it as of archaeological value and destroy it by accident.

Impact of the Present Estate on Archaeology
Much of the forest estate in Ireland today was planted between the 1930s and the 1970s when there was much less sensitivity to, and recognition of, the environmental impact of forestry. Thus, in many planted areas there are known archaeological sites which are not protected in any way. These are particularly at risk during felling (Cooney 1994).

The Impact of Afforestation on Archaeology
Most of the damage to an archaeological feature which has not been recognised or has been ignored is done at establishment phase particularly by ploughing and draining. Thinning, roading and felling are the other major threats.

Regulations, Guidelines and Monitoring
Archaeological sites are protected under the National Monuments Act of 1930 (and amendments 1954, 1987, 1994). The provisions of the latest Amendment Act include the protection of all monuments in the country. All archaeological finds are the property of the State and must be reported to the National Museum of Ireland. Two months prior notice of any intended work or developments on or adjacent to sites must be given to the Office of Public Works. There are also a small number of monuments in full State care and sites with Preservation Orders (approximately 630 and 400 of each respectively) (Cooney, 1994). An Environmental Impact Assessment is required for certain afforestation projects as outlined in Chapter 4.

The Forest Service published guidelines on forestry and archaeology in January 1992 (Forest Service, 1992a). These give advice on how to recognise archaeological features. In the case of private projects, if known archaeological sites are present, maps of proposed afforestation will be forwarded by Forest

---

[48] See Cooney (1983) for further details.

Service to the Office of Public Works for comment within one month. Sites are avoided or mitigation procedures are put in place. In the case of public afforestation, Coillte sends copies of land acquisition maps on a monthly basis to the Office of Public Works for comment.

Monitoring Procedure

For the above guidelines and regulations to be effective, it requires an adequate monitoring procedure. Cooney (1994) points out that the present monitoring procedure is weak since it is based on county Sites and Monuments Records which are rapidly compiled desk-top surveys. These are an inadequate baseline and are least reliable for upland, marginal agricultural areas, blanket and cut-over raised bog which are the areas most likely to afforested. The assessment is totally map based and there is no archaeological field assessment. For those archaeological features which are not recorded, recognition is reliant on the forestry contractor in the case of private afforestation and Coillte foresters in the case of State afforestation. Given that all features are not immediately recognisable as of archaeological value, this may result in the destruction of valuable items.

Conclusion

It is clear that, in the absence of any change in monitoring procedure, afforestation on land that has here-to-fore been relatively undisturbed (such as peatlands and lands formerly used for rough grazing) poses a considerable threat to Ireland's archaeological endowment. Since there is a lack of knowledge of the exact extent and value of this endowment it is not possible to calculate this external cost. For this reason it is omitted from the cost benefit analysis in Chapter 15. However, the cost could be quite significant and should be borne in mind when interpreting the results.

CONCLUSIONS

Land price inflation as a result of subsidies to forestry does not create a true externality. It was not possible to calculate the community integrity value of the Forest Strategy. Neither was it possible to value the external cost of forestry development on archaeology. The absence of both these values should be borne in mind when interpreting the results of the cost benefit analysis in Chapter 15.

CHAPTER 13

PUBLIC PREFERENCE ASSESSMENT

The principal objective of the survey described in this Chapter was to generate the contingent valuation data and recreational use data as described in Chapters 14 and 9 respectively. However, the survey also included questions to elicit the attitude of the public to afforestation. The space available for these questions was very limited. Thus, it is not a full scale public preferences survey but it was the first nation-wide survey which attempted to shed light on the opinions of the Irish public regarding afforestation.

METHODOLOGY

The attitude of the Irish public to afforestation was assessed by surveying a representative sample of households in Ireland.

Survey Vehicle
The data were collected by the Survey Unit of the Economic and Social Research Institute. It was considered appropriate to attach the forestry questionnaire as a supplement to the EU Consumer Survey. This survey gauges public opinion regarding economic issues and elicits consumers' short and medium term purchasing intentions. This includes collecting data on the public's perception of past and future trends with regard to the general economic situation, consumer prices and the financial situation of the respondent household (Williams, 1997).

Attaching the questionnaire to the Consumer Survey was considered appropriate as it both minimised costs and enhanced the credibility of the forestry survey by using professional sampling statisticians and interviewers. In addition, the Consumer Survey had been shown to achieve high rates of response.

Sample Design[49]
The sample design was based on a two-stage clustered sample using the electoral register as a population frame. A preliminary sample was selected using a computerised random sampling system known as RANSAM[50] which selects primary sampling points or clusters. The population across District Electoral Divisions was aggregated up to minimum cluster size thresholds which formed the primary sampling units for the first stage of sample selection. The second stage selected individuals from within each of the primary selection units using a systematic sampling technique.

---

[49] The details in the next two sections are adapted from Williams, 1997.
[50] See Whelan (1979) for further details.

Survey Implementation

The survey was carried out in two stages, the first in October 1996 and the second in March 1997, to allow for tests of consistency to be carried out. A mixed-mode technique was used to implement the sample, i.e. interviewing was carried out using both telephone surveying and face-to-face interviewing. This was to ensure that those without a phone are not under-represented. Each of the primary sampling units represented a geographically restricted area. Each of these geographically restricted areas was then inspected and linked to the telephone directory. A telephone stem was then selected for each of the areas in question. The stem, which represents a valid number for the area minus the last two digits, was generated randomly. This left the interviewer with a potential maximum of 100 telephone numbers (from 00 to 99) for each of the geographical clusters in question. The interviewer telephoned these numbers until a total of 34 interviews were completed. If an interviewer exhausted his or her supply of telephone numbers, a second random stem was supplied and the procedure continued.

When conducting the telephone interviews, the interviewer enforced a set of quota controls on potential respondents which minimised sample selection bias. These controls ensured that the sample of individuals conformed with the structure of the population according to age, sex, and principal economic status. A proportion of the interviews was held in the evenings and at weekends in order to avoid under-representation by those in full-time employment.

In addition to conducting the telephone interviews in the selected clusters, interviewers carried out face-to-face interviews on the respondents directly sampled from the electoral register. Each of the named respondents was contacted by the interviewer and a filter question on whether or not the respondent owned a telephone was asked. If the respondent did not have a telephone then a personally administered interview was carried out. The final data are weighted to ensure the sample is representative of the population.

Response Rates

The first and second rounds of the survey achieved response rates of 78 percent and 75 percent respectively, a combined response rate of 76 percent. This is an excellent response rate in comparison with most surveys. The effective sample sizes of the two rounds of the survey were 1,416 and 1,479 respectively giving a total combined effective sample size of 2,895. Thus, using results from the full sample, one can be 95 percent certain that the results are applicable to the population with a margin of error of plus or minus 1.8 percent at worst, i.e. any differences of 3.6 percent or more are statistically significant. Tests showed the two samples to be from the same population and so the data were combined.

Questionnaire Design

Due to a restriction on space, it was possible to ask respondents only a few questions on their attitudes towards afforestation. It was therefore decided to ask them about their impressions regarding the impact of the present afforestation programme upon the environment. Prior to being questioned, the respondents were given information regarding the land area covered by trees, the rate of increase of planting, and the proportion of conifer planting. In order to avoid information bias, the respondents were presented with two opinions of the impact of afforestation on the environment. The first opinion presented was that more forestry of the type being planted at present is good for the environment because it will improve the landscape, provide better habitats for wildlife, and provide improved recreation areas. The alternative view presented was that more forestry of this sort will spoil the natural landscape, destroy wildlife habitats, and reduce the availability of open spaces for recreation. The respondents were then asked for their opinions regarding the effects of afforestation on landscape, wildlife and recreation. Finally, they were asked whether they believe that, on balance, more forestry would be good for the environment.

A variety of socio-economic and other characteristics of the respondent were recorded so that it could be ascertained whether there is any relation between any particular characteristic of the respondent and their response to the questions.

RESULTS

The results of the survey are presented below. Chi-square tests are used where appropriate to test for independence between variables. The results of these tests are presented in the notes of tables. If a result is reported as "significant", this means that the null hypothesis of independence was rejected at the "level" reported.

Overall Impact of Afforestation on the Countryside
Just over 70 percent believe that, on balance, more forests of the type being planted at present will be good for the countryside with just under 30 percent disagreeing. Only 0.3 percent are unsure (Table 13.1).

TABLE 13.1. "Is Afforestation Good for the Countryside?".

	%
Yes	70.3
No	29.4
Don't Know	0.3

There is not a significant difference between the opinions of males and females of the impact of afforestation on the countryside. However, the percentage of positive responses declines with age. Those between the ages of 16 and 29 have a much more positive attitude to forestry than do older generations (Table 13.2). This is also reflected in an 84 percent approval for afforestation on the part of those in full time training (students) as opposed to a 66 percent approval on the part of retired respondents.

TABLE 13.2. "Is Afforestation Good for the Countryside?" by Age.

	Age			
	16-29	*30-49*	*50-64*	*65 or more*
Yes (%)	80.0	68.0	64.6	64.5
No (%)	20.0	32.0	35.4	35.5

Note:
Significant at 0.01 level.

There is a significant difference in attitudes between those who have had primary education only and those who are educated to a higher level. A smaller proportion of the former respondents views afforestation as being good for the countryside. However, there is not a significant difference between the attitudes of those educated to Intermediate/Junior Certificate level and those educated to Leaving Certificate and Third Level (Table 13.3). This is not surprising given the strong relationship between age and education level, with three quarters of those whose education terminated at primary level being 50 years of age or more.

TABLE 13.3. "Is Afforestation Good for the Countryside?" by Education.

	Education Level			
	Primary	*Intermediate*	*Leaving*	*Third Level*
Yes (%)	66.2	72.1	70.2	72.7
No (%)	33.8	27.9	29.8	27.3

Note:
Significant at 0.10 level.

Just over half of farmers think afforestation will improve the countryside. This is significantly lower than the corresponding proportion of other occupations (Table 13.4).

TABLE 13.4. "Is Afforestation Good for the Countryside?" by Occupation.

	Occupation					
	Self-employed	*Farmer*	*Professional /Managerial*	*Other non-Manual*	*Skilled Manual*	*Unskilled Manual*
Yes (%)	74.5	50.4	71.3	76.9	75.0	72.1
No (%)	25.5	49.6	28.7	23.1	25.0	27.9

Note:
Significant at 0.01 level.

A significantly higher percentage of those who have children think afforestation is good for the countryside (Table 13.5).

A significantly higher proportion of those resident in urban areas think more forestry will improve the countryside (Table 13.6).

TABLE 13.5. "Is Afforestation Good for the Countryside?" by Children.

	Children	No Children
Yes (%)	74.2	64.4
No (%)	25.8	35.6

Note:
Significant at 0.01 level.

TABLE 13.6. "Is Afforestation Good for the Countryside?" by Locality.

	Urban	Rural
Yes (%)	74.2	64.4
No (%)	25.8	35.6

Note:
Significant at 0.01 level

There is a positive relationship between attitudes towards the protection of the environment and attitudes towards the impact of afforestation on the environment (Table 13.7).

TABLE 13.7. "Is Afforestation Good for the Countryside?" by Environmental Concern.

	Importance of Protecting the Environment		
	Very Important	Quite Important	Not Very Important
Yes (%)	74.7	62.6	45.5
No (%)	25.3	37.4	54.5

Note:
Significant at 0.01 level

A significantly higher proportion of respondents from households who had visited a forest in the last year think afforestation would be good for the countryside (Table 13.8).

TABLE 13.8. "Is Afforestation Good for the Countryside?" by Use.

	Recreation Visit in the Last 12 Months	
	Yes	No
Yes (%)	75.2	67.0
No (%)	24.8	33.0

Note:
Significant at 0.01 level

A significantly higher proportion of respondents from counties with a relatively high level of forest cover (as a percentage of land area) do not think that afforestation is good for the countryside (Table 13.9). However, the proportion of respondents holding this view does not differ significantly between counties with a low level of forest cover and those described as medium. It is interesting to note that there are exceptions as shown in the high level of approval of the Forest Strategy in Wicklow (see Chapter 11).

TABLE 13.9. "Is Afforestation Good for the Countryside?" by County Area Afforested.

	Extent to which Respondent's County is Afforested		
	Low	*Medium*	*High*
Yes (%)	75.0	77.7	61.1
No (%)	25.0	22.3	38.9

Note:
Significant at 0.01 level.

TABLE 13.10. Significance of Covariates with "Is Afforestation Good for the Countryside?".

Parameter	*Estimate*	*t-statistic*
Constant	1.165	1.87
Age 16-29	0.647	3.98
Age 30-49	0.134	0.98
Age 50-64	0.052	0.39
Urban	0.552	5.98
"Very important" to protect environment	0.555	2.06
"Quite important" to protect environment	0.515	1.84
Log income	-0.208	-1.71

An instrumental Variables Probit estimate[51] was used to confirm the results of the cross tabulations. Youth, an urban location, a highly forested county and concern about the environment are all positive and significant covariates with a positive attitude regarding the impact of afforestation on the countryside. Interestingly, income is a negative and significant covariate (Table 13.10) suggesting that those on lower incomes have a less favourable view of afforestation all else being equal.

Impact of Afforestation on the Landscape
Almost sixty three percent of respondents believe that more afforestation will improve the landscape, with just under 21 percent saying it will spoil the landscape and 16 percent saying it will make no difference. Less that 1 percent are unsure (Table 13.11).

TABLE 13.11. "How Will Afforestation Affect the Landscape?".

	%
Improve the Landscape	62.5
Make no Difference	16.0
Spoil the Landscape	20.7
Don't Know	0.8

---

[51] See Chapter 14 for explanation. Thanks are due to Anthony Murphy for assistance with this procedure.

There is a very strong correlation between the respondent's answer to the question regarding the overall impact of afforestation on the countryside with their answer to the question regarding the impact of afforestation on the landscape. Again, there is not a significant difference according to gender but younger people and those in full time training are much more positive about the impact of afforestation on the landscape while older people and those whose education ended at primary level are least well disposed to the landscape impact of afforestation. However, the differences are less significant than in the case of the overall impact of afforestation on the countryside. Farmers are virtually evenly split into those who think afforestation improves the landscape and those who think it will spoil it. This breakdown is significantly different than in other occupations in which a large majority has a positive attitude to the impact of afforestation on the landscape (Table 13.12).

TABLE 13.12. "How Will Afforestation Affect the Landscape?" by Occupation.

| | Occupation (%) | | | | | |
	Self-employed	Farmer	Professional /Managerial	Other non-Manual	Skilled Manual	Unskilled Manual
Improve	69.9	45.4	64.6	67.8	67.1	62.2
No Diff.	9.8	12.2	13.7	15.2	16.7	22.2
Spoil	20.2	42.4	21.8	17.1	16.2	15.6

Note:
Significant at 0.01 level.

TABLE 13.13. "How Will Afforestation Affect the Landscape?" by Locality.

	Urban (%)	Rural (%)
Improve	67.4	55.9
Make no Diff.	17.2	14.2
Spoil	15.3	29.9

Note:
Significant at 0.01 level

The presence of children is positively related to the belief that afforestation improves the landscape. A significantly higher percentage of urban residents have a positive attitude to afforestation in relation to its effect on the landscape (Table 13.13).

A significantly higher proportion of those who claim to watch and/or listen to nature programmes on the television and radio very often (67.1 percent) believe that afforestation improves the landscape than of those who claim that they never watch or listen to these programmes (58.5 percent). There is also a very strong relationship between attitudes towards the protection of the environment and beliefs regarding the impact of afforestation of the landscape (Table 13.14). A higher proportion (67.7 percent) of those whose household had visited a forest in the past year than those whose household had not (59.6 percent), think afforestation will improve the landscape.

TABLE 13.14. "How Will Afforestation Affect the Landscape?"
by Environmental Concern.

	Importance of Protecting the Environment (%)		
	Very Important	Quite Important	Not Very Important
Improve	67.8	54.1	34.8
Make no Diff.	10.5	25.9	56.3
Spoil	21.6	20.0	8.9

Note:
Significant at 0.01 level

A significantly higher percentage of respondents from counties with a relatively high level of forest cover (as a percentage of land area) think afforestation will spoil the landscape (Table 13.15).

TABLE 13.15. "How Will Afforestation Affect the Landscape?"
by County Area Afforested.

	Extent to which Respondent's County is Afforested (%)		
	Low	Medium	High
Improve	62.4	72.5	53.7
Make no Diff.	16.1	16.2	16.0
Spoil	21.5	11.3	30.2

Note:
Significant at 0.01 level.

Impact of Afforestation on Wildlife
Sixty five percent of respondents are of the view that more forestry will provide better habitats for wildlife, 13 percent believe it will destroy wildlife habitats and 19 percent believe it will make no difference. Given that the scientific literature does not provide a definitive answer to this question, it is perhaps surprising that only 3.1 percent feel unsure of the effects of afforestation on wildlife (Table 13.16).

TABLE 13.16. "How Will Afforestation Affect Wildlife?".

	%
Provide Better Wildlife Habitats	65.4
Make no Difference	18.6
Destroy Wildlife Habitats	12.9
Don't Know	3.1

The covariates are identical with the covariates of answers to the landscape question, i.e. there is no significant difference according to gender but younger people and those in full time training are much more positive about the impact of afforestation on wildlife than are older people and those whose education ended at primary level. However, substantially more farmers believe afforestation will provide better wildlife habitats than believe it will destroy them (Table 13.17) although the majority is slimmer than in other occupations.

TABLE 13.17. "How Will Afforestation Affect Wildlife?" by Occupation.

	Occupation (%)					
	Self-employed	*Farmer*	*Professional /Managerial*	*Other non-Manual*	*Skilled Manual*	*Unskilled Manual*
Create	73.7	54.2	71.2	73.5	69.7	65.5
No Diff.	15.0	23.2	13.7	15.3	19.6	24.0
Destroy	11.3	22.6	15.1	11.2	10.7	10.5

Note:
Significant at 0.01 level.

Income and the presence of children are positively related to the belief that afforestation improves habitats for wildlife. The difference between the urban and rural divide is significant but smaller than in the case of landscape. A majority in both groups believe that afforestation will provide better habitats for wildlife (Table 13.18).

TABLE 13.18. "How Will Afforestation Affect Wildlife?" by Locality.

	Urban (%)	*Rural (%)*
Improve	69.9	63.7
Make no Diff.	18.8	19.9
Spoil	11.4	16.5

Note:
Significant at 0.01 level

There is a positive correlation between frequency of viewing/listening to nature programmes and a favourable attitude to afforestation in relation to wildlife. Environmental concern has an even stronger positive relationship (Table 13.19).

TABLE 13.19. "How Will Afforestation Affect Wildlife?"
by Environmental Concern.

	Importance of Protecting the Environment		
	Very Important	*Quite Important*	*Not Very Important*
Create	74.2	54.1	33.0
Make no Diff.	12.9	30.6	58.7
Destroy	12.9	15.4	8.3

Note:
Significant at 0.01 level

A significantly higher percentage of respondents from counties with a relatively high level of forest cover (as a percentage of land area) think afforestation will destroy wildlife habitats.

Impact of Afforestation on the Recreational Opportunities

Just under half of the respondents believe that an increase in afforestation will provide more opportunities for recreation, 18 percent say the increase will reduce areas for recreation, and 31 percent believe it will make no difference. Three percent are unsure (Table 13.20).

TABLE 13.20. "How Will Afforestation Affect Recreation?".

	%
Increase Recreation Areas	48.7
Make No Difference	30.5
Reduce Recreation Areas	17.6
Don't Know	3.2

The covariates are the same as for wildlife and landscape except that the presence of children is no longer significant. While there is also a difference in attitudes across age groups and social classes, it is less significant. Farmers are evenly divided between afforestation improving opportunities for recreation, making no difference and reducing opportunities for recreation. There is a significant difference in attitudes between those who had visited a forest in the last 12 months and those who had not, and as expected, those who had visited have a more favourable opinion of the recreational value of afforestation (Table 13.21).

TABLE 13.21. "How Will Afforestation Affect Recreation?" by Use.

	Recreation Visit in the Last 12 Months	
	Yes (%)	No (%)
Increase Recreation Areas	58.5	44.3
Make no Diff.	25.6	35.8
Reduce Recreation Areas	15.8	19.9
Note:		
Significant at 0.01 level		

Other Results

Although not specifically the results of questions regarding afforestation, it is of interest to outline some other results. Seventy percent of the population thinks that protecting the environment is very important with only 4 percent thinking it is not very important. Environmental concern is significantly higher in the 30 to 64 age group than in younger or older age groups. A significantly lower proportion of those who are unemployed view protecting the environment as very important. A smaller percentage of the unskilled and of farmers believes that environmental protection is very important than is the case with other occupations.

The belief in the importance of protecting the environment is positively correlated with education level and the presence of children in the household and, as would be expected, there is a correlation between respondents' views regarding the importance of protecting the environment and their frequency of viewing and/or listening to nature programmes (Table 13.22). Thirty percent of respondents claim to watch or listen to environmental programmes on the television and radio very often with 14 percent never watching them. Slightly more males watch and/or listen regularly but a slightly higher percentage of females view the protection of the environment as very important. Viewing and/or listening to nature programmes is positively correlated with education level and income. However, it is not related to the presence of children in the household.

TABLE 13.22. Importance of Protecting the Environment by Frequency of Viewing/Listening to Nature Programmes on TV/Radio.

| | *Frequency of Viewing/Listening to Nature Programmes* | | | |
	Very Often	*Sometimes*	*When Nothing Else on*	*Never*
Very Important	93.8	67.2	54.4	49.5
Quite Important	6.1	31.5	35.8	35.6
Not very Important	0.1	1.3	9.7	14.9

Note:
Significant at 0.01

The survey suggests that only 2.5 percent of the population is a member of an environmental group[52] so the numbers were too small to examine covariance with other variables.

Further details regarding the results of questions on the subject of forest recreation can be found in Chapter 9 and the results of the contingent valuation survey can be found in the next Chapter.

CONCLUSIONS

This survey provides an interesting insight into the views of the public regarding the impact of afforestation on the environment. A majority of the public feels that afforestation will improve the landscape and provide better

---

[52] Four percent of respondents who claimed to be in an environmental organisation were members of a gun club! 42 percent and 14 percent were in Greenpeace and An Taisce respectively.

habitats for wildlife. Fewer are convinced of the merits of afforestation for recreational opportunities. Over two thirds of the population believe that, on balance, afforestation will have a beneficial effect on the countryside.

Younger people are more favourably disposed to forestry than are older generations. The high correlation between environmental concern and a positive attitude towards forestry suggests that forestry is seen as an environmental good rather than an agricultural good. This view is supported by the finding that those households with children have a more positive attitude towards afforestation and are also more concerned about the environment. In addition, urban dwellers are much more positive than those living in rural areas.

It is not surprising that those who use forests for recreation are more favourably disposed to afforestation particularly in relation to its recreational value. The more favourable response to afforestation from counties with a low or medium level of forest cover compared with those with a high level of forest cover suggests that there are diminishing external benefits of forestry. While farmers are the least well disposed to afforestation, a substantial majority have a favourable attitude to the environmental impact of afforestation.

CHAPTER 14

CONTINGENT VALUATION[53]

This Chapter outlines the methodology and results of the first nation-wide continent valuation study carried out in Ireland. It was ascertained in Chapters 9, 10 and 11 that contingent valuation is the only appropriate valuation method with which to measure the externalities associated with an expansion in the forest estate with regard to recreation, wildlife and landscape. This chapter outlines the methodology employed to measure these externalities and the results obtained.

METHODOLOGY

The survey vehicle used was that outlined in Chapter 13, i.e. a mixed-mode survey of households using both telephone and personal interviews; the questionnaire was attached to the EU Consumer Survey. A pilot study of 50 respondents was used to check for wording difficulties and to choose the appropriate bid vector for willingness to pay. The survey was undertaken in two stages to allow for tests of reliability[54] to be performed. The overall response rate was 76 percent resulting in an effective sample of 2,895 respondents. These results compare very favourably with most contingent valuation surveys.

Allowing for Zero and Negative Valuations
Hanemann and Kriström (1995) state that it is ordinarily assumed that individuals cannot have a zero willingness to pay for an environmental improvement and thus zero bids are normally treated as protest bids. However, a feature of many private goods is that only a subset of all consumers buy them even at a zero price (Kriström, 1995) and there is no reason why this should not also be the case for public goods - if you are not be willing to pay anything for a drink which is not to your taste, why should you be willing to pay for an increase in the forest estate if you do not like forestry? Yet, Kriström (1995) points out that, traditionally, contingent valuation assumes these corner solutions do not arise. To allow for the possibility of zero bids, it is necessary to find a method to distinguish zero bids from protest bids and a model which will allow for the inclusion of the legitimate zero bids.

However, in the case of an expansion in the Irish forest estate, a further development in the methodology is required. There exist two distinct opinions regarding the impact of forestry on the landscape, on recreation and on wildlife.

---

[53] Thanks are due to Anthony Murphy for the econometric analysis contained in this chapter.
[54] Bateman and Turner (1993) suggest that this is desirable but that it is not common practice in contingent valuation studies.

Some people are of the opinion that more forests will spoil the 'natural' landscape, reduce open spaces for recreation and destroy wildlife habitats. Others are of the opinion that more forests will improve the landscape, increase opportunities for recreation and provide better habitats for wildlife. Therefore, while some individuals may experience an increase in utility as a result of an expansion in the forest estate, others may experience a disutility from such an increase, i.e. forestry is both a public good and a public bad. Prior to this study there was no information on the opinions of the population as a whole. However, the 70:30 split in opinions as outlined in Chapter 13 demonstrates the necessity of allowing for winners and losers.

Most CV studies are concerned with measuring willingness to pay for an increase in environmental quality and thus it is reasonable to assume that no one will experience a disutility from the improvement. Thus negative willingness to pay can be ignored. However, in the case of forestry in Ireland it is necessary to find a way to allow for negative willingness to pay.

The most obvious approach would be to ask those who believe afforestation to have a negative impact for their willingness to accept the disutility. However, it was shown in Chapter 3 that there are practical difficulties with eliciting willingness to accept in contingent valuation surveys. For this reason, negative WTP was used as a proxy for WTA. This was considered valid in this case since the elasticity of substitution is not likely to be very low (the agricultural land used is not unique and the damage is not irreversible) and WTP is not likely to be a large proportion of income. Moreover, since the principal competing land use is subsidised and, therefore, the public already pays for its provision, the appropriate measure is the amount of income the consumer is willing to pay to forgo the reduction in the quantity of the good.

The most commonly used approach to allow for negative bids has been to ask respondents for their willingness to pay for an increase in the provision of the public good/bad and then to allow for negative bids by the choice of valuation functional form for parametric estimators, i.e. to make assumptions regarding the negative tail of the distribution of willingness to pay. However, this approach does not explicitly allow respondents themselves to bid negative amounts and therefore the results may be inaccurate.

A second possible approach is to split the sample and ask one sub-sample their willingness to pay for an increase in the forest estate and the other sub-sample their willingness to pay to avoid an increase in the forest estate. This approach has three disadvantages. Firstly, splitting the sample is likely to require a larger total sample to achieve robust results. Secondly, the analysis still requires assumptions regarding zero bids, i.e. it is necessary to decide which of the zero bids would actually be negative bids (if the respondents had been in the other sub-sample), which are protest bids, and which are actual zero bids. Lastly, there is a problem regarding the information given to each of the samples. To ensure that the results are not biased, each sample must be given the same information, i.e., in this example, they should be told the differing opinions as to the effects of forestry on the environment. Having received this information, it may then seem peculiar to a respondent who believes forestry to have a negative impact on the environment if he or she were then asked to pay for an increase in the forest estate and vice versa. Given the uncertainty regarding the way the population divides on the question of the environmental effects of an increase in the forest estate, and the difficulty of interpreting zero bids, it is necessary to find a way to allow explicitly for negative bids in the design of the contingent valuation questionnaire.

Kriström (1995) endeavoured to obtain some information on both positive and negative willingness to pay for a closedown of regular traffic at Bromma Airport in Stockholm. However, while he managed to ascertain whether a respondent had a negative willingness to pay, he was unable to assess the magnitude of the individual's negative willingness to pay. Nevertheless, Kriström (1995) states: "I am not aware of any other study where it has been possible to shed light on both winners and losers of a project, at least not within an experiment with binary valuation questions". The methodology and example below not only outlines how to assess winners and losers but also how to assess the exact magnitude of both positive and negative willingness to pay.

Questionnaire Design

Elicitation Format
To allow for explicit negative bids, the respondents were given some background information regarding forestry in Ireland, i.e. information on the extent of the forest estate in Ireland, the rate of increase of planting, the species type and location of planting. They were then presented with the conflicting opinions regarding the effects of forestry on the environment. The first opinion presented was that more forestry of the type being planted at present is good for the environment because it will improve the landscape, provide better habitats for wildlife, and provide improved recreation areas. The alternative view presented was that more forestry of this sort will spoil the natural landscape, destroy wildlife habitats, and reduce the availability of open spaces for recreation. The respondents were then asked for their opinions regarding the effects of afforestation on landscape, wildlife and recreation. Finally, they were asked whether they believed that, on balance, more forestry would be good for the environment[55].

Those who responded in the affirmative were considered to be likely to experience either no change or an increase in utility if more forests were to be planted and thus would be likely to be willing to pay a zero or positive amount for an increase in the forest estate. Those who responded negatively were considered to be likely to experience no change in utility or experience a disutility if more forests were to be planted and thus would be likely to pay a

---

[55] The answers to these questions are analysed in Chapter 13.

zero or positive amount to *avoid* an increase in the area of forests. The respondents were thereby 'filtered' such that each group was placed in a different contingent market. Figure 14.1 gives a simple outline of the filtering process and the structure of the questionnaire. The requirement for such a process clearly rules out the use of a mail survey.

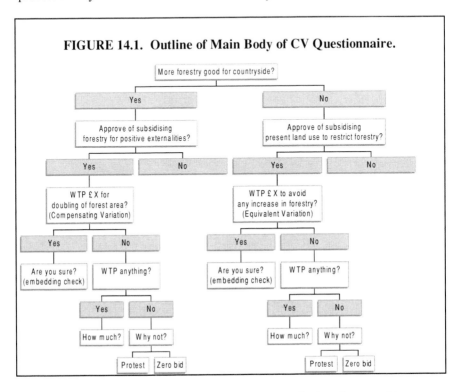

FIGURE 14.1. Outline of Main Body of CV Questionnaire.

Those with a positive view of forestry were asked whether they would approve of a Government programme to double the forest estate over the next 35 years. The scenario presented to respondents was specified such that it mirrored actual plans as put forward in the Forest Strategy. This provided the rationale for payment by the respondents as it was stated that subsidies would be used to compensate those who plant forests for the environmental benefits they provide. The willingness pay on the part of those who approved of the scheme was then assessed.

Meanwhile, those with a negative view of forestry were asked whether they would approve of a government scheme which would give subsidies to landowners to keep land in its present use which would effectively limit any substantial increase in the land area covered by forests over the next 35 years. The scheme suggested would be an expansion of the existing Rural Environmental Protection Scheme. The willingness to pay of those answering in the affirmative was then assessed.

Thus, Compensating Surplus (willingness to pay for a benefit) is used to assess the benefits of an expansion in the forest estate while Equivalent Surplus (willingness to pay to avoid a cost) is used to assess the costs.

Payment Method

Subsidies for forestry will be funded from the exchequer. Thus, income tax was considered to be the most realistic method of financing the Strategy. In addition, this payment method ensured that the respondents did not take the payment decision lightly and they were less likely to forget the goods they would have forgone by paying for the project. Chapter 11 showed that the use of taxation was unlikely to underestimate WTP despite respondents preferring other payment vehicles. Given this result and the benefits of using taxation just mentioned, taxation was considered to be the most appropriate payment vehicle. However, it was necessary to adjust for households which did not pay income tax. Such households may have been very willing to support an increase in taxes since they would not have had to pay such an increase. To allow for this, the payment vehicle was specified as income tax for income tax payers and specified as a reduction in social welfare receipts for social welfare recipients.

Obtaining Bids

The (single-bounded) dichotomous choice format was chosen for the reasons specified in Chapter 3. The respondents were informed that the programme was estimated to cost £X per household each year for ten years and they were asked whether their household would be willing to pay this amount. The bid vector chosen was {£5, £15, £30, £50, £100}. While it would have been preferable to have had a larger distribution of 'cost levels', smaller sub-samples would have reduced the statistical reliability of the results.

It was decided not to ask for a lump sum as it would seem unrealistic that the Government would suddenly raise taxes for one year only. In addition, households have usually made their financial planning decisions early in the year so a yearly amount would avoid answers such as "I could pay it next year but not this year". Ten years was chosen as the length of payment since respondents are thought to find it difficult to think of financial consequences any further into the future.

Checks for Embedding

A follow up question to a positive response to a willingness to pay question was included to check that the respondent was willing to pay the specified amount purely for the programme in question and no other environmental programme.

Partial Validity Checks

Questions regarding sex, age group, household composition (numbers of adults and children), attitude to protecting the environment, and (log) household income, were combined with data on whether the respondents were from urban or rural areas, their geographical area, and whether the counties in which they live are relatively forested or unafforested, and included as potential covariates with willingness to pay.

Checks on Understanding and Acceptance
In order to check for consistency, questions which elicited the attitudes of respondents to the environmental effects of forestry were included prior to the elicitation of their willingness to pay for the good.

Reminders of Alternative Expenditure Possibilities
As outlined in Chapter 13, the survey was included as a supplement to the EU Consumer Survey[56]. As part of this survey, the respondents were asked detailed questions about their perception of the financial situation of their household, their spending plans for the next 12 months, the state of the economy and their plans to save over the next year. Thus, by the time the respondents were asked questions regarding their willingness to pay for forestry they had been more than adequately reminded of alternative expenditure possibilities and of their household budget constraint.

Econometric Modelling
The Dichotomous Choice elicitation method involves choosing m different bids, $A_1, A_2, \ldots, A_m$, and administering these to $n_1, n_2, \ldots, n_m$ households (Hanemann and Kriström, 1995). These bids are disguised in the questionnaire as the "cost" of the programme. At each cost A_i $(i = 1, \ldots, m)$ k_i households are willing to pay A_i and $n_i - k_i$ households are unwilling to pay A_i (Kriström, 1990).

It is difficult to infer much about mean WTP from the "raw" contingent valuation data because most of the relevant data is for open-ended intervals such that precise willingness to pay is unknown. It is therefore necessary to resort to econometric modelling.

Using econometric models it is possible to estimate the mean and the underlying distribution of positive and negative WTP within the sample. The other advantage of econometric modelling is that it facilitates the incorporation of a large number of explanatory variables into the model. The following explanatory variables were used: age group, household composition (numbers of adults and children), urban/rural location, extent of afforestation of the county of the respondent, attitude to protecting the environment, and (log) household income.

Since all the household income data are grouped (into income ranges) and/or censored[57], an econometric "grouped data" probit model of the income data was

---

[56] This questionnaire can be found in Appendix 2.
[57] Some observations on the dependent variable, corresponding to known value(s) of the independent variable, are not observable.

estimated[58]. The model estimates were then used to recover estimates of (log) household income.

WTP and negative WTP were modelled separately using a combination of standard "grouped" and "ordered" probit models. To allow for zero bids, the models also incorporate so called "double hurdles" of zero bids. This means that non-zero WTP bids are only observed if some latent threshold is exceeded. Since estimated as opposed to actual household income was used as an explanatory variable, the models were estimated using Instrumental Variables (IV)[59]. Education, economic activity and occupation were used as instrumental variables.

TESTS OF VALIDITY

WTP for more forests and WTP to avoid more forests were regressed against various potential covariates. The results show that income, positive attitudes towards the protection of the environment and being an urban household are all positive and significant covariates with WTP a positive amount for more forests. Age is not significant. However, age becomes significant with the extent of WTP with younger age groups willing to pay less.

Income is still significant but the small magnitude of the estimator suggests that the landscape, wildlife and recreational benefits of forests are not luxury goods. Support for this result can be found in an interesting paper by Kriström and Riera (1996) which presents evidence that contradicts the common assumption that the income elasticity of environmental improvement is greater than 1. Urban location and a positive attitude to the environment are insignificant.

Only income is a significant and positive covariate with WTP a positive amount to avoid forests. The relationship between extent of WTP to avoid forests and income is insignificant. Interestingly, this suggests that the extent of preferences against forestry is not a function of income.

RESULTS

Table 14.1 shows that out of a total sample of 2,895, 1.7 percent registered protest bids, 0.09 percent failed the embedding check and 2.8 percent failed to answer the required questions. Just less than 30 percent disagreed with the subsidy scheme with which they were presented. The remainder presented legitimate answers to the willingness to pay questions. Of these, 81.7 percent were in contingent market 1 (WTP for more forests) while the remainder were

---

[58] See Greene (1993) for details of the procedure.
[59] Required to produce a consistent estimator where the regressor is correlated with the error

in the second contingent market (WTP to avoid more forests). It is clear from Figure 14.2 that there was a high proportion of zero bids in each contingent market.

TABLE 14.1. Division of the Total Sample.

	Number	Percent
Protested	49	1.69
Failed Embedding Check	27	0.09
Gave no Answer	81	2.80
Disagreed with Subsidy Scheme	860	29.71
Bid	1,878	64.87

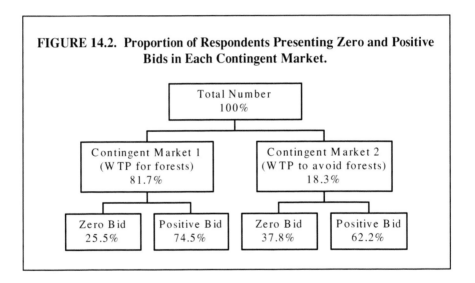

FIGURE 14.2. Proportion of Respondents Presenting Zero and Positive Bids in Each Contingent Market.

Table 14.2 gives the percentage of respondents presented with each cost level in each contingent market. The results show that the interview process was very successful at splitting the sample amongst the bid levels.

TABLE 14.2. Percentage of Respondents Presented with Each Cost Level.

Cost Level (£ per annum for 10 years)	Contingent Market 1 (WTP More Forestry) (%)	Contingent Market 2 (WTP Avoid Forestry) (%)
5	21	21
15	20	20
30	21	20
50	19	21
100	19	18

Omitting zero bids, mean WTP to avoid forests was significantly higher than mean willingness to pay for more forests. This suggests that, as a result of an increase in the forest area, those who dislike forestry will, on average, endure a greater loss of utility than the average increase in utility to those who like forestry, although the overall result is an increase in utility to society.

Mean willingness to pay per household (taking zero and negative bids into account) was calculated to be £14.50. Aggregating up to a total of 1,166,200 households, this amounts to a total willingness to pay of £16.75 m per annum for 10 years (comprising a welfare loss of £6.76 m for those who dislike forestry and a welfare gain of £23.51 m for those who like forestry). Table 14.3 gives the present value of these payments at five test discount rates. At a five percent discount rate, the total landscape, wildlife and recreational benefits of the Forest Strategy amount to £129 m. Unlike the benefits and costs calculated in other chapters, the results are not very sensitive to the discount rate as they are calculated over a much shorter time period.

TABLE 14.3. Landscape, Wildlife and Recreational Value of the Strategy at Test Discount Rates.

Discount Rate (%)	Present Value (£m)
0	168
3	143
5	129
8	112
10	103

CONCLUSIONS

Given that forestry in Ireland was believed to be both a public good and a public bad, it was necessary to advance the contingent valuation methodology to enable the measurement of the exact magnitude of negative as well as positive willingness to pay using binary valuation questions. When applied to the Forest Strategy, the new approach was shown to work successfully. The results indicate that the net present value of the landscape, wildlife and recreational benefits of the Forest Strategy amounts to £129 m.

CHAPTER 15

COST BENEFIT ANALYSIS

This Chapter ties together the various components of Total Economic Value that have been calculated in the preceding chapters. It thereby calculates the net social benefit of the Forest Strategy. The results of a cost benefit analysis are compared with the results that would be provided by a financial analysis, and net external benefits are compared with timber values. Net social benefit is examined under various scenarios using sensitivity analysis.

ASSUMPTIONS

The analysis below does not include figures for the Community Integrity value of the Forest Strategy although this is thought to be negligible. Neither do the figures include any estimates of the costs, if any, that afforestation will impose on the archaeological endowment. The most important assumption to bear in mind when reading the results below is that the cost of acidification of the water supply by future grant-aided afforestation is taken to equal zero. This relies upon the adherence by the Forest Service to restrictions regarding minimum yield class, prohibition of planting in NHAs, consultation with the fisheries boards and the taking into account of the new local authority designations.

Cost of Public Funds

Due recognition must be made of the fact that the provision of subsidies to forestry will create distortions in the economy. If subsidies are to be provided to one activity, such funds have to be raised via the tax system or, if the EU transfers are committed to the project, other projects must be funded from taxation, i.e. there is an opportunity cost. In general, taxation results in distortions in the economy and associated losses such that the cost of raising £1 of revenue costs more than £1 in total costs. In 1996, the marginal cost of public funds was estimated to be 1.5 (Honohan, 1996; 1997) such that the marginal excess burden equals 0.5, i.e. the total cost of raising £1 via the tax system equals £1.50. Multiplying the subsidy by the marginal excess burden gives the Excess Burden of the forestry subsidies. This equals £636 million at a 5 percent discount rate (Table 15.1).

PRINCIPAL RESULTS

At a five percent discount rate, the Department of Finance's recommended rate for assessing the worth of public sector projects, the Forest Strategy fails a cost benefit test, returning a negative Net Social Benefit (NSB) of minus £441 m. At a zero discount rate, NSB is shown to be £66 billion when the time horizon is limited arbitrarily to 300 years, but with an infinite time horizon, NSB would also be infinite. The internal rate of return or "break even" discount rate is around 4 percent.

TABLE 15.1. Costs and Benefits of Strategy (£m).

	Discount Rate (%)				
	0	3	5	8	10
Timber	89,839	3,065	887	204	84
Land	-17,183	-1,193	-552	-250	-167
Labour[1]	-3,105	-258	-136	-74	-55
Other inputs	-2,690	-326	-169	-136	-97
Landscape, wildlife, recreation	168	143	129	112	103
Carbon[2]	261	101	46	16	9
Water	-95	-15	-10	-6	-5
Excess Burden	-1,558	-881	-636	-419	-331
Net Social Benefit	65,638	636	-441	-553	-459

Notes:
[1] Shadow wage equal to market wage.
[2] Carbon permit price stable.

If it is argued that the 75 percent of the subsidy that comes from the EU would not be made available for an alternative use, and, therefore, there is no opportunity cost of committing such funds to afforestation, the Excess Burden would be calculated on Irish Exchequer funds only. This allows the Forest Strategy to pass the cost benefit test at the target discount rate of 5 percent (Table 15.2).

TABLE 15.2. Costs and Benefits of Strategy if EU Funds "Free" (£m).

	Discount Rate (%)				
	0	3	5	8	10
Timber	89,839	3,065	887	204	84
Land	-17,183	-1,193	-552	-250	-167
Labour[1]	-3,105	-258	-136	-74	-55
Other inputs	-2,690	-326	-169	-136	-97
Landscape, wildlife, recreation	168	143	129	112	103
Carbon[2]	261	101	46	16	9
Water	-95	-15	-10	-6	-5
Excess Burden from Irish Funds	-389	-220	-159	-105	-83
Net Social Benefit	66,807	1,279	36	-239	-211

Notes:
[1] Shadow wage equal to market wage.
[2] Carbon permit price stable.

In either case, at a 5 percent discount rate, net external benefits range between £131 m and £350 m depending on assumptions regarding the absolute size and the growth in the price of carbon emissions permits. A conservative estimate of £165 m is 18 percent of the value of timber benefits. At higher discount rates, this percentage increases, since landscape, wildlife and recreational benefits do not show much variation due to the method of measurement (Table 15.3).

TABLE 15.3. Net External Benefits of Strategy.

	Discount Rate (%)				
	0	*3*	*5*	*8*	*10*
Net external benefits (£m)	334	229	165	122	107
As percentage of timber value (%)	0.4	8	18	60	127
Net external benefits: best case[1] (£m)	466	521	350	154	132
Net external benefits: worst case[2] (£m)	140	149	131	111	101

Notes:
[1] High carbon emissions permit price with a 3 percent annual growth rate, slow peat oxidation.
[2] Low carbon emissions permit price with a 3 percent annual decline, fast peat oxidation.

It is of interest to compare the results of the cost benefit analysis with those that would be produced by a financial analysis. Excluding subsidies, the net benefits at a five percent discount rate are negative. This reflects the omission of externalities and the use of the market price of land. The inclusion of subsidies brings net benefits to a figure of £1.2 billion (Table 15.4).

TABLE 15.4. Financial Analysis of Strategy (£m).

	Discount Rate (%)				
	0	*3*	*5*	*8*	*10*
Timber	89,839	3,065	887	204	84
Land[1]	-1,305	-815	-628	-456	-381
Labour	-3,105	-256	-136	-74	-55
Other inputs	-2,690	-326	-169	-136	-97
Net Benefit without Subsidies	82,739	1,666	-46	-462	-449
Net Benefit with Subsidies	85,854	3,428	1,225	375	212

Notes:
[1] Using existing market price of land.

SENSITIVITY ANALYSIS

Using the full excess burden, at a 5 percent discount rate, NSB ranges between minus £530 m and minus £352 m depending on assumptions regarding timber prices (Tables 15.5 and 15.6).

TABLE 15.5. Costs and Benefits of Strategy, High Timber Prices (£m).

	\(0\)	\(3\)	\(5\)	\(8\)	\(10\)
	Discount Rate (%)				
Timber	98,823	3,372	976	224	92
Land	-17,183	- 1,192	-552	-250	-167
Labour	-3,105	-256	-136	-74	-55
Other inputs	-2690	-326	-169	-136	-97
Landscape, wildlife, recreation	168	143	129	112	103
Carbon	261	101	46	16	9
Water	-95	-15	-10	-6	-5
Excess Burden	-1,558	-881	-636	-419	-331
Net Social Benefit	74,621	946	-352	-533	-451

TABLE 15.6. Costs and Benefits of Strategy, Low Timber Prices (£m).

	\(0\)	\(3\)	\(5\)	\(8\)	\(10\)
	Discount Rate (%)				
Timber	80,855	2,759	798	184	76
Land	-17,183	-1,192	-552	-250	-167
Labour	-3,105	-256	-136	-74	-55
Other inputs	-2690	-326	-169	-136	-97
Landscape, wildlife, recreation	168	143	129	112	103
Carbon	261	101	46	16	9
Water	-95	-15	-10	-6	-5
Excess Burden	-1,558	-881	-636	-419	-331
Net Social Benefit	56,653	333	-530	-573	-467

TABLE 15.7. Costs and Benefits of Strategy including Economic Security Value (£m).

	\(0\)	\(3\)	\(5\)	\(8\)	\(10\)
	Discount Rate (%)				
Timber	89,839	3,065	887	204	84
Economic Security Value	701	24	7	1.6	0.7
Land	-17,183	-1,193	-552	-250	-167
Labour	-3,105	-258	-136	-74	-55
Other inputs	-2,690	-326	-169	-136	-97
Landscape, wildlife, recreation	168	143	129	112	103
Carbon	261	101	46	16	9
Water	-95	-15	-10	-6	-5
Excess Burden	-1,558	-881	-636	-419	-331
Net Social Benefit	66,338	660	434	-551	-458

If timber is believed to have strategic importance despite the self-sufficiency of the EU, this might add a further £7 m to NSB (Table 15.7). A lower bound on the shadow wage still fails to make NSB positive (Table 15.8).

TABLE 15.8. Costs and Benefits of Strategy with Reduced Shadow Wage (£m).

	Discount Rate (%)				
	0	*3*	*5*	*8*	*10*
Timber	89,839	3,065	887	204	84
Land	-17,183	-1,193	-552	-250	-167
Labour[1]	-2,484	-206	-109	-59	-44
Other inputs	-2,690	-326	-169	-136	-97
Landscape, wildlife, recreation	168	143	129	112	103
Carbon	261	101	46	16	9
Water	-95	-15	-10	-6	-5
Excess Burden	-1,558	-881	-636	-419	-331
Net Social Benefit	66,258	688	-414	-538	-448

Notes:
[1] Shadow wage equals 80 percent of market wage

TABLE 15.9. Best Case Costs and Benefits of Strategy (£m).

	Discount Rate (%)				
	0	*3*	*5*	*8*	*10*
Timber[1]	98,823	3,372	976	224	92
Economic Security Value	701	24	7	1.6	0.7
Land	-17,183	-1,193	-552	-250	-167
Labour[2]	-2,484	-206	-109	-59	-44
Other inputs	-2,690	-326	-169	-136	-97
Landscape, wildlife, recreation	168	143	129	112	103
Carbon[3]	393	393	230	48	34
Water	-95	-15	-10	-6	-5
Excess Burden from Irish Funds	-389	-220	-159	-105	-83
Net Social Benefit	77,244	1,972	343	-170	-166

Notes:
[1] High timber price.
[2] Shadow wage equals 80 percent of market wage
[3] High carbon emissions permit price with a 3 percent annual growth rate, slow peat oxidation.

TABLE 15.10. Worst Case Costs and Benefits of Strategy (£m).

	Discount Rate (%)				
	0	*3*	*5*	*8*	*10*
Timber[1]	80,855	2,759	798	184	76
Land	-17,183	-1,193	-552	-250	-167
Labour[2]	-3,105	-258	-136	-74	-55
Other inputs	-2,690	-326	-169	-136	-97
Landscape, wildlife, recreation	168	143	129	112	103
Carbon[3]	67	21	11	5	3
Water	-95	-15	-10	-6	-5
Excess Burden	-1,558	-881	-636	-419	-331
Net Social Benefit	56,459	250	-565	-584	-473

Notes:
[1] Low timber price.
[2] Shadow wage equal to market wage.
[3] Low carbon emissions permit price with a 3 annual decline, fast peat oxidation.

At a five percent discount rate a best case NSB of £343 m (Table 15.9) results from historically high timber prices with an economic security premium, a lower bound shadow wage, a high carbon permit price (assuming peat oxidation occurs slowly and the permit price grows at the same rate as the growth of GWP), and the excess burden calculated on Irish funds alone. A worst case scenario results in a NSB of just minus £565 m at a five percent discount rate (Table 15.10).

CONCLUSIONS

This Chapter has shown the Government's Strategic Plan for the Forestry Sector to have an internal rate of return of 4 percent. Therefore, using the Government's test discount rate of 5 percent, the Plan would fail a cost benefit test. However, if it can be argued that EU funds are free in that they will not be made available for an alternative use, the Strategy passes a cost benefit test at the test discount rate. This is explored further in the following chapter. Net external benefits amount to 18 percent of the timber value of the Strategy at a 5 percent discount rate.

CHAPTER 16

SUMMARY AND CONCLUSIONS

The Strategic Plan for the Forestry Sector, published by the Irish Government in June 1996, commits over £3 billion in subsidies to promote the doubling of the forest estate over the next 35 years. There has been considerable controversy regarding the external (environmental) effects of the massive land use change which will ensue. Prior to this study, no assessment of the magnitude of the externalities of afforestation had been undertaken and, therefore, the social efficiency of such a land use change had not been assessed. This book attempts to fill such gaps in knowledge by examining whether investments in afforestation in Ireland are socially efficient, i.e. whether they provide net benefits to society.

METHODOLOGY

A case study of the Strategic Plan for the Forestry Sector in Ireland was taken. This plan was assessed using Cost Benefit Analysis. In undertaking the Analysis, the Total Economic Value framework was employed. Using this approach, adjustments were made for the existence of market failure whereby certain forestry outputs are not captured within markets. These externalities of forestry were estimated using non-market valuation methods including Production Function approaches and Contingent Valuation. Shadow Pricing was employed where appropriate. Benefits and costs were adjusted for time using five test discount rates. A five percent discount rate was used as the target discount rate for the purposes of making policy recommendations as it is that rate recommended by the Department of Finance. Uncertainty was incorporated using Sensitivity Analysis.

In addition to estimating the external effects of afforestation, the book contains the results of the first ever survey of the attitudes of the Irish public to afforestation and an assessment of the regional differences in such attitudes. It also provides estimates of the numbers of domestic and tourist visits to the existing forest estate, and an assessment of the economic value of the estate for tourism.

RESULTS

Results of the Hypothesis Test
Figure 16.1 summarises the results of the cost benefit analysis presented in Chapter 15. This shows that the hypothesis that the planned investment in afforestation is socially efficient is rejected at a discount rate of 5 percent and above but is accepted at rates of 4 percent and below. Thus, using the

Department of Finance (1994) rate of 5 percent rate as the target discount rate, the expansion of the forest estate which will result from the Forest Strategy would be deemed to be inefficient.

Figure 16.2 shows the value of each component of the Total Economic Value of the Strategy. The net external benefit of the Strategy is positive and comprises over 18 percent of the timber value. The value of the timber is by far the greatest benefit of the Strategy and is estimated to be £887 m in present value terms. The total labour costs amount to £136 m while the shadow value of the land requirements amount to £552 m. The total cost of other inputs equals £169 m. Carbon sequestration benefits of the Strategy are estimated to be £46 m. The costs of water supply restriction and pollution are estimated to be in the region of £10 m. The net present value of the landscape, wildlife and recreation benefits of the Strategy are estimated to be approximately £129 m. The Excess Burden imposed on the economy by the raising of the funds and/or the opportunity cost of using EU funds for the purposes of forestry amounts to £636 m.

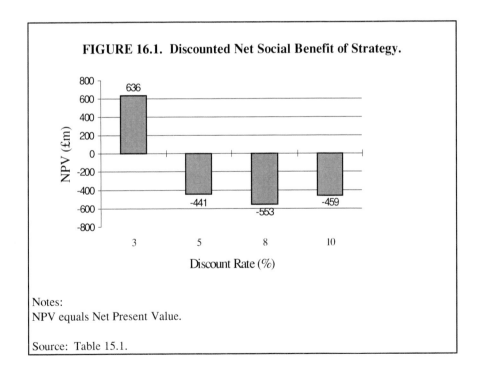

FIGURE 16.1. Discounted Net Social Benefit of Strategy.

Notes:
NPV equals Net Present Value.

Source: Table 15.1.

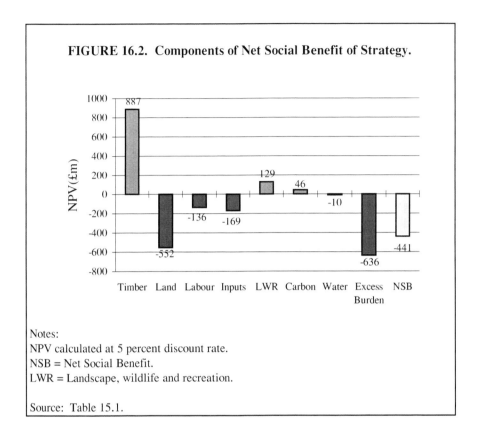

FIGURE 16.2. Components of Net Social Benefit of Strategy.

Notes:
NPV calculated at 5 percent discount rate.
NSB = Net Social Benefit.
LWR = Landscape, wildlife and recreation.

Source: Table 15.1.

What if EU Funds are Free?

As suggested in Chapter 15, if it could be argued that, because funding for forestry is part of CAP reform and, therefore, the EU portion of the afforestation subsidies will not be made available for an alternative use, the Excess Burden could be calculated on Irish Exchequer funds alone. In this instance, the Strategy would pass the cost benefit test at a 5 percent discount rate and, therefore, it would be deemed to be economically efficient and beneficial to the society as a whole.

The difficulty for the Irish Government in justifying such an approach is that it contradicts its own Guidelines for appraisal in the public sector as produced by the Department of Finance (1994). These state:

"The consideration that the EU may aid a project must not lead to a less rigorous appraisal and decision making than if that aid was not forthcoming. Aid from the EU is a national resource and must be used as effectively, and economically, as any other national resource. The EU expects us to ensure this. The availability of EU aid for a project is not a justification for investment in that project; if the project does not go ahead the EU aid can be applied to better effect elsewhere"

These Guidelines also state that, in the context of exchequer cash flow analysis, "EU finance passing through the exchequer should be included".

However, this study need not accept the recommendations of the Department of Finance! Therefore, to conclude on the issue of whether or not the Strategy will be good for society as a whole, on the basis of this study, it is reasonable to state that:

If the EU funds that are committed to afforestation as part of the Strategy could be made available for an alternative use, the Strategy would fail a cost benefit analysis and, therefore, it would be predicted that its implementation would reduce the welfare of Irish society as a whole. However, if the EU funds would not be available for an alternative use, the Strategy would pass a cost benefit analysis and, therefore, it would be predicted that its implementation would improve the welfare of Irish society as a whole.

Other Findings
There has been no secular tendency for real timber prices to rise over time in Ireland and the UK and there is unlikely to be a long run growth in prices in the future. Irish standing timber prices are unreliable as indicators of the social value of Irish timber given the potential in the past for Coillte to exercise monopoly power. However, the evidence is unclear as to whether this potential has been exercised. The expansion of the EU and the resultant shrinkage of the timber deficit renders the economic security value of timber close to zero.

The benefits to the Irish nation of carbon sequestration by the forest estate are likely to be small. However, in the event of a global agreement introducing tradeable carbon emissions permits, it is likely that the forest estate will become of considerable value. The magnitude of this value will depend to a large extent on assumptions regarding the growth in the carbon permit price. The value of afforestation on peatlands is still uncertain as research has not established the rate of oxidation of afforested peat and, consequently, the net carbon sequestration effect is unknown.

The magnitude of the external cost of afforestation with regard to water supply and biodiversity will depend upon the extent to which environmental designations and yield class restrictions prove effective. This would be assisted if statutory backing were to be given to the Guidelines for planting. The effectiveness of all the guidelines should be subject to an ex post assessment.

Total yearly visits to forests by domestic visitors are estimated to be approximately 7.7 m. While more than half of all households do not visit a forest, there is a high frequency of visits on the part of those which do. Annual visits by overseas tourists are estimated to be 744 thousand. Total annual forest visits are estimated to be 8.5 m. It is important to note that the term forest is left open to interpretation by the respondents and so it may include parks which contain some trees etc. Younger people pay more frequent visits to forests as do households with children. The 'uncaptured' benefit of tourist recreation is estimated to be £1.2 million annually which demonstrates the difficulty of internalising recreation benefits. This also might explain the divergence between previous estimates of total forest visits, which were based on monitored site entry to forest parks, and the new estimate reported in this book which is based on a household survey.

The extent of awareness of the Forest Strategy on the part of the public is low. It appears that the Irish public values broadleaves more highly than conifers. A majority of the public feels that afforestation will improve the landscape and provide better habitats for wildlife. Fewer are convinced of the merits of afforestation for recreational opportunities. Over two thirds of the population believe that, on balance, afforestation will have a beneficial effect of the countryside, younger people being most favourably disposed. The high correlation between environmental concern and a positive attitude towards forestry suggests that forestry is seen as an environmental good rather than an agricultural good. This view is supported by the finding that those households with children have a more positive attitude towards afforestation and are also more concerned about the environment. Urban dwellers are much more positive than those living in rural areas. The more favourable attitudes to afforestation in counties with a low or medium level of forest cover compared with those with a high level of forest cover suggests that there are diminishing external benefits of forestry. Farmers are the least well disposed to afforestation, however, a substantial majority have a favourable attitude to the environmental impact of afforestation. Attitudes to afforestation vary considerably from region to region. For example, there is a very positive attitude to the Forest Strategy in Wicklow whereas the population of Leitrim is strongly opposed.

POLICY IMPLICATIONS

The study is limited to assessing the static efficiency of the Forest Strategy, i.e. whether, given the present state of knowledge and the present environment, it is efficient. While this is the most appropriate test for an *ex ante* analysis, ultimately the key criterion for assessment of the Strategy will be whether resources are being used efficiently at each point in time given the state of the environment within which it is operating. While the static analysis in the preceding chapters suggests that the Forest Strategy is not efficient as it fails the cost benefit analysis, *dynamic efficiency* could be achieved if the Strategy has the ability to adapt to new information and new opportunities and to provide flexible and cost effective responses to changes in the policy environment. Whether dynamic efficiency is achieved can only be assessed *ex post*. However, a serious constraint would be if the overriding objective of forest policy was to become the achievement of the planting and timber production targets set out in the Strategy document without regard to changes in the environment within which it operates.

A further consideration required to carry out a complete analysis of policy involves an assessment of the *effectiveness* of the Strategy. It has been assumed in this book that it is certain that the planting and timber production targets set out in the Strategy will be achieved. Coillte has plenty of experience in managing forests and so timber production forecasts for State forestry are likely to be reasonably accurate. However, there is some concern regarding the private sector. Results from a sample of sites afforested by the private sector in 1991 showed one third of the sites to be smaller than four ha (Clinch, 1994). If timber output targets are to be achieved, it will be necessary to ensure that sites planted are commercially viable and it is doubtful if many of these small sites are. It is essential that technical support be given to timber growers to ensure that afforestation is translated into timber production. In order to sustain timber output it will be necessary for sites to be reforested after felling. However, the Strategy makes no provision for reforestation grants and, while the law requires sites to be reforested once felled, it remains to be seen as to whether this will be enforced.

Farrell (1995) points out that most plantation forests consist of exotic species planted on previously unafforested sites and this raises questions regarding their long term sustainability. Climate change may threaten the survival of these species directly by changes in temperature and precipitation or indirectly by improving the environment for pests and altering the hydrological balance. Soil degradation can also result from harvesting and felling operations and due to acidification. In shallow acid soils, acidification may affect forest health and productivity. The reliance on a limited number of exotic species leaves open the possibility of a serious insect attack. Afforestation on peatland results in peat subsidence and oxidation which threatens the sustainability of the peat soil.

The final test of the appropriateness of a policy is *concordance*. This has three elements. The first element relates to equity. The analysis in this book employs the Kaldor-Hicks efficiency test which assesses potential Pareto Optimality, i.e. whether there is the potential for the net benefits of the project to compensate the losers (by definition, there will be so long as the benefits outweigh the costs). Therefore, distributional effects are ignored so it is not possible to get a clear picture of the extent to which the Strategy is equitable. The results of the contingent valuation survey show that there will be winners and losers from the Strategy with regard to its environmental impact and the results of the landscape survey demonstrates that the distribution of costs and benefits will differ geographically. Redistribution of income is not a principal objective of the Strategy. However, it does claim that it will have a positive impact on Community Stability but this is unsubstantiated. What is more clear is that much effort is being put into promoting forestry as an alternative source of income for farmers with particular encouragement of farm forestry. This is probably the only clear-cut redistributive policy of the Strategy. If these individuals are the target of such a policy, a higher weighting for their welfare could result in the Strategy passing the cost benefit test at 5 percent. Apart from those who do not like forestry, the Strategy will not have an adverse impact on any clearly defined section of society.

The second and third elements of concordance relate to administrative feasibility and political sustainability. The Strategy would seem to be feasible from an administrative point of view. However, there is a serious question mark over the ability of the Forest Service to ensure that afforestation is carried out in the most socially efficient manner. This results from the poor quality of information provided by the Forest Service (see below), the lack of an effective monitoring procedure of the location and extent of afforestation, the lack of statutory backing for the forestry Guidelines, and the lack of any *ex post* evaluation to ascertain the effectiveness of the guidelines. The political feasibility of the Strategy will depend upon EU support. EU funding of afforestation is guaranteed up to the year 1999 under the Operational Programme for Agriculture, Rural Development and Forestry. However, the implementation of the Strategy requires further funding to the year 2030. This has not been secured as yet although the document contains an enthusiastic response from the Commissioner for Agriculture and Rural Development.

Subsidy Assessment
General discussions of the limitations of Cost Benefit Analysis (CBA) can be found in Hanley (1992), Hanley and Spash (1993) and Peterson and Brown (1996). However, the most important limitation of CBA in the context of this study is the inability of CBA to take into account the magnitude of subvention. Transfer payments such as taxes and subsidies are excluded from cost benefit analyses since they do not represent a using-up of real resources, but are merely redistributions of money by the government (Hanley and Spash, 1993). It is clear, however, that afforestation on the scale which is to take place under the Forest Strategy would not take place without the provision of subsidies by the Government. However, since transfers are omitted from cost benefit analyses, the results of such studies do not give any indication of the appropriate size of the subsidy.

The Industrial Development Authority (IDA) used a rather arbitrary approach to calculate the appropriate grant level to industry as one quarter of the net social benefit of the project. The discount apparently serves as an allowance for risk, over-optimism etc. (Honohan, 1995). Using this IDA approach to compare the actual subsidy level with the "Advised Subsidy", the results show that, if a positive discount rate is assumed, the extent of subsidisation of the Forest Strategy is not justified. Taking the Government's 5 percent discount rate, the appropriate subsidy is £49 m while the actual subsidy is £1.2 billion. However, this technique has no economic rationale and so is included here for illustrative purposes only (a more detailed explanation of this approach is contained in Appendix 4)

Subsidy Assessment in a First Best World

As stated above, the approach of the IDA is not consistent with an economic efficiency test. Transfer payments such as subsidies should be used to correct failures in the market system. Otherwise, there is no justification for giving one activity a subsidy while leaving another without. It is likely that a cost benefit analysis of many activities such as banks, supermarkets and restaurants would show a higher rate of return than does forestry, but it is not suggested that the government subsidise these activities.

Economic theory tells us that the optimal subsidy equals net marginal external benefits at the optimal level of their provision. Cost benefit analyses generally assess the efficiency of projects rather than the optimality of the projects, i.e. they test whether a project provides positive net benefits to society rather than whether the project itself, and its configuration, provides the best return to society, i.e. whether it the best use of society's scarce resources. Ideally, a cost benefit analysis would be carried out on all competing projects and the optimal project or package of projects can then be supported. However, in practice this does not occur and economists are asked to assess a project in isolation.

Without marginal figures it is not possible to pinpoint the theoretically optimal subsidy. However, Honohan (1995) has gone some way to providing a pragmatic rule for assessing the appropriate magnitude of a subsidy. While he does not include an expression for externalities, this can be built into his model. Based on the rationale of correcting failures in the market system, i.e. to give credit for the non-private benefits (total net social benefit minus net private benefits) of the Strategy, the appropriate grant rate to the Forest Strategy equals:

- net external (environmental) benefits

plus
- the divergence between the shadow and market value of the labour input (to reflect any reduction in unemployment)

plus
- the difference between the shadow and market value of the land required (to adjust for distortions in the price of land as a result of subsidies to agriculture and forestry)

plus
- taxes from forestry (returned to the government) minus any reduction in social welfare payments (as a result of any reduction in unemployment)

all divided by
- the marginal cost of public funds

Figure 16.3 contrasts the actual level of subvention that is required for the Strategy to be implemented with the recommended subsidy level based on the above approach. This suggests that, at all discount rates the level of subvention of the Forest Strategy is far in excess of that which is justified (over £1 billion at a 5 percent discount rate), i.e. there is a government intervention failure.

Thus, while it has been shown that the net external benefits of the Forest Strategy are significant (18 percent of the timber value at a 5 percent discount rate), the cost of obtaining them far outweighs their value.

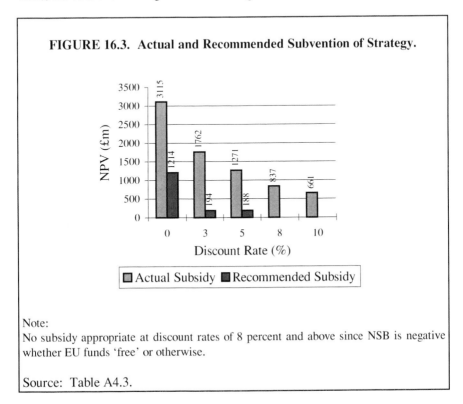

FIGURE 16.3. Actual and Recommended Subvention of Strategy.

Note:
No subsidy appropriate at discount rates of 8 percent and above since NSB is negative whether EU funds 'free' or otherwise.

Source: Table A4.3.

Subsidy Assessment in a Second Best World

The inclusion of EU funds in the calculation of the total subsidy relies on the belief that, if the Forestry Plan was not implemented, Ireland would receive the funds for an alternative use subject to an appropriate plan being put to the Union. In defence of the Forestry Plan, it has been suggested that the EU would not provide any of the funds for an alternative use. If this were true, the subsidy for purposes of comparison should be calculated net of EU funds, i.e. only the 25 percent contribution by the Irish Government should be included as a cost. However, at a five per cent discount rate, the Irish Government's subsidy alone is over one and a half times greater than the appropriate subsidy. Indeed, at all positive discount rates, the Irish Government's share of the subsidy is greater than the appropriate subsidy (Figure 16.4).

Even if the Irish component of the subsidy were less than or equal to the justified subsidy, the Government would find it hard to use this as a justification for funding the Forestry Plan as it contradicts its own guidelines as reproduced earlier in this chapter.

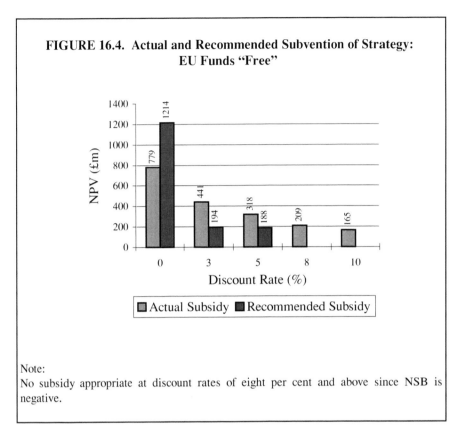

FIGURE 16.4. Actual and Recommended Subvention of Strategy:
EU Funds "Free"

Note:
No subsidy appropriate at discount rates of eight per cent and above since NSB is
negative.

The standard welfare economics approach to subsidy analysis perhaps ignores
that policy is operating in a second best world where there is already a high
level of subsidisation which is not based on the rationale of correcting for
market failure. It is clear that, without large-scale subvention, forestry, on the
scale envisaged, would not be able to compete with agriculture and thereby
assist the political aim of reducing agricultural production as part of the reform
of the Common Agricultural Policy (CAP).

In addition, it is sometimes suggested that subsidisation of forestry is simply a
mechanism for compensating farmers for loss of income resulting from CAP
reform and a politically acceptable way of reducing agricultural production. If
the Strategy is designed as a means of compensating farmers, such a benefit of
the scheme would not be reflected in the subsidy assessment above. All else
being equal, it seems that such large transfers to forestry are not justified.
However, all else is rarely equal and if, under CAP reform, there would be fewer
people employed on the land, then the justification for subsidising forestry
would be greater as the number of otherwise underemployed people would be
greater.   However, to justify the forestry scheme for the purposes of
compensation to farmers it would be necessary to assess whether providing
forestry grants is the most efficient method of compensation. In addition, just

under half of all afforestation is undertaken by non-farmers comprising the semi-state forestry company Coillte (25 per cent) and private individuals/companies (22.5 per cent) so a substantial proportion of the funds does not go to farmers.

The "Strategic Goal" of the Forestry Plan is "to develop forestry to a scale and in a manner which maximises its contribution to national well-being on a sustainable basis and which is compatible with the protection of the environment" (Department of Agriculture, Food and Forestry, 1996). This suggests that increasing the welfare of Irish society is the principal aim of the project. Using the Government's test discount rate of five per cent, the Forestry Plan fails to pass a cost benefit analysis and even if 4 percent is considered a reasonable return, the subsidy is far in excess of that which is justified. This questions the validity of growing timber in Ireland at huge expense to the exchequer rather than importing it from abroad and freeing up the funds for an alternative project or projects which might make better use of the funds. This investment could be comprised of an alternative forestry plan, perhaps on a different scale or with a greater emphasis on the provision of external benefits, or it could be invested in something entirely unrelated to forestry subject to approval from the EU. A weakness of this study is that it is limited to assessing the efficiency of the Governments existing plan and, thus, it does not show whether some other package of measures to promote afforestation would provide a higher (or lower) rate of return and thereby provide a greater justification for the use of the funds. Such measures could include a reduced level of planting, a different species mix, longer rotation periods etc. However, an analysis would have to be carried out to see if this would be a better use of the funds.

It is important to note that this study should not be used as a basis for criticising the Strategy on *environmental* grounds since it has shown that, if the Forest Service enforces its rules and regulations, net environmental benefits will be positive at approximately £165 m. It cannot, therefore, be argued using these figures that, overall, the Strategy will be "bad" for the environment. While there will be some negative environmental impacts of the plan these figures should not be quoted out of context as they are small relative to the other benefits.

Future Areas for Research
Given the conclusions above, it would be desirable for further research to be undertaken to assess the optimal use of these funds such as the planting of community forests where timber production is a secondary objective, direct investment in local communities to promote community stability rather than indirectly through forestry, an expansion of the rural environmental protection scheme to internalise externalities related to landscape and biodiversity etc. However, given that the promotion of afforestation is now part of government policy, it is highly unlikely that it would be abandoned by a future government. Therefore, a greater effort should be made to provide the optimal mix of forest outputs under the present scheme in order to endeavour to maximise the social

benefits of afforestation. The following areas of research would greatly assist this process:

1. The Design of Incentives to Achieve Optimal Forest Outputs

A range of policy measures exists to internalise forest externalities. Thus far the use of mechanisms such as regulation (including zoning) and fiscal instruments has been *ad hoc*. The exact objectives have been unclear and there has been no assessment of the effectiveness of the instruments in achieving whatever the objectives might be. In reality it may be impossible to ascertain the optimal mix of forest outputs. However, further research should be undertaken such that a clear set of objectives can drawn up. Research initiatives 2 to 5 below will assist in achieving this.

Having settled on a set of objectives, research is required to establish the incentives which are necessary to encourage forest owners to provide this mix of forest outputs. A key area for research should be into the use of fiscal instruments. Given the large tranche of funds available for forestry, grant and premia mechanisms can be used to create powerful incentives. At present, apart from the objective of encouraging afforestation, the grant mechanism is used merely to encourage certain species types and mixes. Having drawn up a menu of forest externalities, the loss of timber benefits resulting from the provision of these externalities must be assessed. A more appropriate grant scheme can then be developed to compensate for these losses of revenue. This research initiative will require an interdisciplinary approach. Ideally, a financial appraisal computer package embodying estimates of timber and non-timber benefits and costs would be developed to facilitate the calculation of the appropriate grant.

In regard to regulation, Natural Heritage Areas, areas sensitive for fisheries and landscape, and areas vulnerable to water supply restrictions should be brought together to give an integrated view of the 'areas of constraint'. There is a high geographic coincidence between these areas, and they are, in the main, on land where forest productivity is relatively low so that the opportunity cost of imposing restrictions (in terms of wood production) is likely to be modest. If statutory backing were to be given to the Guidelines and the Rural Environmental Protection Scheme (REPS) were to be fully implemented, this would comprise a reasonably effective land use strategy. This would avoid the bureaucracy and delay involved in setting up a National Authority.

2. Landscape Impacts of Afforestation

A national survey is required to assess the opinions of the public regarding the impact of alternative forest types on different landscapes[60]. This survey should take account of regional differences. Computer simulations provide a cost effective assessment method. A similar study which targets tourists is of particular importance given the value of the Irish landscape for tourism. The

---

[60] Since the final draft of this study but prior to printing, the Forest Service has commissioned UCD and the ESRI to carry out such a survey.

results of the studies could then be used in the development of new landscape guidelines and assist in identifying areas sensitive to afforestation from the point of view of the landscape.

3. Carbon Sequestration on Peat
Thus far, scientists have been unable to ascertain the rate of oxidation of afforested peat. An interdisciplinary research effort is required to assess the net sequestration of CO_2 and methane by afforested peat and the attachment of a monetary value to this process. This is of particular importance given recent EU agreements and likely future global agreements on CO_2 emissions reduction.

4. Water-Forest Relationships
The knowledge of the interaction of forestry with the water supply is very limited. The majority of research in this area has focused on the acidification of water by forest 'scavenging'. A research project is required to assess the extent of pollution other than acidification by afforestation and the costs which this imposes. A study is also required to assess the impact of alternative land uses on hydrology and the associated costs.

5. Community Integrity
An assessment of the extent to which forestry promotes community stability is required. It is a source of some controversy as to whether forestry drives people off the land or whether it provides employment which enables people to stay in their home town. The valuation of this benefit or cost is difficult and, therefore, presents an interesting challenge for researchers in non-market valuation.

It is vital that research such as that listed above be supported and be independent. It is, therefore, most important that the Council for Forest Research and Development (COFORD) be supported in its work and that its be provided with adequate funding.

Information
Information on most aspects of the Irish forest industry is extremely difficult to acquire. The flow of information has deteriorated since the transfer of State forestry from the Forest Service to Coillte in 1989. The Forest Service is failing in its duty to provide information such as the size and location of the forest estate, the location of planting, the species types planted, and annual average timber prices. The difficulty of obtaining such basic information and the reliance upon Coillte to provide information regarding State forestry where it is the duty of the Forest Service to make such information available, seriously hampers research efforts. In addition, it gives ammunition to opponents of forestry. The Forest Service compares most unfavourably with the Forestry Commission in Britain which has a superb information service for the general public and for researchers. During the course of this study, the Forestry Commission were considerably more efficient in providing information than were Coillte and the Forest Service. In view of the huge sums of public money being given in subsidies to Coillte and the private sector it is unacceptable that

information is not more freely available. Unless there is a change in attitude regarding information, the Directive on Freedom to Information on the Environment may come to play a more powerful role in this regard. The Forest Service should publish an annual report and a fact sheet similar to that produced by the Forestry Commission in Britain (Forestry Commission, 1976-1996). Records of compliance and non-compliance with zoning and the Guidelines should be kept in a fashion which facilitates public access, and *ex post* evaluation.

CONCLUSION

To conclude, the study has shown that, if the Forest Strategy is implemented, the resulting expansion of the forest estate will give a rate of return of approximately 4 percent. Therefore, the Plan would fail a cost benefit test at the Government's test rate of 5 percent. This result relies upon the assumption that EU funds committed to afforestation as part of the Strategic Plan could be made available for an alternative use. However, if the EU funds would not be available for an alternative use, the Strategy would pass a cost benefit analysis at a 5 percent discount rate and, therefore, it would be predicted that its implementation would improve the welfare of Irish society as a whole.

However, even if a convincing argument was made that EU funds should be considered as "free", there is still a serious doubt as to whether the social benefits of the programme justify the level of subvention required.

If the Strategic Plan for the Forestry Sector in Ireland is to be justified, a number of issues will need to be clarified:

- Are EU funds restricted to this project and, if so, is there an opportunity cost of using them?
- Is forestry a more viable prospect than an alternative agricultural land use?
- Will forestry subsidies merely replace agricultural subsidies such that there is no net increase in the use of public funds?
- Are subsidies to forestry designed purely to provide income support for farmers and, if so, should Coillte and non-farmers be excluded from the scheme?
- Is funding forestry the best way of transferring income to farmers?
- Would such a plan take the long term unemployed off the dole queue?

The Strategy document does not provide convincing answers to any of these questions. With certain answers to these questions, forestry could be shown to be a wise investment of public funds particularly in comparison to other land uses. However, without such answers, public financing of the Strategic Plan for the Development of the Forestry Sector in Ireland is questionable.

References

Adamowicz, W. (1992). *Non-Timber Values in Canadian Forests: An Assessment of Uses, Techniques and Data Availability*, Project Report 92-02, Department of Rural Economy, University of Alberta.

Alcorn, J. (1989). An Economic Analysis of Huastec Mayan Agroforestry Management, in K. Redford and C. Padock (eds.), *Conservation of Neotropical Forests: Working from Traditional Resource Use*, New York: Columbia University Press.

Allott, N. and Brennan, M. (1993). Impact of Afforestation on Inland Waters, in C. Mollan (ed.), *Water of Life*, Dublin: Royal Dublin Society.

Anderson, A. B. and Ioris, E. M. (1992), The Logic of Extraction: Resource Management and Income Generation by Extractive Producers in the Amazon Estuary, in K. Redford and C. Padock (eds.), *Conservation of Neotropical Forests: Working from Traditional Resource Use*, New York: Columbia University Press.

Anderson, A. R. and Pyatt, D. G. (1986). Interception of Precipitation by Pole Stage Sitka spruce and lodgepole pine at Kielder Forest, Northumberland, *Forestry*, vol. 59, pp. 29-38.

Anderson, A. R., Pyatt, D. G. and Stanard, J. P. (1990). The Effects of Clearfelling a Sitka spruce Stand on the Water Balance of a Peaty Gley Soil at Kershope Forest, Cumbria, *Forestry*, vol. 63, pp. 51-71.

Anderson, D. (1991). *The Forest Industry and the Greenhouse Effect*, report to the Forestry Commission and Scottish Forestry Trust, Edinburgh.

Arnold, M. (1991). *The Long Term Global Demand for and Supply of Wood*, Occasional Paper 36, Edinburgh: Forestry Commission.

Arrow, K., Solow, R., Portney, P. R., Leamer, E. E., Radner, R. and Schuman, H. (1993). Advance Notice of Proposed Rulemaking, Extension of Comment Period and Release of Contingent Valuation Methodology Report, *Federal Register*, vol. 58, pp. 4601-14.

Aylward, B. (1992). Appropriating the Value of Wildlife and Wildlands, in T. M. Swanson (ed.), *Economics for the Wilds*, London: Earthscan.

Ayres, R. U. and Walter, J. (1991). *The Greenhouse Effect: Damages, Costs, and Abatement*, Laxenburg: International Institute for Applied Systems Analysis.

Balick, M. and Mendelson, R. O. (1992). Assessing the Economic Value of Traditional Medicines from Tropical Forests, *Conservation Biology*, vol. 6, pp. 128-30.

Barrow, P., Hinsley, A. P. and Price, C. (1986). The Effect of Afforestation on Hydroelectricity Generation: a Quantitative Assessment, *Land Use Policy*, vol. 3, pp. 141-151.

Bateman, I (1992). The United Kingdom, in S. Wibe and T. Jones (eds.), Forests: *Market and Intervention Failures, Five case Studies*, London: Earthscan.

Bateman, I. (1989). Modified Discounting Method: Some Comments-1, *Project Appraisal*, vol. 4, no. 2, pp. 104-06.

Bateman, I. J. and Turner, R. K. (1993). Valuation of the Environment, Methods and Techniques: The Contingent Valuation Method, in R. K. Turner (ed.), *Sustainable Environmental Economics and Management*, London: Belhaven Press.

Bateman, I. J., Brainard, J. S. and Lovett,, A. A. (1995). *Modelling Woodland recreation Demand Using Geographical Information Systems: a Benefit Transfer Study*, CSERGE Global Environmental Change working paper 95-06.

Baumol, W. J. and Oates, W. E. (1988). *The Theory of Environmental Policy*, 2nd edn., Cambridge: Cambridge University Press.

Bellami, D. (1986). *Bellami's Ireland*, Dublin: Country House.

Benson, J. and Willis, K. (1991), *the Demand for Forest for Recreation*, in Forestry Expansion: a study of technical, economic and ecological factors, Edinburgh: Forestry Commission.

Benson, J. F. and Willis, K. G. (1990). *The Aggregate Value of the Non-Priced Recreation Benefits of the Forestry Commission Estate*, report to the Forestry Commission, Edinburgh.

Birdsall, N. and Steer, A. (1993). Act Now on Global Warming - But Don't Cook the Books, *Finance and Development*, March.

Bishop, R. C. (1982). Option Value: An Exposition and Extension, *Land Economics*, Vol. 58, no. 1, pp. 1-15.

Bishop, R. C. and Herberlein, T. A. (1985). Measuring Values of Extra-Market Goods: Are Indirect Measures Biased?, *American Journal of Agricultural Economics*, vol. 61, pp. 926-30.

Bord Fáilte (1992). *Developing Sustainable Tourism*.

Bord Fáilte (1995). *Tourism Facts 1995*, Dublin: Bord Fáilte.

Bord Fáilte (1995). *Tourism Facts*, July.

Bowes, M. D. and Krutilla, J. V. (1985), Multiple Use Management of Public Forest Lands, in A. Kneese and J. Sweeney (eds.), *Handbook of Natural Resource and Energy Economics*, vol. II, Amsterdam: Elsevier.

Bowes, M. D. and Krutilla, J. V. (1989), *Multiple Use Management: The Economics of Public Forest Lands*, Washington, D.C.: Resources for the Future.

Bowes, M. D., Krutilla, J. V. and Sherman, P. B. (1986), Forest Management for Increased Timber and Water Yields, *Water Resources Research*, vol. 20, no. 6, pp. 655-33.

Bowman, J. (1991). *Acid Sensitive Waters in Ireland*, Dublin: Environmental Research Unit.

Bowman, J. (1997). (EPA), *Personal Communication*.

Bowman, J. J. and Bracken, J. J. (1993). Effect of Run-off from Afforested and Non-afforested Catchments on the Survival of Brown Trout, *Salmo trutta* L. in Two Acid Sensitive Rivers in Wicklow, Ireland, *Biology and Environment*, Proceedings of the Royal Irish Academy, vol. 93B, no. 3, pp. 143-50.

Boyd, R. G. and Hyde, W. F. (1989). *Forestry Sector Intervention: The Impacts of Public Regulation on Social Welfare*, Ames: Iowa State University Press.

Brookshire, D. S., Ives, B. C. and Schulze, W. C. (1976). The Valuation of Aesthetic Preferences, *Journal of Environmental Economics and Management*, vol. 3, pp. 325-46.

Brookshire, D. S., Randall, A., and Stoll, J. (1980). Valuing Increments and Decrements in Natural Resource Service Flows, *American Journal of Agricultural Economics*, vol. 62, no. 3, pp. 478-88.

Brookshire, D., Thayer, M., Schulze, W. and d'Arge, R. (1982). Valuing Environmental Goods: A Comparison of Survey and Hedonic Approaches, *American Economic Review*, vol. 71, pp. 165-77.

Brookshire, D., Thayer, M., Tschirhart, J. and Schulze, W. (1985). A Test of the Expected Utility Model: Evidence from Earthquake Risks, *Journal of Political Economy*, vol. 93, pp. 369-89.

Brown, G. and Henry, W. (1990), *The Economic Value of Elephants*, London Environmental Economics Centre, paper no. 89-12, London: International Institute for Environment and Development.

Brown, K. and Pearce, D. W. (1994), The Economic Value of Non-Market Benefits of Tropical Forests: Carbon Storage, in J. Weiss (ed.), *The Economics of Project Appraisal and the Environment*, London: Edward Elgar.

Bruce, J. P., Yi, H. and Haites, E. F. (1996). *Climate Change 1995: Economic and Social Dimensions of Climate Change*, contribution of Working Group III to the second assessment report of the Intergovernmental Panel on Climate Change, Cambridge: Cambridge University Press.

Bulfin, M. (1987), *Determining the Role of Private Forestry on Highly Productive Forest Sites in Agriculturally Disadvantaged Areas*, Dublin: An Foras Taluntais.

Burke, W. (1968). Drainage of Blanket Peat in Glenamoy, *Transactions of the Second Annual Peat Congress*, Leningrad, pp. 809-17.

Caldecott, J. (1987). *Hunting and Wildlife Management in the Sarawak, Malaysia*, Washington, D.C.: World Wildlife Fund.

Calder, I. R. (1979). Do Trees Use More Water than Grass?, *Water Services*, 83, pp. 11-14.

Calder, I. R. and Newson, M. D. (1979). Land Use and Upland Water Resources in Britain - a Strategic Look, *Water Resources Bulletin*, vol. 15, no. 6, pp. 1628-39.

Cameron, T. A. (1988). A New Paradigm for Valuing Non-market Goods Using Referendum Data: Maximum Likelihood Estimation by Censored Logistic Regression, *Journal of Environmental Economics and Management*, vol. 15, pp. 355-79.

Cannell, M. and Cape, J. (1991), *International Environmental Impacts: Acid Rain and the Greenhouse Effect*, Forestry Commission Occasional Paper 35, Edinburgh: Forestry Commission.

Cannell, M. G. R., Dewar, R. C. and Pyatt, D. G. (1993). Conifer Plantations on Drained Peatlands in Britain: a Net Gain or Loss of Carbon?, *Forestry*, vol. 66, no. 4.

CEC (1995). *The Agricultural Situation in the EU (1994)*, Luxembourg: Office for Official Publications of the European Communities.

Chopra, K. (1993). The Value of Non-timber Forest Products: An Estimate from India, *Economic Botany*, vol. 47, pp. 251-57.

Ciriacy-Wantrup, S. V. (1947). Capital Returns from Soil Conservation Practices, *Journal of Farm Economics*, vol. 29, pp. 1181-96.

Clark, C. W. (1990). *Mathematical Bioeconomics: the optimal management of renewable resources*, 2nd edn., New York: John Wiley and Sons.

Clawson, M and Knetsch, J. (1966). *Economics of Outdoor Recreation*, Baltimore: Johns Hopkins University Press.

Clinch, J. P. (1994). *The Economics of Private Sector Investment in Forestry in the Republic of Ireland*, Unpublished National University of Ireland Master of Arts Thesis, Department of Economics, University College Dublin.

Cline, W. (1993). Give Greenhouse Abatement a Fair Chance, *Finance and Development*, March.

Cline, W. R. (1992). *The Economics of Global Warming*, Washington DC: Institute for International Economics.

COFORD (1994). *Pathway to Progress: A Programme for Forest Research and Development*, Dublin: COFORD.

Collett, M. E. W. (1970). External Costs arising from the Effects of Forests upon Streamflow in Britain, *Forestry*, vol. 43, pp. 87-93.

Conver,y F. (1979). *Irish Forestry Policy*, NESC Report No. 46, Dublin: Stationery Office.

Convery, F. J., Flanagan, S. and Parker, A. J. (1989). *Tourism in County Wicklow - Maximising the Potential*, Dublin: UCD Environmental Institute.

Convery, F. (1988). The Economics of Forestry in the Republic of Ireland, *Irish Banking Review*, Autumn.

Convery, F. J. (1972). *Impacts of Alternative Rural Land-Uses: A Case Study*, unpublished Ph.D. thesis, State University College of Forestry at Syracuse University.

Cooney, G. (1983). Archaeology as a Resource, in J. Blackwell and F. Convery (eds.), *Promise and Performance*, Dublin: UCD Resource and Environmental Policy Centre.

Cooney, G. (1994). *Submission from the Irish Association of Professional Archaeologists on the Impact of Forestry on the Archaeological Resource*, unpublished paper.

Cospoir (1994). *Walking Routes (Ireland).*

Crabbe, P. J. and Long, N. V. (1989). Optimal Forest Rotation under Monopoly and Competition, *Journal of Environmental Economics and Management*, vol. 17, pp. 54-65.

Cruz, W., Francisco, H. A. and Conway, Z. T. (1988). The On-site and Downstream Costs of Soil Erosion in the Magat and Pantabangan Watersheds, *Journal of Philippine Development*, vol. 26.

CSO (1973-1993). *Trade Statistics*, Dublin: Stationery Office.

Cunnane, F. (1994). (Irish Orienteering Association), *Personal Communication.*

Curran, S. (1994). *Personal Communication* (Coillte).

d'Arge, R. and Shorgren, J. (1989). Non-Market Asset Prices: a Comparison of Three Valuation Approaches, in H. Folmer and E. van Ierland (eds.), *Valuation and Policy Making in Environmental Economics*, Amsterdam: Elsevier.

Davis, R. K. (1964). The Value of Big Game Hunting in a Private Forest, in *Transactions of the Twenty-ninth North American Wildlife Conference*, Washington D.C.: Wildlife Management Institute.

Department of Agriculture, Food and Forestry (1995). *Schemes and Services 1995*, Dublin: Department of Agriculture, Food and Forestry.

Department of Agriculture, Food and Forestry (1996). *Growing for the Future: a strategic plan for the development of the forestry sector in Ireland*, Dublin: Stationery Office.

Department of Finance (1994), *Guidelines for the Appraisal and Management of Capital Expenditure Proposals in the Public Sector*, July.

Department of the Environment (1996). *Howlin Tightens Environmental Controls on Forestry*, Press Release, 16 April.

Department of the Environment (1997a). *Forestry Development: Consultation draft of Guidelines for Planning Authorities*, January.

Department of the Environment (1997b). *Sustainable Development: A Strategy for Ireland*, Dublin: Stationary Office.

Desvousges, W. H., Johnson, F. R., Dunford, R. W., Boyle, K. J., Hudson, S. P. and Wilson, K. N. (1993). <u>Measuring Natural Resource Damages With Contingent Valuation: Tests of Validity and Reliability</u>, in J. A. Hausman (ed.), *Contingent Valuation: A Critical Assessment*, Contributions to Economic Analysis 220, Amsterdam: North Holland.

Desvousges, W. H., Smith, V. K. and McGivney, M. P. (1983). *A Comparison of Alternative Approaches for Estimating Recreation and Related Benefits of Water Quality Improvements*, Report no. 30-05-83-001, US Environmental Protection Agency, Washington D.C.

Diamond, P. A. and Hausman, J. A. (1994). <u>Contingent Valuation: Is Some Number Better than No Number</u>?, *Journal of Economic Perspectives*, Vol. 8, No. 4, pp. 3-17.

Diamond, P. A., Hausman, J. A., Leonard, G. K. and Denning, M. A. (1993). <u>Does Contingent Valuation Measure Preferences? Experimental Evidence</u>, in J. A. Hausman (ed.), *Contingent Valuation: A Critical Assessment*, Contributions to Economic Analysis 220, Amsterdam: North Holland.

Dickie, M, Fisher, A. and Gerking, S. (1987). <u>Market Transactions and Hypothetical Demand Data: A Comparative Study</u>, *Journal of the American Statistical Association*, vol. 82, pp. 69-75.

Drèze, J., and Stern, N. (1994). <u>Shadow Prices and Markets: Policy Reform</u>, in R. Layard and S. Glaister (eds.) *Cost-Benefit Analysis*, 2nd edn., Cambridge: Cambridge University Press.

Duffield, J. W. and Patterson, D. A. (1991). *Field Testing Existence Values: An Instream Flow Trust Fund for Montana Rivers*, paper presented at annual meeting of American Economic Association, New Orleans, January, 1991.

Dupuit, J. (1933). *De l'utilité et de la mesure* (reprints of works published in 1844 and the following years). La Riforma Sociale, Turin.

duQuesne (1993). EC Funds and Irish Forestry: a thematic evaluation of EC co-financed forestry measures in Ireland, Dublin: duQuesne Ltd.

Economist, February 5th-11th, 1994.

Edwards, P. and Christie, J. (1981). *Yield Models for Forest Management*, Booklet 48, Edinburgh: Forestry Commission.

Englin, J. and Mendelson, R. (1991). A Hedonic Travel Cost Analysis for Valuation of Multiple Components of Site Quality: the Recreation Value of Forest Management, *Journal of Environmental Economics and Management*, , vol. 21, pp. 275-290.

Environmental Resources Ltd. (1993). *The Valuation of Biodiversity in UK Forests*, report for the Forestry Commission, Edinburgh.

Fankhauser, S. (1995). *Valuing Climate Change: the Economics of the Greenhouse*, London: Earthscan.

FAO (1982). *Yearbook of Forest Products (1969-80) 1980*, Rome: UN Food and Agriculture Organisation.

FAO (1993a). *Forestry: Statistics Today for Tomorrow 1961-1991: 2010*, Rome: UN Food and Agriculture Organisation.

FAO (1993b). *Yearbook of Forest Products (1980-91) 1991*, Rome: UN Food and Agriculture Organisation.

FAO (1996). *European Timber Trends and Prospects: Into the 21st Century*, ECE/TIM/SP/11, Geneva: UN Food and Agriculture Organisation.

Farrell, E. P. (1983). Land Acquisition for Forestry, in J. Blackwell and F. Convery (eds.), *Promise and Performance*, Dublin: UCD Resource and Environmental Policy Centre.

Farrell, E. P. (1995). Sustainability of the Forest Resource, in F. Convery and J. Feehan (eds.), *Assessing Sustainability in Ireland*, Dublin: UCD Environmental Institute.

Farrell, E. P. and Kelly-Quinn, M. (1992). Forestry and the Environment, in J. Feehan (ed.), *Environment and Development in Ireland*, Dublin: UCD Environmental Institute.

Faustmann, M. (1849), Berechnung des Wertes welchen Waldboden sowie noch nicht haubare Holzdestände für die Waldwirtschaft besizen (Calculation of the Value which Forest land and Immature Stands Possess for Forestry), *Allgemeine Forst- und Jagd-Zeitung*, vol. 15, reprinted in English in *Journal of Forest Economics*, vol. 1, no. 1, 1995, pp. 7-44.

Fitz Gerald, J. and Johnson, J. (1996). *The Economic of Biomass in Ireland*, unpublished paper, Dublin: Economic and Social Research Institute.

Ford, E. D. and Deans, J. D. (1978). The Effects of Canopy Structure on Stemflow, Throughfall and Interception Loss in a Young Sitka spruce Plantation, *Journal of Applied Ecology*, vol. 15, pp. 905-17.

Forest and Wildlife Service (1974). *Analytic Study of State Forest Undertaking*, Confidential Report.

Forest Authority (1993). *Woodland Grant Scheme*, Edinburgh: Forestry Commission.

Forest Service (1992a). *Forestry and Archaeology Guidelines*, Dublin: Department of Energy (Forest Service).

Forest Service (1992b). *Forestry and Fisheries Guidelines*, Dublin: Department of Energy (Forest Service).

Forest Service (1992c). *Forestry and Landscape Guidelines*, Dublin: Department of Energy (Forest Service).

Forest Service (1992d). *Taxation Provisions Relating to Private Forestry*, Dublin: Department of Energy.

Forest Service (1994a). *Afforestation Grant and Premium Scheme*, Dublin: Department of Agriculture, Food and Forestry.

Forest Service (1994b). *Personal Communication*, 19th September.

Forest Service (1996). *Addendum to Afforestation Grant and Premium Scheme*, Dublin: Department of Agriculture, Food and Forestry.

Forest Service (undated a). *Amenity Woodland Scheme*, Dublin: Department of Agriculture, Food and Forestry.

Forest Service (undated b). *Urban Woodland Scheme*, Department of Agriculture, Food and Forestry.

Forest Service (undated). *Amenity Woodland Scheme*, Dublin: Department of Agriculture, Food and Forestry.

Forestry Commission (1976-1996). *Forestry Facts and Figures*, Edinburgh: Forestry Commission.

Forestry Trust, *Information Leaflet*.

Freeman, A. M. (1993). *The Measurement of Environmental and Resource Values: Theory and Methods*, Washington D. C.: Resources for the Future.

Friedman, M. (1962). *Capitalism and Freedom*, Chicago: University of Chicago Press.

Garrod, G. D. and Willis, K. G. (1990). *Contingent Valuation Techniques: A Review of their Unbiasedness, Efficiency and Consistency*, Working Paper no. 10, Countryside Change Unit, University of Newcastle Upon Tyne.

Garrod, G. D. and Willis, K. G. (1992). Valuing Goods' Characteristics: An Application of the Hedonic Price Method to Environmental Attributes, *Journal of Environmental Management*, vol. 34, pp. 59-76.

Giller, P. S., O'Halloran, J., Hernan, R., Roche, N., Clenaghan, C., Evans, J., Kiely, G. K., Morris, P., Allott, N., Brennan, M., Reynolds, J., Cooke, D., Kelly-Quinn, M., Bracken, J., Coyle, S. and Farrell, E. P. (1993). An Integrated Study of Forested Catchments in Ireland, *Irish Forestry*, vol. 50, no. 1, pp. 70-83.

Gillmor, D. (1993). Afforestation in the Republic of Ireland, in A. S. Mather (ed.), *Afforestation: Policy, Planning and Progress*, London: Belhaven.

Godoy, R., Lubowski, R. and Markandya, A. (1993). A Method for the Economic Valuation of Non-Timber Tropical Forest Products, *Economic Botany*, vol. 47, no. 3, pp. 220-233.

Good, J., Newton, I., Miles, J., Marus, R. and Greatorex-Davies, J. N. (1991). *Forests as a Wildlife Habitat*, Forestry Commission Occasional Paper 40, Edinburgh: Forestry Commission

Government of Ireland (1991). *Forestry Operational Programme 1989-1993*, Dublin: Stationery Office.

Government of Ireland (1994). *Operational Programme for Agriculture, Rural Development and Forestry 1994-1999*, Dublin: Stationery Office.

Gray, H. J. (1963). *The Economics of Irish Forestry*, Journal of Statistical and Social Inquiry Society of Ireland, vol. XXI, part III, pp. 18-54.

Greene, W. (1993). *Econometric Methods*, 2nd edn., London: Macmillan

Gregory, G. R. (1955). An Economic Approach to Multiple Use, *Forest Science*, vol. 1, no. 1, pp. 6-13.

Griliches, Z. (1971). *Price Indexes and Quality Change*, Cambridge: Harvard University Press.

Grimes, A., Loomis, S., Jahnige, P., Burham, M., Onthank, K., Alarcon, W., Ceron, C., Neill, Balick, M., Bennett, B. and Mendelson, R. (1993). *Valuing the Rain Forest: the Economic Value of Non-Timber Forest Products in Equador*. Unpublished Report, Yale School of Forestry.

Gurnell, J. and Pepper, H. W. (1991). *Conserving the Red Squirrel*, Forestry Research Information Note 205, Farnham: Forestry Commission Research Division.

H.M. Treasury (1972). *Forestry in Great Britain: an Interdepartmental Cost/Benefit Study*, London: Her Majesty's Stationery Office.

Halstead, J. M., Lindsay, B. E. and Brown C. M. (1990). Use of the Tobit Model in Contingent Valuation: Experimental Evidence from the Pemigewasset Wilderness Area, *Journal of Environmental Economics and Management* vol. 33, pp. 79-89.

Hammack, J. and Brown, G. M. (1974). *Waterfowl and Wetlands: Toward Bioeconomic Analysis*, Baltimore: Johns Hopkins.

Hanemann, W. M. (1991). Willingness To Pay and Willingness to Accept: How Much Can they Differ, *American Economic Review*, Vol. 81, No. 3, pp. 635-47.

Hanemann, M. (1984). Welfare Evaluations in Contingent Valuation Experiments with Discrete Response Data: Reply, *American Journal of Agricultural Economics*, vol. 71, pp. 1057-61.

Hanemann, M. (1989). Welfare Evaluations in Contingent Valuation Experiments with Discrete Responses, *American Journal of Agricultural Economics*, vol. 66, pp. 332-41.

Hanemann, M. and Kriström, B. (1995). Preference Uncertainty, Optimal Designs and Spikes, in P.-O. Johansson, B. Kriström and K-G. Mäler (eds.), *Current Issues in Environmental Economics*, Manchester: Manchester University Press.

Hanemann, W. M. (1992). Preface, in S. Navrud (ed.), *Pricing the European Environment*, Oslo: Scandinavian University Press.

Hanemann, W. M. (1994). Valuing the Environment Through Contingent Valuation, *Journal of Economic Perspectives*, Vol. 8, No. 4, pp. 3-17.

Hanley, N. (1989). Valuing Rural Recreation Benefits: an empirical comparison of two approaches, *Journal of Agricultural Economics*, vol. 40, pp. 361-74.

Hanley, N. (1992). Are There Environmental Limits to Cost Benefit Analysis?, *Environmental and Resource Economics*, vol. 2, pp. 33-59.

Hanley, N. and Craig, S. Wilderness Development Decisions and the Krutilla-Fisher model: the case of Scotland's 'Flow Country', *Ecological Economics*, vol. 4, pp. 145-164.

Hanley, N. and Ruffell, R. (1993). The Valuation of Forest Characteristics, in W. Adamowicz, W. White and W. E. Phillips, *Forestry and the Environment: Economic Perspectives*, Wallingford: CAB International.

Hanley, N. and Spash, C. (1993). *Cost-Benefit Analysis and the Environment*, Aldershot: Edward Elgar.

Hanley, N. D. and Common, M. S. (1988). *Estimating Recreation, Wildlife and Landscape Benefits Attached to Queen Elizabeth Forest Park*, report to the Forestry Commission, Edinburgh.

Hanley, N., Shogren, J. F. and White, B. (1997). *Environmental Economics in Theory and Practice*, London: Macmillan.

Hanley, N., Simpson, I, Wright, R., MacMillan, D., Bullock, C. and Crabtree, B. (1996). *Valuing the Landscape and Wildlife Benefits of Woodlands in an Agricultural Context*, paper presented at the International Symposium on the Non-market Benefits of Forestry, Edinburgh, June 1996.

Hanley, N., Spash, C. and Walker, L. (1995). <u>Problems in Valuing the Benefits of Biodiversity Protection</u>, *Environmental and Resource Economics*, vol. 5, pp. 249-272.

Harriman, R. (1978). <u>Nutrient Leaching from Fertilised Forest Watersheds in Scotland</u>, *Journal of Applied Ecology*, vol. 15, pp. 933-42.

Harrison, G. W. and Kriström, B. (1995). <u>On the Interpretation of Responses in Contingent Valuation Surveys</u>, in P.-O. Johansson, B. Kriström and K-G. Mäler (eds.), *Current Issues in Environmental Economics*, Manchester: Manchester University Press.

Hartman, R. (1976). <u>The Harvesting Decision when a Standing Forest has Value</u>, *Economic Inquiry*, vol. 14, pp. 52-58.

Harvey, D. (1991). *The Agricultural Demand for Land: Its Availability and Cost for Forestry*, in Forestry Commission Occasional Paper 47, Edinburgh: Forestry Commission.

Harvey, D. R. and Hall, J. (1989). *PSE's, Producer Benefits and Transfer Efficiency of the CAP and Alternatives*, Discussion Paper DP 3/89, Department of Agricultural Economic and Food Marketing, University of Newcastle Upon Tyne.

Hausman, J. A. (ed.) (1993). *Contingent Valuation: A Critical Assessment*, Contributions to Economic Analysis 220, Amsterdam: North Holland.

Hayden, T. J. (1995). <u>Irish Wildlife: A Knowable and Renewable Resource?</u>, in F. Convery and J. Feehan, *Assessing Sustainability in Ireland*, Dublin: UCD Environmental Institute.

Heal, G. M. (1981). <u>Economics and Resources</u>, in R. Butlin (ed.), *Economics of Environmental and Natural Resource Policy*, Boulder: Westview Press.

Hickey, B. and Bulfin, M. (1978). <u>Economics of Forest Production in Leitrim</u>, in An Foras Taluntais, *County Leitrim Resource Survey*, Dublin: An Foras Taluntais.

Hickie, D. (1990). *Forestry in Ireland: Policy and Practice*, Dublin: An Taisce.

Hickie, D. (1996). *Evaluation of Environmental Designations in Ireland*, Dublin: Heritage Council.

Hickie, D. (1997). *Personal Communication*.

Hicks, J. (1939). <u>The Foundations of Welfare Economics</u>, *Economic Journal*, vol. 49, pp. 696-712.

Honohan, P. (1995). *Cost-Benefit Analysis of Industrial Policy Incentives*, unpublished paper, Dublin: Economic and Social Research Institute.

Honohan, P. (1996). *Methodological Issues in Evaluation of Irish Industrial Policy*, Working Paper 69, Dublin: Economic and Social Research Institute.

Hornung, M. and Adamson, J. (1991). *The Impact of Forestry Expansion on Water Quality and Quantity*, Forestry Commission Occasional Paper 42, Edinburgh: Forestry Commission.

Houghton, J. T., Meira Filho, L. G., Callander, B. A., Harris, N., Kattenberg, A., Maskell, K. (1996). *Climate Change 1995: The Science of Climate Change*, contribution of Working Group I to the second assessment report of the Intergovernmental Panel on Climate Change, Cambridge: Cambridge University Press.

Hudson, J. A. (1988). The Contribution of Soil Moisture Storage to the Water Balances of Upland Forested and Grassland Catchments, *Journal of Hydrological Science*, vol. 33, pp. 289-309.

Hulme, M. and Jones, P. D. (1988). *Climatic Change Scenarios for the UK*, report for the Institute of Hydrology, NERC. Climatic Research Unit, University of East Anglia.

Hunter Blair, P. (1994).   (Northern Ireland Forest Service), *Personal Communication.*

Hutchinson, W. and Chilton, S. (1994).   *How Site Specific are Rural Environmental Benefits for Forest Recreation?*, paper presented to the Agricultural Economics Society Annual Conference, University of Exeter, April.

Hutchinson, R. W. (1989). Modified Discounting Method: Some Comments-3, *Project Appraisal*, vol. 4, no. 2, pp. 108-09.

Irish Timber Growers Association (1995). *Yearbook and Directory of Services, 1995*, Dublin: ITGA.

Irish Timber Growers Association (1997). *Yearbook and Directory of Services, 1997*, Dublin: ITGA.

Jaakko Pöyry (1994). *Long Term Development of Timber Prices*, paper given at the launch of IFUT, Dublin, 9 March.

Johansson, P-O (1989).   Valuing Public Goods in a Risky World: an Experiment, in H. Folmer and E. Van Ierland (eds.), *Valuation Methods and Policy Making in Environmental Economics*, Amsterdam: Elsevier.

Johansson, P-O (1990). Willingness to Pay Measures and Expectations: An Experiment, *Applied Economics*, vol. 22, pp. 313-29.

Johansson, P-O, Kriström, B. and Mäler, K. G. (1989). Welfare Evaluations in Contingent Valuation Experiments with Discrete Response Data: Comment, *American Journal of Agricultural Economics*, vol. 71, pp. 1054-56.

Johansson, P.-O. (1993).   *Cost-Benefit Analysis of Environmental Change*, Cambridge: Cambridge University Press.

John Clegg and Co. (1993). *The Rural Property Market: the Influence of Woods on Property Values in 1993*, report to the Forestry Commission, Edinburgh.

Johnson, R. C. (1990). The Interception, Throughfall and Stemflow in a Forest in Highland Scotland and the Comparison with Other Upland Forest in the UK, *Journal of Hydrology*, vol. 118, pp. 281-87.

Johnson, R. C. (1995). *Effects of Upland Afforestation on Water Resources: the Balquhidder Experiment 1981-1991*, report no. 116, Wallingford: Institute of Hydrology.

Kahneman, D. (1986). Comments, in R. G. Cummings, D. S. Brookshire and W. D. Schulze (eds.), *Valuing Environmental Goods*, Totwa: Rowman and Allenhead.

Kahneman, D. and Knetsch, J. L. (1992). Valuing Public Goods: The Purchase of Moral Satisfaction, *Journal of Environmental Economics and Management*, vol. 22, pp. 90-4.

Kaldor, N. (1939). Welfare Propositions of Economics and Interpersonal Comparisons of Utility, *Economic Journal*, vol. 49, pp. 549-552.

Kangas, J. and Kuusipalo, J. (1993). Estimation and Use of Biodiversity in Forest Management Planning, *Scandinavian Forest Economics*, no. 34.

Kearney, B. and O'Connor, R. (1993). *The Impact of Forestry on Rural Communities*, Dublin: Economic and Social Research Institute.

Kennedy, J. J. and McCusker, P. (1983). State Forest Amenity Policies for a growing Urban Irish Population, in J. Blackwell and F. Convery (eds.), *Promise and Performance*, Dublin: UCD Resource and Environmental Policy Centre.

Kilroy, M. and Murphy, M. (1980). A Summary of the Glenamong River Survey 1979, in *Annual Report of the Salmon Research Trust of Ireland*, no. 24, pp. 30-31.

Klaassen, G. (1997). *Emissions Trading in the European Union: Practice and Prospects*, unpublished paper, European Commission, DGXI.

Kramer, R., Sharma, N. and Munasinghe, M. (1995*), Valuing Tropical Forests: Methodology and Case Study if Madagascar*, Environment Paper no. 13, Washington D.C.: World Bank.

Kriström, B. and Riera, P. (1996). Is the Income Elasticity of Environmental Improvements Less than One?, *Environmental and Resource Economics*, vol. 7, pp. 45-55.

Kriström, B. (1989). On the Benefits of Preserving Virgin Forest, *Scandinavian Forest Economics*, No. 30, pp. 141-66.

Kriström, B. (1990). *Valuing Environmental Benefits using the Contingent Valuation Method - An Econometric Analysis*, Umeå Economic Studies No. 219, Umeå: University of Umeå

Kriström, B. (1995). *Spike Models in Contingent Valuation: Theory and Illustrations*, Arbetsrapport 210, Umeå: Department of Forest Economics, Swedish University of Agricultural Sciences.

Krutilla, J. V. (1967). Conservation Reconsidered, *American Economic Review*, vol. LVII, no. 4, pp. 777-86.

Kula, E. (1988a). Future Generations: The Modified Discounting Method, *Project Appraisal*, vol. 3, no. 2, pp. 85-88.

Kula, E. (1988b). *The Economics of Forestry: Modern Theory and Practice*, London: Croom Helm.

Kula, E. (1989). Modified Discounting Method: Rejoinder, *Project Appraisal*, vol. 4, no. 2, pp. 110-12.

Kumari, K. (1994). *Sustainable Forest Management in Peninsular Malaysia: Towards a Total Economic Valuation Approach.*, unpublished PhD thesis, University of East Anglia.

Lampietti, J. A. and Dixon, J. A. (1995). *To see the Forest for the Trees: A Guide to Non-Timber Forest Benefits*, Environment Department Paper no. 013, Washington, D. C.: World Bank.

Law, F. (1956). The Effect of Afforestation upon Yield of Water Catchment Areas, *Journal of the British Water Works Association*, vol. 38, pp. 484-94.

Layard, R. and Glaister, S. (1994). Introduction, in R. Layard and S. Glaister (eds.) *Cost-Benefit Analysis*, 2nd edn., Cambridge: Cambridge University Press.

Layard, R. and Walters, A. (1994). Income Distribution, in R. Layard and S. Glaister (eds.) *Cost-Benefit Analysis*, 2nd edn., Cambridge: Cambridge University Press.

Leslie, A. J. (1989). On the Economic Prospects for Natural Management in Temperate Hardwoods, *Forestry*, vol. 62, pp. 147-66.

Lind, R. C., Arrow, K. J., Corey, G. R., Dasgupta, P., Sen, A. K., Stauffer, T., Stiglitz, J. E., Stockfisch, J. A. and Wilson, R. (1982). *Discounting for Time and Risk in Energy Policy*, Washington D.C.: Resources for the Future.

Little, I. (1957). *A Critique of Welfare Economics*, 2nd edn., Oxford: Clarendon Press.

Little, I. M. D. and Mirrlees, J. A. (1968). *Manual of Industrial Project Analysis in Developing Countries*, vol. 1, Paris: Organisation for Economic Co-operation and Development.

Little, I. M. D. and Mirrlees, J. A. (1974). *Project Appraisal and Planning for Developing Countries*, New York: Basic Books.

Little, I. M. D. and Mirrlees, J. A. (1994). *The Costs and Benefits of Analysis: Project Appraisal and Planning Twenty Years On*, in R. Layard and S. Glaister (eds.) *Cost-Benefit Analysis*, 2nd edn., Cambridge: Cambridge University Press.

London Economics (1993). *National Forest Cost Benefit Analysis: Final Report*, unpublished report.

Loomis, , J. B. and Cooper, J. (1988). *The Net Economic Value of Antelope Hunting in Montana*, Department of Fish, Wildlife and Parks, Helena, Montana.

Lucey, C. (1995). Letter to the Editor, *Sunday Tribune*, 13 October.

Lynam, J. (1994). (Long Distance Walking Groups Committee), *Personal Communication*.

M. C. O'Sullivan Ltd. (1996). *Greater Dublin Water Supply: Strategic Study*, Dublin: Department of the Environment.

Magrath, W. and Arens, P. (1989). *The Costs of Soil Erosion on Java: A Natural Resource Accounting Approach*. Environment Department paper no. 15, Washington D.C.: World Bank.

Maitland, P. S., Newson, M. D. and Best, G. A. (1990). *The Impact of Afforestation and Foresty Practice on Freshwater Habitats*, Focus on Nature Conservation no. 23, Peterborough: Nature Conservancy Council.

Malcom, D. C. and Cuttle, S. P. (1983). The Application of Fertlisers to Drained Peat 1: Nutrient Losses in Drainage, *Forestry*, vol. 56, pp. 155-74.

Marglin, S. (1963). The Social Rate of Discount and the Optimal Rate of Investment, *Quarterly Journal of Economics*, vol. 77, pp. 95-111.

Marglin, S. A., Sen, A. and Dasgupta, P. S. (1972). *Guidelines for Project Evaluation*, Vienna: United Nations Industrial Development Organisation.

Markandya, A. and Pearce, D. (1988). Natural Environments and the Social Rate of Discount, *Project Appraisal*, vol. 3, no. 1, pp. 2-12.

Markandya, A. and Pearce, D. (1990). *Economic Security Arguments for Afforestation in the United Kingdom*, unpublished paper, CSERGE, University College London.

Markandya, A., Pearce, D., and Knight, I. (1988). *Economic Security Arguments for Afforestation*, Report to the Forestry Commission.

Mattsson, L. (1990). Hunting in Sweden: Extent, Economic Values and Structural Problems, *Scandinavian Journal of Forest Research*, vol. 5, pp. 563-73.

McCloskey, D. (1985). *The Rhetoric of Economics*, Madison: University of Wisconsin Press.

McConnell, K. E. (1983). Existence and Bequest Value, in R. D. Rowe and L. G. Chestnut (eds.), *Managing Air Quality and Scenic Resources at National Parks and Wilderness Areas*, Boulder: Westview Press.

McCormack, A. and O'Leary, T. (1993). Classification of Landscape Sensitivity for Visual Impact Assessment, *Irish Forestry*, vol. 50, no. 1.

McWilliams, B. (1994). Implications for Ireland of Climate Change - an Overview, in J. Feehan (ed.), *Climate Variation and Climate Change in Ireland*, Dublin: UCD Environmental Institute.

Milner, N. J. and Varallo, P. V. (1990). Effects of Acidification on Fish and Fisheries in Wales, in R. W. Edwards, A. S. Gee and J. H. Stoner (eds.), *Acid Waters in Wales*, Dordrecht: Kluwer.

Minister for Agriculture, Food and Forestry (1996). Press Release of 1 July.

Mishan, E. J. (1988). *Cost-Benefit Analysis: an informal introduction*, 4th edn., London: Unwin Hyman.

Mitchell, R. C. and Carson, R. T. (1995). Current Issues in the Design, Administration and Analysis of Contingent Valuation Surveys, in P.-O. Johansson, B. Kriströmand K-G. Mäler (eds.), *Current Issues in Environmental Economics*, Manchester: Manchester University Press.

Mitchell, F. (1990). *The Way that I Followed*, Dublin: Country House.

Mitchell, R. C. and Carson, R. T. (1989). *Using Surveys to Value Public Goods: The Contingent Valuation Method*, Washington D.C.: Resources for the Future.

Mori, S. A. (1992). The Brazil Nut Industry: Past, Present and Future, in M. Plotkin and L. Famolare (eds.), *Sustainable Harvest and Marketing of Rain Forest Products*. Washington D. C.: Island Press.

Mulloy, F. (1992). Forestry Development: Review of Existing and Prospective EC Policies and Implementation, in. J. Feehan (ed.), *Environmental and Development in Ireland*, Dublin: UCD Environmental Institute.

Murphy, G. (1994). *Personal Communication* (Coillte).

Navrud, S. (1989). *The Use of Benefits Estimates in Environmental Decision Making: Case Study on Norway*, Paris: OECD.

Navrud, S. (1993). Economic Value of Biodiversity in Norway, *Scandinavian Journal of Forest Economics*, no. 34, pp. 74-97.

Neeson, E. (1991). *A History of Irish Forestry*, Dublin: Lilliput.

Newbery, D. M. (1992). *Long Term Discount Rates for the Forest Enterprise*, report to the Forestry Commission, Edinburgh.

Newson, M. D. (1979). The Results of Ten Years Experimental Study on Plynlimon, mid-Wales and Their Importance for the Water Industry. *Journal of the Institute of Water Engineering Science*, vol. 33, pp. 321-33.

Ní Dhubháin, A., Gardiner, J. J., Davis, J., Hutchinson, W. G., Chilton, S., Thompson, K., Psaltopoulos, D. and Anderson, C. (1994). *The Socio-Economic Impact of Afforestation on Rural Development*, European Community CAMAR Contract no. 80001-0008.

Nordhaus, W. D. (1991). To Slow or Not to Slow: The Economics of the Greenhouse Effect, *Economic Journal*, vol. 101, pp. 920-37.

Nordhaus, W. D. (1993). Rolling the 'DICE': An Optimal Transition Path for Controlling Greenhouse Gases, *Resource and Energy Economics*, vol. 15, no. 1, pp. 313-17.

Noss, R. F., Cline, S. P., Csuti, B. and Scott, J. M. (1992). Monitoring and Assessing Biodiversity, in E. Lykke (ed.), *Achieving Environmental Goals*, London: Belhaven Press.

O' Connor, R. and Conlon, F. (1993). *Agricultural and Forestry Land Prices in Ireland*, Dublin: Economic and Social Research Institute.

O'Brien, D. (1997). (Coillte), *Personal Communication*.

O'Connor, R. and Kearney, B. (1993). Economic Issues in Irish Forestry, *Journal of the Statistical and Social Inquiry Society of Ireland*, vol. XXVI, Part V, pp. 179-204.

O'Halloran, J. and Giller, P. (1993). Forestry and Ecology of Streams and Rivers: Lessons from Abroad?, *Irish Forestry*, vol. 50, no. 1, pp. 35-52.

O'Hegarty, D. (1994). *Woodland Taxation in Ireland*, in ITGA Yearbook and Directory of Services, Dublin: ITGA.

Ohlin, B. (1921). Till frågan om skogarnas omloppstid (Concerning the Question of the Rotation Period in Forestry), *Ekonomisk Tidskrift*, vol. 22, reprinted in *Journal of Forest Economics*, vol. 1, no. 1, 1995, pp. 89-114.

Ozanne, C. M. P. (1996). Managing Woodlands for Invertebrates, *Forestry and British Timber*, June.

Pearce, D. (1991). *Assessing the Returns to the Economy and Society from Investments in Forestry*, Forestry Commission Occasional Paper 47, Edinburgh: Forestry Commission.

Pearce, D. (1996). *Can Non-Market Values Save the World's Forests?*, presented at the International Symposium on the Non-market Benefits of Forestry, Edinburgh, June 1996.

Pearce, D. and Moran, D. (1994). *The Economic Value of Biodiversity*, London: Earthscan.

Pearce, D. W. and Nash, C. (1981). *The Social Appraisal of Projects*, London: Macmillan Press.

Pearce, D. W. and Turner, R. K. (1990). *Economics of Natural Resources and the Environment*, Hemel Hempstead: Harvester Wheatsheaf.

Pearce, D. W. and Warford, R. (1993). *World Without End*, Oxford: Oxford University Press.

Pearce, D., Markandya, A., and Barbier, E. B. (1989). *Blueprint for a Green Economy*. London: Earthscan.

Pearce, D.W. (1983). *Cost Benefit Analysis*, 2nd edn., London: Macmillan.

Peck, S. C. and Teisberg, T. J. (1992). CETA: A Model for Carbon Emissions Trajectory Assessment, *Energy Journal*, vol. 13, no. 1, pp. 222-30.

Peterken, G. F. (1996). *Natural Woodland, Ecology and Conservation in Northern Temperate Regions*, Cambridge: Cambridge University Press.

Peterson, G. L. and Brown, T. C. (1996). *Trains are Pretty Good but they Can't Take You to Australia.....Yet*, paper presented at the International Symposium on the Non-Market Benefits of Forestry, Edinburgh, June 24-28.

Pigou, A. C. (1932). *The Economics of Welfare*, London: Macmillan.

Pinedo-Vazquez, M, Zarin, D. and Jipp, P. (1992). Economic Returns from Forest Conservation in the Peruvian Amazon, *Ecological Economics*, vol. 6, pp. 163-73.

Polinsky, A. M. (1972). Probabilistic Compensation Criteria, *Quarterly Journal of Economics*, vol. 86, no. 3, pp. 407-425.

Portney, P. R. (1994). The Contingent Valuation Debate: Why Economists Should Care, *Journal of Economic Perspectives*, Vol. 8, No. 4, pp. 3-17.

Power, R. and Roche, M. (1996). *National Farm Survey 1995*, Dublin: Teagasc.

Preßler, M. R. (1860). Aus der Holzzuwachlehre (zweiter Artikel) (For the Comprehension of Net Revenue Silviculture and the Management Objectives Derived Thereof), *Allgemeine Forst- und Jagd-Zeitung*, 36, 173-191, reprinted in *Journal of Forest Economics*, vol. 1, no. 1, 1995, pp. 45-87.

Price, C. (1991a). *Evaluating the Benefits of Amenity Trees*, unpublished report, School of Agricultural and Forest Sciences, University of Wales, Bangor.

Price, C. (1991b). *Landscape Valuation and Public Decisions Making*, unpublished report, School of Agricultural and Forest Sciences, University College of North Wales, Bangor.

Price, C. (1993). *Time, Discounting and Value*, Oxford: Blackwell.

Price, C. (ed.) (1994). *Landscape Research*, vol. 19, no. 1, pp. 1-56.

Price, C. (1997). 25 Years of Forestry Cost-Benefit Analysis in Britain, *Forestry*, vol. 70, pp. 171-89.

Price, C. and Willis, R. W. (1993). Time, Discounting and the Valuation of Forestry's Carbon Fluxes, *Commonwealth Forestry Review*, vol. 72, pp. 265-71.

Prins, R., Adamowicz, W. and Phillips, W. (1990), *Non-Timber Values and Forest Resources: An Annotated Bibliography*, Project Report 90-03, Department of Rural Economy, University of Alberta.

Ramsey, F. (1928). A Mathematical Theory of Saving, *Economic Journal*, Vol. 38.

Randall, A. (1984). The Conceptual Basis of Benefit Cost Analysis, in G. L. Peterson and A. Randall (eds.), *Valuation of Wildland Resource Benefits*, Boulder: Westview Press.

Randall, A. (1991). The Value of Biodiversity, *Ambio*, vol. 20, no. 2.

Randall, A. (1993). Thinking About the Value of Biodiversity, *Scandinavian Forest Economics*, no. 34.

Randall, A. and Stoll, J. R. (1980). Consumer's Surplus in Commodity Space, *American Economic Review*, vol. 70, no. 3, pp. 449-55.

Rea, T. (1976). *A New Pulpwood Industry, Its Timing and Location*, unpublished M.Sc. thesis, Department of Statistics, University of Dublin.

Review Group on Forestry (1985). *Report to the Minister for Fisheries and Forestry*, Dublin: Stationery Office.

Rigby, M. W. (1989). Modified Discounting Method: Some Comments-2, *Project Appraisal*, vol. 4, no. 2, pp. 107-08.

Roberts, G. (1988). Forest Fertilisation, in G. Roberts, B. Reynolds and J. Talling (eds.), *Upland Management and Water Resources*, NERC Contract Report to Department of the Environment and Welsh Office.

Rose, A. and Tietenberg, T. (1993). An International System of Tradeable CO_2 Entitlements: Implications for Economic Development, *Journal of Environment and Development*, vol. 2, pp. 1-36.

Rosen, S. (1974). Hedonic Prices and Implicit Markets: Product Differentiation in Pure Competition, *Journal of Political Economy*, vol. 82, pp. 34-55.

Rowe, R., d'Arge, R. and Brookshire, D. (1980). An Experiment on the Economic Value of Visibility, *Journal of Environmental Economics and Management*, vol. 7, pp. 1-19.

Ruitenbeek, H. J. (1988). *Social Cost-Benefit of the Korup Project, Cameroon*, London: World Wide Fund for Nature.

Ruitenbeek, H. J. (1989). *Economic Analysis of Issues and Projects Relating to the Establishment of the Proposed Cross River National Park (Oban Division) and Support Zone*, London: World Wide Fund for Nature.

Salmon Research Agency of Ireland Incorporated (1995). *Annual Report no. 40*, Newport.

Samuelson, P. (1947). *Foundations of Economic Analysis*, Cambridge M.A.: Harvard University Press.

Samuelson, P. (1954). The Pure Theory of Public Expenditure, *Review of Economics and Statistics*, vol. 36, pp. 387-89.

Samuelson, P. (1976). Economics of Forestry in an Evolving Society, *Economic Inquiry* vol. 14, reprinted in *Journal of Forest Economics*, vol. 1, no. 1, 1995, pp. 115-149.

Schwartzman, S. (1989). *Extractive Reserves in the Amazon, in J. Browder (ed.), Fragile Lands of Latin America: Strategies for Sustainable Development*, Boulder: Westview Press.

Scitovsky, T. (1941). A Note on Welfare Propositions in Economics, *Review of Economic Studies*, vol. 9.

Scully, B. (1994). *National Monuments and Historic Properties*, paper presented at conference on Investing in Tourism, University College, Dublin, March 29.

Sedjo, R. A. (1989). Forests: a Tool to Moderate Global Warming?, *Environment*, vol. 31, no. 1, pp. 14-20.

Seventh Joint Committee on State-Sponsored Bodies (1997). *Fifth Report: Coillte Teoranta*, Dublin: Government of Ireland.

Sheehy, S. J. (1992), Evaluation of Current Proposals to Reform the Common Agricultural Policy, in. J. Feehan (ed.), *Environmental and Development in Ireland*, Dublin: UCD Environmental Institute.

Simons (1991). *The Irish Timber Industry, and Export Development Plan for the 90s*, Report prepared for Coillte Teoranta, the Irish Timber Council, the IDA and CTT.

Smith, K. (1977). Catchment Area Experiences at Plynlimon, *Water Reports*, vol. 81, no. 977, pp. 394-401.

Smith, V. K. (1992). Arbitrary Values, Good Causes and Premature Verdicts, *Journal of Environmental Economics and Management*, vol. 22, pp. 71-89.

Smith, V. K. and Desvousges, W. H. (1986). *Measuring Water Quality Benefits*, Boston: Kluwer-Nijhoff.

Smyth, P. (1997). Decision to Cut Greenhouse Gas Emissions Means EU Leads Fight Against Global Warming, *Irish Times*, March 4.

Sodal, D. (1989), The Recreational Value of Moose Hunting in Norway: Towards Modelling Optimal Population Density, *Scandinavian Forest Economics*, No. 30, pp. 62-78.

Spash, C. L. and Hanley, N. (1994). *Preferences, Information and Biodiversity Preservation*, discussion paper in Ecological Economics 94/1, University of Stirling.

Squire, L. and van der Tak, H. G. (1975). *Economic Analysis of Projects*, Baltimore: Johns Hopkins Press.

Stretton, C. (1984). Water Quality and Forestry - A Conflict of Interests: Cray Reservoir, a Case Study, *Journal of the Institute of Water Engineers*, vol. 38, pp. 323-30.

Swanson, T. M. (1992). Wildlife and Wildlands, Diversity and Development, in T. M. Swanson (ed.), *Economics for the Wilds*, London: Earthscan.

Swift, D. W. (1986). *Phosphorous Run Off from Glenorchy Forest*, Report PRV 1699-M, Medmenham: Water Research Centre.

Temple-Lang, J. and Hickie, D. (1996). The Wildlife Act and EC Conservation Measures, in J. Feehan (ed.), *Environment and Development in Ireland*, Dublin: UCD Environmental Institute.

Thayer, M. (1981). Contingent Valuation Techniques for Assessing Environmental Impacts: Further Evidence, *Journal of Environmental Economics and Management*, vol. 8, pp. 27-44.

Thompson, K. (1988). Future Generations: The Modified Discounting Method: A Reply, *Project Appraisal*, vol. 3, no. 3, pp. 171-72.

Thorbjarnarson, J. H. (1991). An Analysis of the Spectacled Caiman (*Caiman crocodilus*) Harvest Program in Venezuela, in K. Redford and J. Robinson (eds.), *Neotropical Wildlife Use and Conservation*, Chicago: University of Chicago Press.

Tickell, O. (1994). Conifer Forests are Not the 'Deserts' They Seem, *New Scientist*, September 1994.

Tobias, D. and Mendelson, R. (1991), Valuing Ecotourism in a Tropical Rainforest Reserve, *Ambio*, vol. 20, no. 2.

Tourism Development International Ltd (1994). *1993 Visitor Attractions Survey*.

UNEP (1993), *Guidelines for Country Studies on Biodiversity*, Nairobi: United Nations Environment Programme.

van der Sleesen, A. (1997). (University College Galway), *Personal Communication*.

van Kooten, G. C., Thompson, W. A. and Vertinsky, I (1993). Economics of Reforestation in British Columbia when Benefits of CO_2 Reductions are Taken into Account, in W. Adamowicz, W. White and W. Phillips (eds.), *Forestry and the Environment: Economic Perspectives*, Wallingford: CAB International.

Varian, H. R. (1990). *Intermediate Microeconomics: A Modern Approach*, New York: W. W. Norton & Co.

Walsh, P. D. (1980). The Impacts of Catchment Afforestation on Water Supply Interests, *Aqua*, vol. 4, pp. 82-85.

Walsh, R. G., Sanders, L. D. and Loomis, J. B. (1985), *Wild and Scenic River Economics: Recreation Use and Preservation Values*, Department of Agricultural and Natural Resource Economics, Colorado State University, Fort Collins.

Watson, R. T., Zinyowera, M. C., Moss, R. H. (1996). *Climate Change 1995: Impacts, Adaptations and Mitigation of Climate Change*, contribution of Working Group II to the second assessment report of the Intergovernmental Panel on Climate Change, Cambridge: Cambridge University Press.

Weisbrod, B. A. (1964). Collective-Consumption Services of Individual-Consumption Goods, *Quarterly Journal of Economics*, vol. 78, pp. 471-77.

Whelan, B. J. (1979). A Random Sample Design for Ireland, *Economic and Social Review*, vol. 10, no. 2, pp. 169-174.

Whelan, K. (1995). *The Role of Peatlands in the Management of Freshwater Fisheries*, Newport: Salmon Research Agency.

Whiteman, A. (1991). *A Cost-Benefit Analysis of Forest Replanting in East England*, Edinburgh: Forestry Commission Development Division.

Whiteman, A. (1991a). *UK Demand for and Supply of Wood and Wood Products*, Occasional Paper 37, Edinburgh: Forestry Commission.

Whiteman, A. and Sinclair, J. (1994), *The Costs and Benefits of Planting Three Community Forests: Forest of Mercia, Thames Chase and Great North Forest*, Edinburgh: Forestry Commission Policy Studies Division.

Wibe, S. (1995). *Non Wood Benefits in Forestry: A Survey of Valuation Studies*, Geneva: United Nations Economic Commission for Europe/Food and Agriculture Organization.

Wiley, S. (1994). The Market for Irish Timber: A Perspective from 1994, in *ITGA Yearbook*, Dublin: ITGA.

Wilkie, D. S. (1989). Impact of Roadside Agriculture on Subsistence in the Ituri Forest of Northeastern Zaire, *American Journal of Physical Anthropology*, vol. 78, pp. 485-94.

Wilkie, D. S. and Curran B. (1991). Why do Mbuti Hunters use Nets? Ungulate Hunting Efficiency of Archers and Net Hunters in the Ituri Rain Forest, *American Anthropologist*, vol. 93, pp. 680-89.

Williams, J. (1997). *Personal Communication*, January.

Willig, R. D. (1976). Consumer's Surplus Without Apology, *American Economic Review*, vol. 66, no. 4, pp. 587-97.

Willis K. G., Benson, J. F. and Whitby, M. C. (1988). *Values of Use-Benefits of Forest Recreation and Wildlife*, report to the Forestry Commission, Edinburgh.

Willis, K. and Garrod, G. (1991). An Individual travel Cost Method of Evaluating Forest Recreation, *Journal of Agricultural Economics*, vol. 42, no. 1, pp. 33-42.

Willis, K. G. and Benson, J. F. (1989). *Values of User-Benefits of Forest Recreation: Some Further Site Surveys*, report to the Forestry Commission, Edinburgh.

Willis, K. G. and Garrod, G. D. (1992). Amenity Value of Forests in Great Britain and its Impact on the Internal Rate of Return from Forestry, *Forestry*, vol. 65, pp. 341-46.

Willis, K. G. and Garrod, G. D. (1993). Valuing Landscape: a Contingent Valuation Approach, *Journal of Environmental Management*, vol. 37, pp. 1-22.

Worrell, R. (1991). *Trees and the Treasury: Valuing Forests for Society*, Godalming: World Wide Fund for Nature.

Zerbe, R. and Dively, D. (1994). *Benefit Cost Analysis in Theory and Practice*, New York: Harper Collins.

APPENDIX 1

APPENDIX TABLES

TABLE A1.1 Afforestation, 1984 to 1995.

Year	Public (ha)	Private (ha)	Total (ha)
1984	5192	284	5476
1985	4625	617	5242
1986	4689	2280	6969
1987	5395	2954	8349
1988	7112	4596	11708
1989	6629	8498	15127
1990	6670	9147	15817
1991	7855	11292	19147
1992	7565	9134	16699
1993	6827	9171	15998
1994	6431	12837	19268
1995	6400	17300	23700

Source: Department of Agriculture, Food and Forestry, 1996.

TABLE A1.2. Forest Strategy Planting Statistics.

End Year	Planting (ha)	Forested area (ha)	Forests % land	Productive Forest (ha)	Conifers (ha)	Broadl. (ha)
1996	25,000	570,000	8	464,000	20,000	5,000
1997	25,000	595,000	9	489,000	20,000	5,000
1998	25,000	620,000	9	514,000	20,000	5,000
1999	25,000	645,000	9	539,000	20,000	5,000
2000	25,000	670,000	10	564,000	20,000	5,000
2001	20,000	695,000	10	589,000	16,000	4,000
2002	20,000	715,000	10	609,000	16,000	4,000
2003	20,000	735,000	11	629,000	16,000	4,000
2004	20,000	755,000	11	649,000	16,000	4,000
2005	20,000	775,000	11	669,000	16,000	4,000
2006	20,000	795,000	12	689,000	16,000	4,000
2007	20,000	815,000	12	709,000	16,000	4,000
2008	20,000	835,000	12	729,000	16,000	4,000
2009	20,000	855,000	12	749,000	16,000	4,000
2010	20,000	875,000	13	769,000	16,000	4,000
2011	20,000	895,000	13	789,000	16,000	4,000
2012	20,000	915,000	13	809,000	16,000	4,000
2013	20,000	935,000	14	829,000	16,000	4,000
2014	20,000	955,000	14	849,000	16,000	4,000
2015	20,000	975,000	14	869,000	16,000	4,000
2016	20,000	995,000	14	889,000	16,000	4,000
2017	20,000	1,015,000	15	909,000	16,000	4,000
2018	20,000	1,035,000	15	929,000	16,000	4,000
2019	20,000	1,055,000	15	949,000	16,000	4,000
2020	20,000	1,075,000	16	969,000	16,000	4,000
2021	20,000	1,095,000	16	989,000	16,000	4,000
2022	20,000	1,115,000	16	1,009,000	16,000	4,000
2023	20,000	1,135,000	16	1,029,000	16,000	4,000
2024	20,000	1,155,000	17	1,049,000	16,000	4,000
2025	20,000	1,175,000	17	1,069,000	16,000	4,000
2026	20,000	1,195,000	17	1,089,000	16,000	4,000
2027	20,000	1,215,000	18	1,109,000	16,000	4,000
2028	20,000	1,235,000	18	1,129,000	16,000	4,000
2029	20,000	1,255,000	18	1,149,000	16,000	4,000
2030	20,000	1,275,000	19	1,169,000	16,000	4,000
end 2030		1,295,000	19	1,189,000		
Totals	725,000				580,000	145,000

Source: Adapted from Department of Agriculture, Food and Forestry, 1996.

TABLE A1.3. Forest Strategy Financial Statistics.

End Year	Total grants (£)	Total premia (£)	Exchequer cost (£)	EU share @ 75% (£)
1996	38,825,123	4,162,500	42,987,623	32,240,717
1997	38,825,123	8,325,000	47,150,123	35,362,592
1998	38,825,123	12,487,500	51,312,623	38,484,467
1999	38,825,123	16,650,000	55,475,123	41,606,342
2000	38,825,123	20,812,500	59,637,623	44,728,217
2001	31,060,000	24,142,500	55,202,500	41,401,875
2002	31,060,000	27,472,500	58,532,500	43,899,375
2003	31,060,000	30,802,500	61,862,500	46,396,875
2004	31,060,000	34,132,500	65,192,500	48,894,375
2005	31,060,000	37,462,500	68,522,500	51,391,875
2006	31,060,000	40,792,500	71,852,500	53,889,375
2007	31,060,000	44,122,500	75,182,500	56,386,875
2008	31,060,000	47,452,500	78,512,500	58,884,375
2009	31,060,000	50,782,500	81,842,500	61,381,875
2010	31,060,000	54,112,500	85,172,500	63,879,375
2011	31,060,000	57,442,500	88,502,500	66,376,875
2012	31,060,000	60,772,500	91,832,500	68,874,375
2013	31,060,000	64,102,500	95,162,500	71,371,875
2014	31,060,000	67,432,500	98,492,500	73,869,375
2015	31,060,000	70,762,500	101,822,500	76,366,875
2016	31,060,000	73,072,500	104,132,500	78,099,375
2017	31,060,000	75,382,500	106,442,500	79,831,875
2018	31,060,000	77,692,500	108,752,500	81,564,375
2019	31,060,000	80,002,500	111,062,500	83,296,875
2020	31,060,000	82,312,500	113,372,500	85,029,375
2021	31,060,000	82,377,500	113,437,500	85,078,125
2022	31,060,000	82,442,500	113,502,500	85,126,875
2023	31,060,000	82,507,500	113,567,500	85,175,625
2024	31,060,000	82,572,500	113,632,500	85,224,375
2025	31,060,000	82,637,500	113,697,500	85,273,125
2026	31,060,000	82,702,500	113,762,500	85,321,875
2027	31,060,000	82,767,500	113,827,500	85,370,625
2028	31,060,000	82,832,500	113,892,500	85,419,375
2029	31,060,000	82,897,500	113,957,500	85,468,125
2030	31,060,000	82,962,500	114,022,500	85,516,875
Total	1,125,925,615	1,989,387,500	3,115,313,115	2,336,484,836

Source: Adapted from Department of Agriculture, Food and Forestry, 1996.

TABLE A1.4. Cork and Wood (Div. 24) Net Exports, 1975 to 1992[1].

Year	Total Quantity (MT)	Real Value[2] (1991£000s)
1975	-150,157	-56,540
1976	-203,620	-70,728
1977	-170,899	-68,745
1978	-201,861	-74,837
1979	-267,582	-93,969
1980	-141,500	-80,802
1981	-42,104	-77,953
1982	120,937	-51,924
1983	68,367	-47,560
1984	53,603	-48,023
1985	86,799	-37,267
1986	27,425	-40,291
1987	116,567	-36,524
1988	130,781	-33,996
1989	91,943	-44,386
1990	57,134	-57,726
1991	217,584	-37,510
1992	349,016	-37,487

Notes:
[1] Comparable figures unavailable post 1992.
[2] Deflated with GDP Deflator

Source: CSO, 1976 to 1993.

TABLE A1.5. **Pulp and Waste Paper (Div. 25) Net Exports,**
1975 to 1992[1].

Year	Total Quantity (MT)	Real Value[2] (1991£000s)
1975	-22,447	-11,170
1976	-5,145	-8,828
1977	6,518	-7,103
1978	2,298	-6,254
1979	24,604	-5,360
1980	15,664	-6,949
1981	-20,385	-13,300
1982	10,697	-2,370
1983	12,639	-2,385
1984	4,550	-4,664
1985	11,267	-4,278
1986	-3,604	-9,046
1987	4,991	-5,438
1988	8,627	-4,306
1989	19,250	-4,778
1990	14,765	-4,900
1991	17,051	-6,361
1992	17,290	-5,268

Note:

[1] Comparable figures unavailable post 1992.

[2] Deflated with GDP Deflator

Source: CSO, 1976 to 1993.

TABLE A1.6. Cork and Wood Manufactures (excluding furniture)
(Div. 63) Net Exports, 1974 to 1992[1].

Year	Total Quantity (MT)	Real Value[2] (1991£000s)
1974	-14,821	-20,392
1975	-16,670	-12,506
1976	-12,263	-13,329
1977	-21,161	-20,995
1978	-41,632	-28,812
1979	-90,659	-48,422
1980	-78,139	-45,438
1981	-95,510	-48,668
1982	-71,710	-35,717
1983	-62,689	-29,844
1984	-83,340	-34,651
1985	-50,031	-29,311
1986	-51,455	-31,764
1987	-41,496	-31,808
1988	48,199	-2,309
1989	28,159	-13,568
1990	242	-25,915
1991	15,596	-21,578
1992	20,645	-17,173

Note:
[1] Comparable figures unavailable post 1992.
[2] Deflated with GDP Deflator

Source: CSO, 1975 to 1993.

TABLE A1.7. ROI, NI and British Timber Real Price Indices Compared.

Year	ROI Price Index[1]	NI Price Index[2]	British Price Index[2]
1974	na	208.1	na
1975	na	215.1	na
1976	163.5	145.9	na
1977	187.9	58.3	221.9
1978	219.5	171.9	161.4
1979	170.9	119.4	145.6
1980	127.8	89.0	154.0
1981	98.4	86.9	70.3
1982	78.7	69.3	79.2
1983	69.3	69.5	84.7
1984	88.4	77.9	109.9
1985	115.8	76.6	117.5
1986	96.1	106.2	141.9
1987	102.7	123.5	157.2
1988	101.8	133.4	160.4
1989	118.2	115.5	160.8
1990	137.6	103.7	135.6
1991	100.0	100.0	100.0
1992	98.7	85.6	96.0
1993	95.2	80.7	91.1
1994	127.1	85.3	110.14
1995	123.7	108.4	133.11
1996	136.6	105.3	111.52

Notes:

[1] Deflated with ROI GDP Deflator to base 1991=100.

[2] Deflated with UK GDP Deflator to base 1991=100.

TABLE A1.8. ROI CSO "Rough Timber" and "Other Timber"
Real* WPIs.

Year	Rough Timber WPI	Other Timber WPI
1975	109.4	110.3
1976	103.9	99.5
1977	113.6	103.5
1978	96.8	99.3
1979	95.6	93.7
1980	100.0	95.2
1981	104.7	97.3
1982	90.3	88.0
1983	88.8	86.8
1984	94.2	92.3
1985	91.7	90.3
1986	86.6	85.9
1987	85.7	85.9
1988	85.2	84.4
1989	95.9	91.1
1990	103.6	99.4
1991	100.0	100.0
1992	96.3	97.3
1993	93.3	91.9
1994	103.8	92.0
1995	111.7	96.1
1996	104.1	99.0

Note:
* Deflated with GDP Deflator to base 1991=100.

Source: CSO.

TABLE A1.9. Selected UK Forest Products Real[1] Price Indices.

Year	FCSSPI[2]	FCCSLI[3]	SSOPI[4]	SPWPI[5]
1971	184.8	na	na	na
1972	199.6	na	na	na
1973	274.5	na	na	na
1974	377.9	na	253.1	236.3
1975	221.2	183.5	171.7	163.1
1976	222.6	209.0	161.8	154.5
1977	206.0	214.8	189.5	179.0
1978	140.9	174.8	166.4	160.3
1979	199.5	205.6	159.7	155.6
1980	124.4	168.1	152.3	147.9
1981	61.6	112.1	127.4	124.9
1982	79.0	112.7	120.5	118.1
1983	86.3	118.4	119.4	116.6
1984	110.6	127.8	127.2	123.3
1985	120.3	129.3	125.5	122.1
1986	139.2	127.4	122.5	120.0
1987	162.2	161.9	123.3	121.2
1988	157.4	72.4	121.9	119.7
1989	153.3	134.5	117.7	115.9
1990	131.3	131.3	118.7	117.6
1991	100.0	100.0	100.0	100.0
1992	101.8	102.2	91.6	93.2
1993	95.6	110.4	102.2	104.9
1994	119.0	124.4	na	na
1995	155.7	123.4	na	na
1996	135.7	110.2	na	na

Notes: [1] Deflated with UK GDP Deflator; [2] Forestry Commission Softwood Standing Sales Price Index; [3] Forestry Commission Competitive Softwood Log Index.; [4] UK CSO Sawn Softwood Output Price Index; [.5] UK CSO Sawmilling, Planing etc. of Wood Price Index.

Source: Forestry Commission; UK CSO.

TABLE A1.10. Selected ROI Real[1] Export Price Indices[2].

Year	Div. 24	Div. 25	Div. 26
1975	89.2	187.4	153.7
1976	105.2	162.5	127.2
1977	90.3	139.4	110.6
1978	70.6	119.6	113.1
1979	89.2	124.3	179.2
1980	71.9	120.3	202.3
1981	63.2	82.5	234.8
1982	57.2	103.1	177.8
1983	70.9	78.7	158.6
1984	86.3	105.0	146.5
1985	77.3	106.6	109.5
1986	91.9	101.2	109.3
1987	95.7	111.7	115.3
1988	111.3	129.9	91.3
1989	112.5	146.8	86.4
1990	136.4	149.9	97.7
1991	100.0	100.0	100.0
1992	94.7	93.6	103.0

Notes:

[1] Deflated with Import Price Index to base 1991=100.

[2] Unit values calculated from value of exports divided by quantity, comparable figures unavailable post 1992.

Source: CSO, 1976 to 1993.

TABLE A1.11. UK Cork and Wood and Softwood Lumber Real* Import Price Indices.

Year	Cork and Wood IPI	Softwood Lumber IPI
1974	120.6	89.4
1975	99.3	71.6
1976	98.2	88.5
1977	106.0	81.1
1978	93.4	74.8
1979	94.5	81.7
1980	97.2	83.2
1981	85.0	69.3
1982	78.4	66.7
1983	83.9	74.4
1984	88.4	76.2
1985	83.4	72.9
1986	87.4	77.9
1987	90.0	81.3
1988	95.1	85.7
1989	99.5	91.7
1990	109.2	101.2
1991	100.0	100.0
1992	91.3	na
1993	113.7	na
1994	121.1	na
1995	107.6	na
1996	103.3	na

Note:
* Deflated with UK IPI to base 1991=100.

Source: Forestry Commission, UK CSO.

APPENDIX 2

TECHNICAL DESCRIPTION OF METHODOLOGY

WELFARE CRITERION

In using CBA to assess the costs and benefits of a project or policy to society, it is first necessary to define the social efficiency criterion. This study relies predominantly on allocative efficiency as a measure of social efficiency. Allocative efficiency reflects the possibility of reallocating resources so as to achieve an increase in the net value of output produced by those resources and is measured using the Kaldor-Hicks test (Kaldor, 1939 and Hicks, 1939).

The Kaldor-Hicks test embodies the potential compensation principle. Kaldor categorised an action as efficient if those who gain from the action could compensate the losers and still be better off. Hicks framed the question slightly differently and labelled the action efficient if the potential losers from the action could compensate the potential beneficiaries of the action for not going ahead. In both cases the action is an improvement *regardless of whether the compensation is actually paid*.

The potential compensation principle differs from the welfare criterion known as Pareto Optimality which requires that an action which makes one person better off leaves nobody else feeling worse off. For an investment to pass the Pareto Optimality test, compensation must be paid to those bearing the costs so as to leave them indifferent between their welfare *ex post* and *ex ante*. Most policies and investments leave somebody worse off and thus most would fail to meet the Pareto criterion. However, Freeman (1993) points out that the Kaldor-Hicks criterion is essentially one of *potential* Pareto improvement since if the compensation were paid nobody would be worse off. Even if the compensation is not paid it has been argued (see Polinsky, 1972 and Musgrave, 1969) that a large number of efficient projects will spread benefits sufficiently widely so that everyone is a net gainer from the set of projects as a whole. Layard and Glaister (1994) describe the acceptance of this proposition as "putting excessive trust in princes" (or politicians perhaps). Pearce and Nash (1981) point out that the principal problem with the Kaldor-Hicks criterion is that whether or not a project passes the potential compensation test depends on the distribution of income e.g. the rents from establishing a gold mine near a very poor village will be more than sufficient to compensate those in the village who suffer from the pollution. If the existing distribution of income is optimal then the Kaldor-Hicks test is sufficient to show that the project is justified on social efficiency grounds. However, if the distribution of income is not optimal and villagers should have more income, then the rents may not be sufficient to compensate the villagers and, if not, the project would fail the Kaldor-Hicks test. Another problem with the potential compensation test results from the Scitovsky Paradox

(Scitovsky, 1941). This shows that, if there is a change in relative prices as a result of a project going ahead, losers may be able to compensate winners to go back to the original situation.

Layard and Walters (1994) suggest that despite the shortcomings of the Kaldor-Hicks criterion, it is often useful to measure the effects of a change in the total value of output independently of the distribution of output, however, in judging the social efficiency of a project equity aspects should also be considered. Zerbe and Dively (1994) suggest that using Kaldor-Hicks is justified where the costs of determining a policy's distributional effects or the costs of responding to them are larger than the expected benefits from taking the distributional effects into account.

Little (1957) suggests a two part test whereby a project or policy is put to the Kaldor-Hicks test and then tested to see if it improves the distribution of income. Approaches that consider questions of equity[61] therefore allow the possibility of acceptance of a project or policy which returns a negative figure for the sum of individual welfare changes if the gains from income distribution outweigh these losses. However, the difficulty when considering equity is the assignment of weights to individual welfare changes according to the relative 'deservingness' of the different individuals (Freeman, 1993). Given this difficulty, this study does not attempt to explicitly address equity considerations in an attempt to judge 'deservingness'.

WELFARE MEASURES[62]

In order to assess the costs and benefits of a project or policy it is necessary to examine the strength of consumers' preferences for or against the project (Pearce and Nash, 1981). Neoclassical consumer theory assumes that the goal of consumption is utility maximisation[63]. Suppose there is an individual, i, who consumes N private commodities, x_j, bought at prices, P_j, $(j = 1,......., N)$.

The utility of individual i can then be expressed as a continuous and increasing function:

$$U_i = U(x_1, x_2, ..., x_N) \qquad (A2.1)$$

The change in utility from an action that changes the quantity of a good or service, x_j, is the change in the quantity of x_j going to person i, (dx_{ij}),

---

[61] See Pearce and Nash, 1981 and Layard and Glaister, 1994 for an outline of various approaches.
[62] The model presented here can be expanded to takes into account utility interdependence resulting from vicarious value (see Zerbe and Dively, 1994).
[63] The approach taken here follows closely that of Zerbe and Dively, 1994

multiplied by the marginal utility of j for i $\left(\partial U_i/\partial x_{ij}\right)$ summed over all the x_j affected goods (for i), i.e.

$$dU_i = \sum_{ji} \frac{\partial U_i}{\partial x_{ij}} dx_{ij} \qquad (A2.2)$$

The additional utility to i of one more unit of good j equals the price of j $\left(P_j\right)$ times i's marginal utility of income $(\partial U_i/\partial Y_i)$, where Y represents income, i.e.

$$\frac{\partial U_i}{\partial x_{ij}} = \frac{\partial U_i}{\partial Y_i} P_j \qquad (A2.3)$$

Substituting (A2.3) into (A2.2) gives,

$$dU_i = \sum_{ji} \frac{\partial U_i}{\partial Y_i} P_j dx_{ij} \qquad (A2.4)$$

where dx_{ij} is the change in the amount of good j consumed by i and the remainder of the right hand side of (A2.4) is the additional utility to i to one more unit of good j.

Now that we have an expression for a change in the individual's welfare as a result of a change in the quantity of a good, it is worth returning to the issue of aggregation and the welfare criterion.

Using a Samuelson-Bergson utility function, social welfare can be expressed a function of the utility of all M individuals,

$$W = W\left(U_1, U_2, \ldots, U_M\right) \qquad (A2.5)$$

Totally differentiating gives the change in welfare from a change in the ith person's utility,

$$dW = \sum_{i=1}^{M} \frac{\partial W}{\partial U_i} dU_i \qquad (A2.6)$$

where $\partial W/\partial U_i$ is the marginal social utility of i (MSU_i) which is the weight given to the ith person's utility. Substituting the expression for individual i's welfare, (A2.4), into (A2.6) gives,

$$dW = \sum_{j} \sum_{i} \frac{\partial W}{\partial U_i} \frac{\partial U}{\partial Y_i} P_j dx_{ij} \qquad (A2.7)$$

Equation (A2.7) can be rearranged to give,

$$dW = \sum_j \sum_i P_j dx_{ij} + \sum_j \sum_i \left(\frac{\partial W}{\partial U_i} \frac{\partial U_i}{\partial Y_i} - 1 \right) P_j dx_{ij} \qquad \text{(A2.8)}$$

The first term on the right hand side of (A2.8) can be thought of as the 'efficiency effect' (the change in incomes) while the second term can be thought of as the 'distributional effect' which weights income changes by the individual's marginal utility of income and by the social weight given to the individual. If we call $\dfrac{\partial W}{\partial U_i} \dfrac{\partial U}{\partial Y_i}$ the Marginal Social Utility of Income, α_i, then:

$$dW = \sum_j \sum_i P_j dx_{ij} + \sum_j \sum_i (\alpha_i - 1) P_j dx_{ij} \qquad \text{(A2.8b)}$$

When the Kaldor-Hicks criterion is employed, it is assumed that each individual has the same α_i, such that a pound is counted the same regardless of who receives it. In this case, the welfare change is similar to that of an individual, i.e.

$$dW = \sum_j \sum_i P_j dx_{ij} \qquad \text{(A2.9)}$$

Choice of Benefit Measures

The traditional measure of consumer benefits[64], was proposed by Dupuit in 1844 and championed by Marshall (Mitchell and Carson, 1989). He described the consumer's surplus as being the difference between the price actually paid when purchasing a good or service and the price the consumer would have been willing to pay (Hanley and Spash, 1993), thus consumers' surplus is the area under the (Marshallian) demand curve above the price line. However, Samuelson (1947) among others pointed out a number of problems with this measure. These problems are largely the result of the fact that the Marshallian demand curve does not hold the level of utility constant but rather holds the level of income constant. In a series of papers, Hicks suggested alternative methods of measuring costs or benefits by holding utility constant. The Hicksian consumer surplus measures may be thought of as Marshallian consumer surplus measures calculated from demand curves where total utility is held constant at different specified levels (Mitchell and Carson, 1989). These measures are known as Compensating Variation (Surplus) and Equivalent Variation (Surplus).

---

[64] Producer benefits as measured by producer's surplus are not discussed here as the analytics are identical to those of consumer surplus measures (Randall, 1984).

The approach of Johansson (1993) is worth summarising because it is particularly useful in the development of contingent valuation methodology. Using an indirect utility function, he examines welfare measures of a change in the level of a public good although the analysis can easily be applied to a change in the price or quantity of private goods. In this case, for the *ith* individual, in addition to a vector of private goods, $(x_1, x_2, \ldots, x_N)$, there is also a vector of public goods, $(z_1, z_2, \ldots, z_N)$, in his or her utility function. The individual's income is spent purchasing some or all of the private goods bought at prices P_j where $j = 1, \ldots, N$. The individual maximises his or her utility subject to the budget constraint and thus the indirect utility function can be written as,

$$V = U[x(P,Y,z), z] = V(P,Y,z) \tag{A2.10}$$

where the vector x is interpreted as $x(P,Y,z) = [x_1(P,Y,z), \ldots, x_N(P,Y,z)]$, i.e. a vector of demand functions for private goods with quantity demanded being a function of prices, income and the provision or quality of the public good. The indirect utility function is decreasing in price, and increasing in income and the provision of the public good.

If there is a change in the quantity or quality of the public good, *ceteris paribus*, the change in utility is expressed as,

$$\Delta V = V(P,Y,z^1) - V(P,Y,z^0) \tag{A2.11}$$

where z^0 is the initial endowment of the public good and z^1 is the final level. The utility function is not observable and so a money measure must be found to measure the change in utility. Compensating Variation (CV) is the maximum amount of money that can be taken from the individual after an increase in the quantity/quality of the public good such that the individual will be left with the same level of utility, i.e.,

$$V(P, Y - CV, z^1) = V(P,Y,z^0) \tag{A2.12}$$

Thus, CV measures the maximum Willingness To Pay (WTP) for the increase in the quantity/quality the public good. However, if there is a decrease in the quantity/quality of the public good, CV measures the minimum compensation required to leave the individual with the same level of utility after the change as before. Thus CV measures the minimum Willingness To Accept (WTA) a reduction in the quantity/quality of the public good.

Equivalent Variation (EV) is the minimum amount of compensation which must be given to the individual to give them the same utility as they would have had after a proposed increase in the quantity/quality of the public good, i.e.

$$V(P, Y + EV, z^0) = V(P, Y, z^1) \qquad\qquad (A2.13)$$

Thus, EV measures the minimum compensation the individual is willing to accept to forgo an increase in the quantity/quality of the public good. If there is a proposed decrease in the quantity/quality, EV measures the maximum amount of money that can be taken from an individual that would give them the same utility prior to the decrease in the quantity/quality of the public good as the individual would have had after the decrease. Thus, EV in this case measures the individual's maximum WTP to avoid a decrease in the quantity/quality of the public good.

The same analysis can be used in the case of externalities by treating the z terms as positive externalities or with the sign reversed as negative externalities (Johansson, 1993).

Randall and Stoll (1980) suggest that the Hicksian Variation measures are to be used when the consumer is free to vary the quantity of the good considered, and the Hicksian Surplus measures used when the consumer may only purchase fixed quantities of the good.

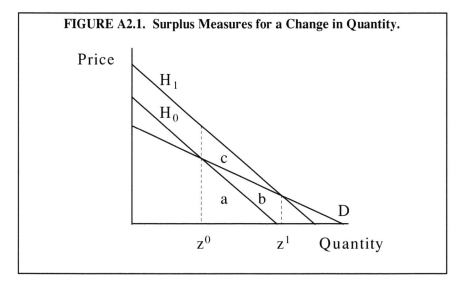

FIGURE A2.1. Surplus Measures for a Change in Quantity.

Mitchell and Carson (1989) present a useful diagrammatic analysis of surplus measures for a change in quantity (Figure A2.1). Holding price at zero, if there is a quantity increase in the good from z^0 to z^1, Marshallian Consumer Surplus (MCS) is the area under the demand curve D between z^0 and z^1, i.e. (a + b). Compensating Surplus (CS) is the area under the Hicksian compensated demand curve H_0, i.e. (a), and Equivalence Surplus (ES) is the area under the Hicksian compensated demand curve H_1, i.e. (a+b+c). Thus, for a quantity increase:

$$CS \le MCS \le ES \qquad \text{(A2.14)}$$

and for a quantity decrease:

$$ES \le MCS \le CS \qquad \text{(A2.15)}$$

A discussion of the difference in magnitude between WTP and WTA can be found in the discussion of the Contingent Valuation Method below.

DISCOUNTING

A single payment in the future $q(t)$ is measured in present value terms $q(0)$ according to the following formula where $0 \le \partial \le 1$ represents the discount factor at time t, $(t = 0,.......,T)$, and r represents the discount rate,

$$q(0) = \partial q(t) \qquad \text{(A2.16)}$$

where,

$$\partial = \frac{1}{(1+r)^t} \qquad \text{(A2.17)}$$

The discount factor can also be written as an exponential,

$$\partial = e^{-rt} \qquad \text{(A2.18)}$$

Having calculated the costs (C) and benefits (B) of a project, it is necessary to compare them in present value terms. This gives the net present value of the investment,

$$NPV = \sum_{t=0}^{T}(B_t - C_t)e^{-rt} \qquad \text{(A2.19)}$$

Inflation is controlled for by expressing values in real terms and assuming that costs and benefits increase at the same rate in nominal terms. The discount rate is assumed constant throughout the life of the investment.

The project is accepted if and only if,

$$NPV > 0 \qquad \text{(A2.20)}$$

The efficiency of the investment can also be assessed by calculating a benefit cost ratio,

$$\frac{B}{C} = \frac{\sum_{t=0}^{T} B_t (e^{-rt})}{\sum_{t=0}^{T} C_t (e^{-rt})} \qquad \text{(A2.21)}$$

The project is accepted if and only if,

$$\frac{B}{C} > 1 \qquad \text{(A2.22)}$$

In the case of more than one project having a positive net present value and where a budget constraint means a choice must be made, CBA can be used as a ranking device (see Pearce, 1983).

Rationale for Discounting

Hanley and Spash (1993) and Worrell (1991) provide succinct discussions of the literature on discounting from which much of this outline is drawn[65]. The first candidate for the discount rate is the social rate of time preference. This concept arises from the observation that members of society treat the future as less important than the present. The second candidate for the discount rate is the opportunity cost of capital which reflects the fact that the cost of tying up resources in one project is the rate of return which could be earned if the resources were put into some other project. Neoclassical economics shows that, in simplified world, a unique discount rate is determined by the market where the production possibilities curve is at a tangent to the social indifference curve. Using similar notation as before, except now $U_1 ...... U_M$ represent the total utilities of the t generations $(t = 1 ...... M)$, the utilitarian social welfare function is written,

$$W = W(U_1, U_2, ..., U_M) \qquad \text{(A2.23)}$$

For W to be maximised, marginal utilities must be equated across time. If future utility is discounted at some positive discount rate r $(0 < r < 1)$, then this is referred to as "pure time preference". Thus, in continuous, infinite time, the above equation becomes,

$$W = \int_{t=0}^{\infty} e^{-rt} U_t \, dt \qquad \text{(A2.24)}$$

To avoid the problem of measuring utility directly, the utility function can be made a function of consumption at time t (K_t),

---

[65] see also Lind *et al.* for an excellent collection of papers on this topic.

$$W = \int_{t=0}^{\infty} e^{-rt} U_t(K_t) dt \qquad (A2.25)$$

Another rationale for a positive marginal rate of time preference is diminishing marginal utility with respect to income, i.e. while $\partial U / \partial K > 0$, $\partial^2 U / \partial K^2 < 0$, such that, as future generations become more wealthy, a unit of consumption is valued less highly. Thus, time preference depends on three factors:

1.   The pure rate of time preference, r;

2.   The elasticity of marginal utility, $\theta(K_t) \equiv -\dfrac{\partial^2 U / \partial K^2 (K_t) K_t}{\partial U / \partial K (K_t)} > 0$;

3.   The rate of change of consumption, $\dot{K}_t / K_t$.

Letting the consumption rate of interest be i_t, this gives,

$$i_t = r + \theta(K_t) \frac{\dot{K}}{K_t} \qquad (A2.26)^{66}$$

i_t, is sometimes known as the Social Time Preference Rate (STPR) or the Social Rate of Time Preference (SRTP). Individual time preference rates determine consumption and savings decisions. These savings provide funds for investment and thus deferring current consumption increases future income via the marginal productivity of capital. Under perfect competition, savings and investment schedules intersect to define a unique equilibrium where the marginal rate of return on capital equals the marginal rate of time preference and thus there exists a single discount rate. This result is intuitive since, if capital markets work effectively, the rate of return on projects must equal the interest rate that savers would require which equals individuals' time preference (Pearce, 1983).

Problems with Discounting
There have been a number of criticisms of discounting. Firstly, many environmentalists find it unacceptable because it rules out certain projects they would see as desirable and encourages certain activities they would see as undesirable e.g. it encourages more rapid exploitation of resources, discourages certain long-term projects such as the planting of broadleaved forests, reduces the costs of potential damage in the long run such as the consequences of global warming.

More technical arguments have focused on the following potential problems:

---

[66] Thus, even if there is a zero rate of time preference, a positive discount rate, i_t, exists so long as consumption is growing.

- a single discount rate cannot accurately express time preference, the opportunity cost of capital and diminishing marginal utility of income simultaneously;

- it is unlikely that all these factors discount future net benefits exponentially with time;

- diminishing marginal utility does not apply to all goods e.g. wilderness, and so it may not be possible to apply the same discount rate to all costs and benefits.

- time preference does not allow people to 'regret' early consumption of benefits.

Hanley and Spash (1993) show that the social rate of discount, i.e. the rate of discount society would choose to express its time preference, may be lower than the marginal rate of time preference for three possible reasons:

1.   Since savings provide external consumption benefits in the future, the market will under-supply savings in the present. The government s hould account for this by applying a lower discount rate[67].

2.   The time preference rate revealed in individuals' consumption behaviour may differ from their inter-temporal preferences as members of a society. The government should account for this by using a lower discount rate than the rates revealed by individuals in their saving decisions.

3.   Individuals of one particular generation have a different rate of time preference to a society with an infinite life. Thus, savings will be lower and therefore the level of investment will be too low to make adequate provisions for future generations[68].

There are also problems using the opportunity cost of capital as the discount rate. The social rate of discount is likely to be lower than the market rate of return to capital due to taxation resulting in sub-optimal investment. Company taxation makes the opportunity cost of capital higher than the social rate of time preference such that the company can pay off investors and have enough residual funds to pay the tax. If projects in the private sector are more risky than those in the public sector, there will be an even greater divergence between the two rates (Pearce, 1983).

Other rates have been suggested including:

---

[67] see Marglin, 1963.
[68] see Ramsey, 1928 and Pigou, 1932.

- a weighted average of the consumption rate of interest and the market rate of return to capital;

- the real cost of borrowing on the world market;

- the rate of return on the marginal (excluded) project where capital is rationed;

- using the shadow price of capital to adjust cost/benefit flows to take account of their impact on private investment and then discounting these adjusted flows at the consumption rate of interest[69].

Worrell (1991) summarises three schools of thought concerning the use of discounting:

1.   Provided externalities are included in the CBA, and the preferences of future generations are accounted for by sustainability constraints, discounting provides an accurate picture of consumer behaviour. These sustainability criteria would maintain a constant stock of natural capital or provide compensation for environmental damage by implementing shadow (environmental) projects or by replacing natural capital with man-made capital[70].

2.   Alternatives to straightforward discounting should be used such as a modified discounting method, which allows new individuals in new generations to discount costs and benefits from the start of their lives and this effectively reduces the discount rate[71], or disaggregating the determinants of the discount rate (time preference, diminishing marginal utility of income etc.) with their individual effects being explicitly included separately in analyses.

3.   Discounting is unacceptable and counter to sustainable resource use and therefore a zero discount rate should be used[72]. The case for a zero rate is weak since the opportunity cost of capital will be positive so long as alternative projects exhibit a positive rate of return. If long run growth in GNP is assumed and marginal utility with regard to income is diminishing, the time preference rate will also be positive since future consumption will be valued less highly. In any case, if a zero rate is applied, many more projects will pass a cost benefit test and this is unlikely to enhance sustainability.

---

[69] see Lind, 1982.

[70] see Pearce *et al.*, 1989 and Markandya and Pearce, 1988 for further details.

[71] See Kula, 1988a, 1988b, 1989, Bateman, 1989, Rigby, 1989 and Hutchinson, 1989 for further details.

[72] see Price, 1993 for an in-depth critique of discounting.

SHADOW PRICING

Shadow prices must be used when there are distortions within an economy which render certain prices invalid as indicators of social opportunity costs or values (Drèze and Stern, 1994). If a project is proposed which will consume some goods and services and produce others, this can be thought of as an objective function to be maximised subject to some constraint (Layard and Glaister, 1994),

$$\text{Maximise} \quad f(q_1, q_2, \ldots, q_n) \tag{A2.27}$$

$$\text{subject to} \quad g(q_1, q_2, \ldots, q_n) \leq b \tag{A2.28}$$

As b is varied, the solution values for each of the q_i will vary as will the maximised value of the objective. If $V(b)$ describes the relationship between the maximised value of the objective and b, then the shadow price of the constraint is given by,

$$\frac{\partial V(b)}{\partial(b)} \tag{A2.29}$$

Thus the shadow price of the constraint is the rate of change of the maximised objective with respect to a unit relaxation of the constraint.

If the money value of the benefits of a project is greater that the money value of the costs, the project is worthwhile if, and only if, the prices used in calculating the costs and benefits are correct shadow prices. These shadow prices measure the 'worth' of a unit of each of the commodities as measured by the objective function (Layard and Glaister, 1994). The fact that shadow prices sometimes differ from market prices is partially what distinguishes financial analysis (which uses market prices) from CBA (which uses shadow prices).

In the case of a perfectly competitive market, market prices and shadow prices are equivalent. This flows from the First and Second Theorems of Welfare Economics. The First states that a competitive market will exhaust all of the gains from trade and an equilibrium allocation achieved by a set of competitive markets will necessarily be Pareto Efficient. The Second asserts that under certain conditions, every Pareto efficient allocation can be achieved as a competitive equilibrium (Varian, 1990). However, in the real world, market prices may not reflect the social value of goods or services because of distortions in the market.

EXTERNALITIES AND PUBLIC GOODS

Baumol and Oates (1988) provide two conditions for the existence of an externality:

1.   An externality is present whenever an agent's utility or production relationships contain real (non-monetary) variables whose values are chosen by other agents without attention to the effects on the first agent's utility.

2.   The decision maker whose activity affects others' utility or production functions does not pay (receive) compensation for this activity an amount equal to the resulting costs (benefits) to others.

Condition 2 is necessary for the existence of an externality, however, condition 1 is sufficient for existence.

It is important to distinguish true 'technological externalities' from what are known as 'pecuniary externalities'. Pecuniary externalities arise when one individual's activity level affects the financial circumstances of another individual but which need not produce a misallocation of resources in pure competition (Baumol and Oates, 1988). This concept is referred to in Chapter 12.

An individual undertaking an activity that produces an external cost will, if not forced to bear that cost, engage in a higher level of the activity than is socially optimal. Conversely, an individual undertaking an activity that produces an external benefit will, if not compensated for that benefit, engage in a level of that activity that is below the socially optimal level. This sub-optimal outcome in the presence of externalities can be explained in the context of the rotation of a forest:

OPTIMAL FOREST ROTATION

Privately Optimal Forest Rotation[73]
Although a forest produces a number of outputs other than timber, the profit maximising owner benefits solely from timber production. The other outputs are externalities.

The commercial value V of a single tree is dependent on the volume and quality of the tree. Thus, V is a function of the age t of the tree,

$$V = V(t) \tag{A2.30}$$

---

[73] The presentation here is based upon that of Clark, 1990. More complete analyses can be found in Bowes and Krutilla, 1985 and 1989.

Letting c be the cost of felling, $V(t) - c$ is the value of the stand. This must be discounted at a rate r to give the present value (PV) of the stand[74]. The objective is to maximise the present value of the stand,

$$\text{Maximise } PV = e^{-rt}[V(t) - c] \qquad (A2.31)$$

This gives the solution,

$$\frac{V'(T)}{V(T) - c} = r \qquad (A2.32)$$

However, this does not take into account the opportunity cost of land, i.e. the cost of keeping the land under this forest measured in terms of the opportunity forgone of planting a new forest or using the land for some other purpose[75]. Taking a series of times $T_1 < T_2 < \ldots\ldots$ with the property that, at each time T_k, the existing forest is felled and a new forest is planted, and letting c now represent the sum of harvesting and planting costs, the total present value of all future harvests is given by,

$$PV = e^{-rT_1}[V(T_1) - c] + e^{-rT_2}[V(T_2 - T_1) - c] + e^{-rT_3}[V(T_3 - T_2) - c] + \ldots\ldots \qquad (A2.33)$$

All rotations are of equal length since, if all parameters are assumed constant for all time, then the first problem is equal to the second problem, thus, they both have the same solution so $T_2 - T_1$ must equal T_1, i.e.

$$T_k = kT, \quad k = 1,2,\ldots\ldots \qquad (A2.34)$$

Substituting (A2.36) into (A2.35) gives,

$$PV = \sum_{k=1}^{\infty} e^{-krT}[V(T) - c] = \frac{V(T) - c}{e^{rT} - 1} \qquad (A2.35)$$

Maximising the above equation with respect to time gives,

$$\frac{V'(T)}{V(T) - c} = \frac{re^{rT}}{e^{rT} - 1} = \frac{r}{1 - e^{-rT}} \qquad (A2.36)$$

---

[74] This is what distinguishes the Faustmann Formula from what is known as Maximum Sustainable Yield (sometimes called the biological harvesting decision) which gives the rotation length which provides the maximum sustainable yield of timber from the forest (see Bowes and Krutilla, 1985).

[75] This is often excluded from calculations by foresters.

This is the Faustmann Formula[76] which provides the privately optimal rotation period T.

Socially Optimal Forest Rotation
A social planner would be concerned with all outputs from a forest including externalities. Taking the simple case where net external benefits grow proportionally with the volume of standing timber $V(t)$, the total discounted net external benefits over one rotation is given by,

$$Q_r(T) = \beta \int_0^T e^{-rt} V(t) dt \tag{A2.37}$$

where β is a proportionality constant. The total discounted present value of these net external benefits is given by,

$$PV_{externalities} = Q_r(T)(1 + e^{-rT} + e^{-2rT} + ...) \tag{A2.38}$$

$$= \frac{Q_r(T)}{1 - e^{-rT}} \tag{A2.39}$$

The present value of timber harvests has already been derived in equation (A2.35),

$$PV_{timber} = \frac{e^{-rT}[V(T) - c]}{1 - e^{-rT}}$$

Comparing the optimal rotation for externalities with the optimal rotation for timber,

$$\frac{Q'_r(T)}{Q_r(T)} = \frac{re^{-rT}}{1 - e^{-rT}} \qquad \text{externalities} \tag{A2.40}$$

$$\frac{V'(T)}{V(T) - c} = \frac{r}{1 - e^{-rT}} \qquad \text{timber} \tag{A2.41}$$

If net external benefits are positive, $T^*_{externalities} > T^*_{timber}$ (A2.42)

If net external benefits are negative, $T^*_{timber} > T^*_{externalities}$ (A2.43)

The socially optimal rotation will lie somewhere in between the two. Unless there is intervention in the market to correct for externalities, their supply will be non-optimal.

---

[76] See Faustmann, 1849 and Samuelson, 1976 for further details.

When carrying out a CBA, the existence of forestry externalities makes it essential to use what are known as the Total Economic Value approach and non-market valuation methods.

NON-MARKET VALUATION METHODS

Production Function Approaches
Production Function Approaches are indirect methods of valuing externalities. Environmental goods often enter into the production functions of firms and households e.g. a fishery combines water quality (q) with purchased inputs (x), labour (l) and capital (k). Where F is the output of fish, the production function would take the form:

$$F = f(l,k,x,q) \tag{A2.44}$$

Thus, if forestry causes a deterioration in water quality and $\partial F/\partial q > 0$, F will be reduced. This cost can be estimated in two ways:

1.   By the cost of the increase in other inputs which would be necessary to achieve the same level of output after the reduction in water quality as before e.g. by liming a river to reduce acidification (Defensive Expenditures/ Avoided Cost Approach) or by the cost of restoring the damage done e.g. restocking a river (Replacement Cost).

2.   By the value of productivity changes, i.e. the value of the lost output of fish (Dose-Response Functions);

Avoided Cost Approach
If there is a deterioration in water quality defensive expenditures may be necessary to reduce the impact on productivity. These expenditures can be used as a proxy for the cost of the damage to the water supply. In most of the literature this is expressed from another point of view, i.e. the benefits of an improvement in environmental quality can be measured by the defensive costs avoided, hence it is known as the Avoided Cost Approach. If the productivity with defensive expenditures is equal to the productivity prior to the deterioration of the quality of the water, then the defensive expenditures give a reasonable approximation of the external cost imposed by the activity which causes the pollution. If productivity with defensive expenditures is less than the productivity prior to the deterioration in water quality then this approach underestimates the external cost. If the defensive expenditures result in benefits other than the maintenance of productivity e.g. if for some reason liming was to improve the quality of the fish, then this approach would overestimate the external cost. Hanley and Spash (1993) conclude that in most cases, the avoided cost approach is likely to provide a lower bound on willingness to pay for environmental quality.

Dose-Response Functions
Hanley and Spash (1993), from which this explanation is taken, provide a clear outline of this approach. Dose-response methods seek a relationship between environmental quality variables and the output level of a marketed commodity. These methods take natural science information and include it in an economic model. There are three economic approaches:

The Traditional Model
The traditional model multiplies yield changes based on current area in production by the current price of the crop. Thus, this assumes that resource use and prices (and therefore consumer surplus) remain constant. Therefore, for the answers to be legitimate, it is necessary to assume that any reduction in yield will leave prices unaltered.

Optimisation Models
Optimisation models consist of Linear Programming models and Quadratic Programming Models. These are normative models which are specified as cost minimising or profit maximising models. In Linear Programming, changes in environmental quality can be simulated by using biological dose-response functions to alter the quantity of output produced from the set of inputs required for each production activity. The disadvantages of these models is that they require large data sets and it is often unclear as to the cause of discrepancies between the model solutions and the real world. This can either be due to misspecification of the model or due to the inaccuracy of the assumption of optimality in the real world.

Econometric Models
Econometric models resolve some of the problems just mentioned since they rely upon historical data. However, the institutional setting is taken as given and the models cannot capture changes in technology that have not been captured in the data.

In conclusion, while the accuracy of the traditional approach relies on very strict assumptions, it is the most simple dose-response approach and it requires very little data. While optimisation and econometric models are more sophisticated, they require larger data sets and depending on the way in which responses are modelled, widely varying estimates emerge.

Contingent Valuation
The advantage of the CVM is that, unlike other methods, it can elicit option and existence values. In addition, it can measure Hicksian consumer surplus directly. The CVM is the most controversial of all non-market valuation methods. Therefore, it is worth exploring the methodology and the controversies surrounding the method in some detail.

History of CVM

According to Hanemann (1992) the CVM was first suggested by S. V. Ciriacy-Wantrup in 1947 although its significance was not immediately appreciated. In 1958 the United States (US) National Park Service was the first to use the CVM when a survey of outdoor recreational activities was undertaken on their behalf which elicited the willingness to pay a site entry charge to publicly owned recreation areas. In 1961, Davis (1964) carried out the second Contingent Valuation (CV) study when he used a survey to value hunting in the Maine woods[77].

Up until the mid 1980s, the CVM did not stand out from other non-market valuation measures. Since then, however, this method has become the most widely used approach for valuing public goods and there has been an explosion in the number of CV studies (Mitchell and Carson, 1995).

Appropriate Welfare Measures: Willingness to Pay vs. Willingness to Accept

In the case of the valuation of an increase in the quantity of a public good, the following are the valuations which may be elicited using the CVM:

Compensating Surplus (CS): The maximum willingness to pay (WTP) on the part of the population for a specified increase in the quantity of the public good (leaving them as well off after the increase as before).

Equivalent Surplus (ES): The minimum amount of compensation the population is willing to accept (WTA) to forgo the increase (and be as well off as they would have been after the increase).

There are two key problems in choosing an appropriate consumer surplus measure. Firstly, there is the theoretical observation that WTP and WTA can differ in size. Secondly, it has been observed that respondents to CV questionnaires react differently to each approach.

Mitchell and Carson (1989), from which much of this discussion is drawn, give an outline of the development of the literature on the appropriate measure. Hammack and Brown (1974) compared WTA with WTP for waterfowl benefits. Their study showed that WTA amounts were over four times greater than WTP amounts for the same amenity. However, many people accredited this result to some peculiarity in their CV study since the results were in conflict with Willig's classical work (1976). This research had shown that the difference between WTP and WTA should be relatively small in most cases.

While Willig's results were for price changes, Randall and Stoll (1980) extended these results to cover quantity changes where expenditures on the good were a small proportion of income. They suggested that, in contingent

---

[77] Some authors suggest that this was the first CV study.

valuation experiments, the difference between WTP and WTA should not be more than 5 percent.

Brookshire, Randall and Stoll (1980) showed that if the price flexibility of income ξ could be estimated in a similar fashion to an ordinary income elasticity by regressing the log of WTP on the logs of the quantity of the good, income Y, and other explanatory variables then an upper bound on WTA (ES) could be measured from WTP (CS). Mitchell and Carson (1989) give the following example: Taking a household with an income of \$18,000 and a WTP of £250 and estimating $\xi = 0.7$, then using the following equations from Randall and Stoll (1980),

$$(M - CS)/M \approx \xi M /2Y \qquad (A2.45)$$
$$ES - CS \approx \xi M^2 /Y \qquad (A2.46)$$

This gives,

$$CS(\$250) < ES(\$252.45) \qquad (A2.47)$$

As ξ increases, the difference increases.

However, empirical studies still showed a large divergence between WTP and WTA measures. The following possible reasons emerged to explain this divergence:

Rejection of WTA Property Right
This occurs when respondents do not accept the property right implied by the question e.g. they may refuse to 'sell' the environmental asset at any price, regarding this as unethical. More frequently, individuals do not see the property right as plausible e.g. they may be asked how much compensation they would accept for the deterioration of air quality in their area, however, if they have never been compensated for environmental damage in the past, they may see this as implausible. This tends to result in 'protests' and/or infinite bids.

The Cautious Consumer Hypothesis
Under conditions of uncertainty, risk-averse individuals will offer smaller WTP amounts and larger WTA amounts than they would under certainty.

Prospect Theory
According to prospect theory, the value function is steeper for losses than for gains from a neutral position, i.e. people value a loss more highly than a gain since the former is considered the loss of a 'right' and the latter is considered only as a 'bonus'.

Other Results from Economic Theory
Hanemann (1991) shows that price flexibility of income cannot be interpreted in a similar fashion to a standard income elasticity as Randall and Stoll had suggested and that ξ is, in fact, the ratio of the income elasticity of demand η to the elasticity of substitution between the public good being valued and all other goods in the economic system σ_0,

$$\xi = \frac{\eta}{\sigma_0} \tag{A2.48}$$

Supposing $\eta = 2$ and $\sigma_0 = 0.1$ then $\xi = 20$ so in the example mentioned earlier the difference between CS and ES is substantial,

$$CS(\$250) < ES(\$350) \tag{A2.49}$$

If substitution possibilities are such that σ_0 is small relative to η, WTP and WTA will be far apart. However, for public goods with many substitutes, WTP and WTA should be close together. Since the elasticity of WTP with respect to income obtained from a regression estimate of the valuation function is not equal to ξ, it is hard to estimate the magnitude of ξ.

The question now arises as to whether, in order to avoid the rejection of the property right, WTP can be used where economic theory suggests the correct measure is WTA without providing inaccurate estimates. Mitchell and Carson (1989) suggest that WTP rather that WTA is the correct measure where "the consumer is asked to set the highest amount she would be willing to pay annually in taxes for a given program which guarantees to maintain the present level of supply of a good for the next and succeeding fiscal years".

The Validity of the CVM
Mitchell and Carson (1989) suggest examining validity under three headings:

Content Validity
Content Validity involves the issue of whether the measure adequately covers the construct's domain. Since, by definition, public goods are not captured within a market, it is very difficult to test for content validity. The responsibility rests on the researcher to ask the right questions in an appropriate manner such that the WTP of respondents reflects what they would actually pay if the good was available in a market. A general improvement in survey design has meant that content validity has not been regarded as too great a problem in recent years (Garrod and Willis, 1990).

Criterion Validity
Criterion Validity is concerned with whether the measure of the construct is related to other measures which may be regarded as criteria. Criterion validity can be assessed under the following sub-headings:

Theoretical Validity: Questions about the respondents' characteristics and their preferences relevant to the good should be used in a regression equation for the good. If these variables 'explain' the valuations of the individuals as the theory would suggest then this is a partial test of reliability. Mitchell and Carson (1989) recommend a minimum r^2 of 0.15 but the significance of the coefficients should be judged using t-tests.

Convergent Validity: The results of a CV study can be compared with results from revealed preference methods to check for consistency. This is problematic in the case of the CVM since there is no other method which can measure existence values and therefore the methods are usually measuring different constructs. However, studies by Brookshire *et al.* (1982), Brookshire *et al.* (1985) and d'Arge and Shogren (1989) support the convergent validity of CV by comparing results from the Hedonic Pricing Method. Hanley (1989), Thayer (1981), Smith and Desvousges (1986) and others have carried out similar tests using the Travel Cost Method.

Criticisms of the CVM
Up until the mid 1980s, the majority of the research on the CVM had been carried out in agricultural economics departments in the "State" universities in the US, where the fields of resource and environmental economics developed.

However, the lack of interest on the part of 'mainstream' economists quickly disappeared in the aftermath of the Exxon Valdez Alaskan oil spill in 1989 when the state and federal governments decided to undertake a contingent valuation study to assess the magnitude of the damages. Whereas the government assembled a group of resource economists to carry out the CV, the Exxon Corporation hired a panel of economists mainly from outside this discipline in an attempt to prove that the CVM was an unreliable method for valuing natural resource damage (Mitchell and Carson, 1995). A book of the papers produced by the Exxon economists was published in 1993 (see Hausman, 1993 and also Diamond and Hausman, 1994). The main criticisms of the CVM relate to sources of bias:

Sources of Bias
Free-Riding and Strategic Bias: Samuelson (1954) suggested that the individual has an incentive to understate her WTP for a public good on the understanding that others will pay for it and therefore she will benefit from its provision in any case. On the other hand, the individual may engage in strategic behaviour to raise the mean bid by overstating her WTP on the basis that the level of provision is subject to the size of the mean bid. Brookshire *et al.* (1976) test for and reject strategic bias while the results from Rowe *et al.*

(1980) suggest that WTP bids are a good reflection of true valuations. While experiments suggest free-riding does occur, it appears to be less prevalent than standard Neoclassical theory would predict (Bateman and Turner, 1993).

Hypothetical Bias: Critics of the CVM suggest that the hypothetical nature of the market renders the answers invalid. Bishop and Herberlein (1979) showed a significant difference between hypothetical WTA for duck hunting licences and their true WTA when offered 'real' money. However, Mitchell and Carson (1989) show that the significance of the difference relied on the truncation decisions in the original analysis. Further studies suggest that actual and hypothetical WTP differences are much smaller than in the case of WTA (Bateman and Turner, 1993).   Duffield and Patterson (1991) show that hypothetical willingness to contribute to charitable organisations is higher than actual contributions. However, the authors suggest that the differences are small enough for CV to be used to estimate real WTP. Evidence produced from a study comparing hypothetical WTP for strawberries with actual purchases (Dickie et al., 1987) was reinterpreted by Diamond et al. (1993) as showing that the CV approach tends to systematically overestimate quantity demanded at each price. However, Arrow et al. (1993) qualify the results in two ways: Firstly, the quality of the survey was poor and secondly, it is going too far to conclude that systematic overestimation means that CV can tell us nothing about the demand for strawberries.

Part-Whole (Mental Account) Bias: Some authors testify that results from CV studies are invalid as they are inconsistent with rational choice. Several authors have found that WTP does not increase with the size of the good. Kahneman (1986) found that there was no significant difference between WTP for the cleanup of lakes in a small area of a province and WTP for cleanup of all the lakes in the province. This 'embedding' effect was also shown by Kahneman and Knetsch (1992) by giving one sample group a more inclusive public good and the other sample group a less inclusive good. The results showed no significant difference between the mean WTP for each good. The authors proposed that this is due to a 'warm glow' whereby people are contributing because they feel good about improving the welfare of society. Thus, WTP does not measure their true valuation of the good. A number of other papers have also demonstrated this phenomenon (e.g. Desvousges et al., 1993 and Diamond et al., 1993). Smith (1992), Hanemann (1994) and Mitchell and Carson (1995) have argued that Kahneman and Knetsch's findings result from poor instrument design and poor information (see 'General Responses to the Critics' below).

Information Bias: One of the most controversial issues in CV relates to the quantity of information which is supplied to the respondent. It should go without saying that if individuals are given incorrect information, the use of the results in making policy decisions is invalid. The more disputed claim is that the provision of more information elicits a higher WTP. However, there is no reason why WTP should not be a function of information and thus information bias should not be an overriding problem (Bateman and Turner, 1993).

Another criticism of CV surveys is that they often provide only vague descriptions of the good in question (this has also been a criticism of the CV studies carried out by economists wishing to demonstrate the flaws of the CVM).

Payment Vehicle Bias: Choice of payment vehicle e.g. an increase in taxes or a contribution to a 'fund', has been shown to influence WTP (see Desvousges *et al.*, 1983 and Navrud, 1989). It is therefore suggested that controversial payment methods be avoided and the payment vehicle should be that which is most likely to be used in reality. The method of payment should also be such that the respondent is aware of the substitutes for the public good in question. This is important due to the criticisms of opponents of the CVM who question the large mean WTP figures for environmental improvements that emerge from CV studies. They ask whether individuals would really be willing (or able) to pay similarly large amounts if asked to pay for all environmental improvements. In addition, there is a common criticism that respondents do not consider their budget constraints when stating their WTP if the payment vehicle is unrealistic. Arrow *et al* (1993) state that "to date very few CV surveys have reminded respondents of the very real economic constraints within which spending decisions must be made".

Bid Level Bias: There are a number of ways of eliciting bids in CV studies (Hanley and Spash, 1993):

1.   As a bidding game:
The interviewer asks the individual whether he or she will pay a specified amount. If the respondent says 'no', the interviewer lowers the amount until he or she says 'yes'. If, in the first instance, the respondent says 'yes' then the amount is raised until he or she says 'no'. This approach often results in a large number of 'protests' since some respondents find this 'auctioning' of a public good either unethical or unrealistic. It also can suffer from what is known as 'starting point bias' whereby the initial bid suggested influences the WTP of the individual. Mitchell and Carson (1989) suggest that the provision of a starting point reduces the effort people put into making their choice of WTP.

2.   As an open-ended question:
Individuals are asked their maximum WTP with no value being suggested to them. Respondents tend to find it difficult to answer questions of this type when they have no experience of trading in the commodity in question. Open ended CV studies are subject to 'free-rider' bias much more so than the other approaches.

3.   As a payment card:
A range of values is presented on a card which helps respondents to calibrate their replies. This is less problematic than the bidding game, however, in some instances, respondents also may find the approach rather unrealistic. This approach can produce 'anchoring bias' whereby the respondent assumes that the

'correct' valuation is one of the values on the card and therefore he or she is reluctant to go outside that range.

4.   As a closed-ended referendum:
This approach is also known as 'take-it-or-leave-it' or 'Dichotomous Choice'. The sample is split into sub-samples and a single payment is suggested to which the respondent must agree or disagree. A different amount is presented to each of the sub-samples. This is the most incentive-compatible approach. However, the analysis of binary responses requires more sophisticated econometric techniques and larger samples. Sometimes the question is followed up by a higher or lower offer depending on whether the answer to the first question is 'yes' or 'no'. This is called the Double Bounded Dichotomous Choice approach. The Dichotomous Choice approach may be subject to anchoring bias if the payment amounts chosen do not cover the full range of WTP. In addition it may be subject to 'yea-saying' whereby individuals may just say 'yes' in order to avoid having to think carefully.

Interviewer Bias: The interviewer may intentionally or unintentionally put pressure on the respondent to give particular answers to questions. This is most common in face-to-face surveys.

Other Criticisms
Some economists have a much simpler objection to the CVM out of their suspicions regarding the use of surveys in economic analysis. McCloskey (1985) observes[78]: "Economists are so impressed by the confusions that might possibly arise from questionnaires that they have turned away from them entirely, and prefer the confusions that result from external observation". However, while some economists would never dream of undertaking a survey themselves, many of these rely on data produced from other people's surveys such as the Census, the Labour Force Survey, the Household Survey, etc. In addition, it may be better to oversee your own survey, the methodology and administration of which you can be sure.

General Responses to the Critics
Hanemann (1994) criticises the papers referred to in Diamond and Hausman (1994) and Hausman (1993) for the weakness of the CV studies they use to back up their claims of the inappropriateness of the CVM. He states: "none uses in-person interviews. Many are self-administered. Most use open-ended questions. None is cast as voting. Many ask questions with a remarkable lack of detail. Several seem designed to highlight the symbolic aspects of valuation at the expense of substance. The Exxon surveys were designed and fielded in great haste, with little pre-testing, just at a time when federal agencies were gearing up for natural resource damage regulations. The only way to justify this is to make the tacit assumption that, if contingent valuation is valid, details of its implementation should not matter. This is fundamentally wrong:

---

[78] As quoted by Hanemann (1994).

measurement results are not invariant with respect to measurement practice in *any* science".

Mitchell and Carson (1995) explain two misconceptions about contingent valuation that arise in the debate of the validity of the CVM. Firstly, they reprimand the critics of the CVM for failing to realise that a CV question involves much more than just asking a respondent to express a WTP for some good. Asking respondents whether they are willing to pay £50 for cleaner air is an 'attitudinal' WTP question. Neither the payment vehicle nor the good are specified clearly. A CV question measures 'behavioural intention' by setting out the specific details of the good which is being sold to the respondent, how the good would be provided and how the good would be paid for. Mitchell and Carson (1995) criticise Kahneman and Knetsch (1992) for presuming that an attitudinal WTP question is a sufficient basis upon which to test the reliability of CV. In one experiment Kahneman and Knetsch ask one sample of Vancouver residents how much they would be willing to pay "to improve sport fish stocks in British Columbia fresh water" and ask the other sample "how much they would be willing to pay to improve sport fish stocks in Canada fresh water". They do not explain: the meaning of "fish-stocks" and "fresh water", the size of the improvement, how long the improvement would be maintained, who will provide the good, how it will be provided, when it will be provided, and how the respondents will pay for it. It is not surprising therefore that the respondent would provide a quick and not so meaningful answer. Studies that test the CVM using attitudinal surveys are not a reasonable basis upon which to discount the CVM.

The second observation made by Mitchell and Carson is that all CV surveys are not equally reliable and therefore it is not reasonable to choose surveys selectively in order to criticise the method. This amounts to asserting that CV results are averse to CV practice.

Guidelines for CVM
With such conflicting views on the validity of the CVM, the US National Oceanic and Atmospheric Administration (NOAA) convened a Blue Ribbon panel of experts (known as the NOAA Panel) to deliberate on all the evidence produced an to answer the question: "Is the contingent valuation method capable of providing estimates of lost non-use or existence values that are reliable enough to be used in natural resource damage assessments" (Portney, 1994). This was chaired by Nobel prize winners Kenneth Arrow and Robert Solow and had four other members[79]. The panel reported its findings in 1993 (Arrow *et al.*, 1993) and drew the overall conclusion that:

---

[79] Edward Leamer, Paul Portney, Roy Radner and Howard Schuman were the other members of the panel.

CV studies can produce estimates reliable enough to be the starting point for a judicial or administrative determination of natural resource damages - including lost passive value.

The report suggests that, so long as the study is well designed, the CVM is a reliable tool. In this regard they issued a comprehensive set of 'best practice' guidelines for the carrying out of such studies. Except where otherwise stated, the following guidelines come from the NOAA Panel's recommendations:

Sample Type and Size
The guidance of a professional sampling statistician should be sought when selecting a sample. Weighting is necessary to adjust the sample to the characteristics of the population (Mitchell and Carson, 1995).

Non-Response and Protests
Survey non-response and item non-response should be minimised. Mitchell and Carson (1995) state that it is almost unheard of to achieve response rates higher that 80 percent. This can be partially justified on the grounds that it also occurs in official referenda. An open-ended follow-up to a 'no' answer to a question about willingness to pay for a good should be included to allow for the elimination of 'protests'.

Interview Method
Face-to-face interviews are preferable although telephone interviews have some advantages in terms of cost and centralised supervision. The choice between these two approaches depends on the requirements of the survey. Telephone surveys must be shorter, photographs cannot be used and non-response tends to be higher. However, telephone interviews are much cheaper to administer. If the results of a CV study are to be used as a basis for a legal or policy decision, it is preferable if the use of mail surveys can be avoided. This is based on results which show the inability of many respondents in the US to comprehend the type of written information which CV surveys must convey (Mitchell and Carson, 1995). However, some very successful mail surveys have been carried out in parts of Europe. Mitchell and Carson (1995) recommend the use of professional interviewers.

Pre-testing
A pilot survey must be carried out to ensure that the respondents can understand the wording of the questionnaire and that they find the description of the good in question realistic and the payment method plausible. It is important that the interviewer also finds the questions easy to read. Mitchell and Carson (1995) recommend a pilot of 10 to 50 respondents.

Survey Design
A conservative design increases the reliability of the survey.

Elicitation Format
The WTP format should be used instead of WTA because the former is the conservative choice.

Payment Method
It is usually recommended that the payment method should be as close a possible to the actual way the project is to be financed. Mitchell and Carson (1995) suggest that, in the case of a population who resent paying taxes and are reluctant to increase their tax burden, using increased taxation as a payment method ensures that respondents do not taken the decision lightly. In addition, they are less likely to forget the other goods that they would forgo if they pay for the project.

Referendum Format
The Dichotomous Choice format is the most desirable form of CV elicitation as it is the most incentive compatible, i.e. it mimics our day-to-day market decisions, and it reduces the incentive to engage in strategic behaviour since it is more difficult for the respondent to influence mean WTP (Kriström, 1990). Harrison and Kriström (1995) strongly recommend against the double-bounded dichotomous choice approach as it does not display the incentive compatibility properties of the single-bounded approach and they show that it produces "sizeable" upward bias.

Accurate Description of Program or Policy
"Adequate" information must be provided to respondents about the environmental programme that is offered.

Pre-testing of Photographs
If photographs are to be used they should be pre-tested carefully to explore their effect on responses.

Cross Tabulations
The survey should include a variety of information on variables such as such as income, interest in the environment and use of the asset in question which are likely to be correlated with WTP. A good CV study has WTP responses which vary systematically with the covariates one might expect to influence that measure (Mitchell and Carson, 1995).

Aggregation Issues
In order to estimate the value of the good to the population, the mean or median must be multiplied by the population size. In CV surveys there are generally a large number of respondents who are willing to pay small amounts and a few who are willing to pay large amounts. Thus, the distribution of WTP is usually skewed rightwards. Therefore the mean is greater than the median. The median is often the preferred choice for two reasons: Firstly the median, unlike the mean, can be reliably estimated and secondly the median provides a more conservative measure. However, Harrison and Kriström (1995) state that there

is virtually no rationale behind the *exclusive* use of the median where the goal is to assess aggregate damages to a population. They show that there "appears to be no consistent statistical basis for eliminating the mean from consideration" and that using the median because it is more conservative "begs the reason that we want to bias the estimates in the first place". The authors also question the rationale of excluding the mean because it does not address distributional consequences. If a Majority Rule social welfare function is assumed, then the median would be the correct choice, however, if the Kaldor-Hicks (potential Pareto) criterion is used then the mean is the correct choice as the project is considered desirable if the net benefit to society is positive (see also Johansson *et al.*, 1989 and Johansson, 1993 and Kriström, 1990).

Checks on Understanding and Acceptance
In order to check consistency, questions should be asked which ascertain the respondent's attitude to the good in question before she is asked her WTP for the good.

Alternative Expenditure Possibilities
The NOAA panel states that, even in the best CV studies, respondents are not adequately reminded that their payment for an environmental good will reduce their expenditure possibilities on other goods.

It is important to bear in mind that the NOAA Panel's guidelines are for CV studies which are to be used in natural resource damage assessment. Mitchell and Carson (1995) note that these guidelines set a "very high" and "very costly" standard. They suggest that the extent to which the guidelines must be adhered to will depend on the importance of the policy question being examined.

Appendix 3

MAPS

FIGURE A3.1. Forestry Production Potential in Ireland.

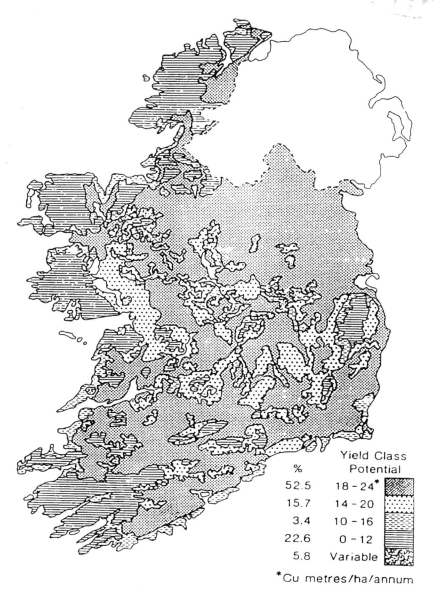

%	Yield Class Potential
52.5	18 - 24*
15.7	14 - 20
3.4	10 - 16
22.6	0 - 12
5.8	Variable

*Cu metres/ha/annum

Source: Bulfin, M., Teagasc, Kinsealy Research Centre.

FIGURE A3.2. Natural Heritage Areas.

Source: Hickie, 1996.

FIGURE A3.3. Acid Sensitive Areas.

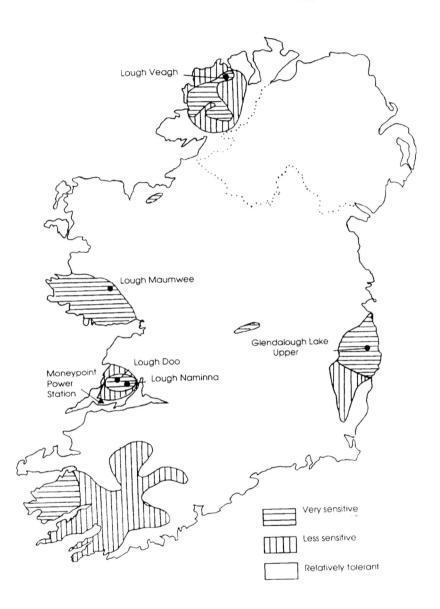

Source: Bowman, 1991.

APPENDIX 4

SUBSIDY ASSESSMENT

The rule that has been used by the Industrial Development Authority (IDA) to assess the appropriate grant is as follows,

$$Grant \leq \frac{1}{4}\left[\sum_i x_i(p_i - v_i) + \lambda\pi\right] \tag{A4.1}$$

where x_i is a vector of inputs, p_i is a vector of market prices of inputs, v_i is a vector of shadow prices of inputs, π represent profit and λ is the fraction of the firm which is Irish owned. Rearranging,

$$Maximum\ Grant = \frac{1}{4}\left[\sum_i x_i p_i + \lambda\pi - \sum_i x_i v_i\right] \tag{A4.2}$$

Since total sales revenue equals total costs $\sum_i x_i p_i$ plus profit, Honohan (1995) suggests that the maximum grant can then be written as[80],

$$Maximum\ Grant = \frac{1}{4}\left[Yv_0 - \sum_i x_i v_i\right] \tag{A4.3}$$

where v_0 is the shadow value of output. However, this is clearly only the case where the market and shadow price of output are the same. This assumes that there is no market power in the market for this product. If this is the case, the maximum grant level equals one quarter of the net social benefit of the project. The discount apparently serves as an allowance for risk, over-optimism etc.

Equation A4.3 was used to calculate the "Advised Subsidy". This is compared with the actual subsidy under the five test discount rates and the results are presented in Table A4.1. The results show that, if a positive discount rate is assumed, the extent of subsidisation of the Forest Strategy is not justified. Taking the Government's 5 percent discount rate, the appropriate subsidy is £49 m while the actual subsidy is £1.2 billion.

---

[80] Assuming the firm is Irish owned.

TABLE A4.1. 'IDA Advised' Subsidy and Actual Subsidy to Strategy.

Discount Rate (%)	Net Social Benefit (£m)	Advised Subsidy (£m)	Actual Subsidy (£m)
0	64,196	16,799	3,115
3	1,519	380	1,762
5	195	49	1,271
8	-133	0[1]	837
10	-128	0[1]	661

[1] No subsidy is appropriate since net social benefit is negative.

Honohan's (1995; 1996) rule builds in a shadow price of public funds. This is a factor greater than unity which is multiplied by the subsidy outlay to take account of the extra taxation that would have to be imposed elsewhere in the economy in order to make good any loss of revenue arising from the project being evaluated. Dividing the non-exchequer net revenues by this shadow price makes them commensurate with grant and tax funds in the calculation (Honohan, 1996). The shadow price of public funds (ϕ) was estimated to be between 1.74 and 2.44 in the late 1980s but, since then, marginal tax rates have been falling and a figure of 1.5 is more appropriate (Honohan, 1996).

The maximum grant is also adjusted downwards to reflect 'deadweight' or leakage whereby some projects would have gone ahead with a lower grant rate or none at all. This is done by multiplying by a factor $(1-\theta)$ where θ is the probability that some of the projects would have gone ahead without any subsidy or with a lower subsidy. An optimal policy would give the minimum grant necessary for the project to go ahead. The correct value of the grant to benefit ratio $(1-\theta)$ is estimated by examining the responsiveness of aggregate project benefits to the grant level and the extent to which grant costs increase with an increase in the maximum allowable grant to benefit ratio. Taking the case where the grant rate applies uniformly across projects (as it does in the case of afforestation grants), the maximum grant benefit ratio $(1-\theta)$ is maximised where the marginal impact of the grant rate of benefits is equal to its marginal impact of costs. Honohan's (1996) approach is based on a simplified model of the grant process in which both the benefits and the grants are proportional to jobs. He estimates a value for $(1-\theta)$ of 0.076 using an average grant to wage ratio of 0.15 and an elasticity of demand for labour of (-)0.55. This latter figure is the estimate for high tech manufacturing. A lower elasticity of 0.15 for traditional industry reduces the value of $(1-\theta)$ to 0.022.

Finally, the calculation takes account of the fact that tax revenues consisting of taxes on inputs, including an allowance for the reduced welfare payments from a fall in unemployment (assuming a shadow wage of less than the market wage), at a rate t_i, and on profits, at a rate t_0, will be returned to the government. The maximum grant is, therefore, given by the following expression,

$$Maximum\ Grant = (1-\theta)\left\{\sum_i x_i\left[\phi^{-1}(p_i - v_i)+t_i\right]+t_0\pi\right\} \qquad (A4.4)$$

Honohan (1995) does not include an expression for externalities. He recommends that they be left out of the analysis since industrial projects are subject to planning approval. However, while this may be the case, planning approval does not imply that no external costs will be imposed, it is just implies that the costs are not above some predetermined level. In the case of the Forest Strategy it is also necessary to allow for external benefits. Thus, the appropriate subsidy level for the Forest Strategy is given by the following expression,

$$Maximum\ Grant = (1-\theta)\{\phi^{-1}[\varepsilon + (\mu - \vartheta)+(M-\Omega)+T+\omega+\tau]\} \qquad (A4.6)$$

where,

proportion of project which would have gone ahead without subsidy = θ
net external benefits = ε
market wage bill = μ
shadow wage bill = ϑ
market land bill = M
shadow land bill = Ω
tax revenue on inputs = T
reduction in social welfare payments = ω
tax revenue from timber sales = τ
shadow price of public funds = ϕ

TABLE A4.2. Value of Parameters for Equation A4.6 under Various Assumptions.

		Discount Rate (%)			
	0	*3*	*5*	*8*	*10*
ε	£334m	£229m	£165m	£122m	£107m
ϕ	1.5	1.5	1.5	1.5	1.5
T	£1,672	£139m	£73m	£40m	£29m
M [1]	£17,183m	£1,192m	£552m	£250m	£167m
Ω	£1,305m	£815m	£628m	£456m	£381m
μ	£3,105m	£258m	£136m	£74m	£55m
ϑ when $\vartheta = \mu$	£3,105m	£258m	£136m	£74m	£55m
ϑ when $\vartheta = 0.8\mu$	£2,484m	£206m	£109m	£59m	£44m
ω when $\vartheta = \mu$	0	0	0	0	0
ω^2 when $\vartheta = 0.8\mu$	£331m	£28m	£15m	£8m	£6m

Notes:
[1] Mean market price of forestry land taken to be £1,800 per ha.
[2] Unemployment benefit taken to be £80 per week.

Table A4.2 gives the values of each of the parameters in equation A4.6 under various assumptions. Honohan's (1996) estimates of $(1-\theta)$ rely on his simple model that the grant is proportional to employment. This is not the method used to calculate the afforestation grant. However, in terms of the total afforestation project it could be assumed that, while there will be leakage, it will be quite small such that $(1-\theta)$ would also be small. For the purposes of this analysis it will be assumed to be zero. When the shadow wage is believed to equal the market wage $(\vartheta = \mu)$, unemployment will not be reduced by the Forest Strategy so there will be no unemployment benefit saving by the Government, i.e. ω equals zero.

TABLE A4.3. Recommended Subsidy to Strategy.

Discount Rate (%)	Recommended Subsidy (£m) $(\vartheta = \mu)$	Recommended Subsidy (£m) $(\vartheta = 0.8\mu)$	Actual minus Recommended (£m) $(\vartheta = \mu)$	Actual minus Recommended (£m) $(\vartheta = \mu)$
0	1,214	2,112	1,901	1,004
3	194	537	1,568	1,226
5	188	401	1,083	870
8	0[1]	0[1]	837	837
10	0[1]	0[1]	661	661

[1] No subsidy is appropriate since net social benefit is negative.

Table A4.3 shows the recommended subsidy level (according to equation A4.6) at the five test discount rates when assuming the shadow wage equals the market wage $(\vartheta = \mu)$ and when the shadow wage is assumed to be 80 percent of the market wage $(\vartheta = 0.8\mu)$. The difference between the actual subsidy and the recommended subsidy is given in the final column.

Seventy five percent of the subsidy is being provided by the EU and, given that Ireland is a net recipient of funds from the EU, all of the funds will not be raised from Irish taxes. However, the maximum grant should be compared with the total subsidy if the use of these funds for forestry involves an opportunity cost. The figures show that the actual subsidy is far higher than the recommended subsidy at all five test discount rates. At the five percent rate, the Strategy is oversubsidised by more than £1 billion. Even if the upper bound estimate of net external benefits is used, the oversubsidisation amounts to £910 m.

If EU funds would not be available for an alternative use they can be considered as free. However, as shown in Chapter 16, the Irish Government subsidy alone is higher than the recommended subsidy at all positive discount rates.

Index

Acidification, xxi, 20, 22, 103-104, 127, 175, 188, 195, 248, 263
Adamowicz, W., 9
Adamson, J., 92, 93, 94, 95, 96, 97, 99
Agriculture, xx, xxii, xxiii, xxv, 2, 3, 4, 10, 31, 33, 69, 70, 93, 94, 99, 104, 113, 127, 139, 146, 149, 150, 190, 192
Agriculture, Food and Forestry, Department of, xxvi, 3, 4, 11, 13, 25, 37, 50, 51, 52, 71, 141, 151, 193, 221, 222, 223
Alcorn, J., 8
Allocative efficiency, 15
Allott, N., 96, 98
Amenity. See Recreation
Anderson, A. B., 8, 10, 80, 96
Annual Payments. See Premium Scheme
Anthropomorphism, 20
Archaeology, xxiii, 27, 149, 151-153, 176, 177
Arens, P., 8
Arnold, M., 40, 41, 42, 43
Arrow, K., 254, 255, 257
Avoided Cost of Compliance Approach, 80-81, 82, 94
Aylward, B., 132
Ayres, R. U., 81, 82

Balick, M., 8
Barrow, P., 10, 99
Bateman, I., 9, 10, 117, 167, 243, 254
Baumol, W. J., 18, 149, 245
Benson, J., 10, 117, 120
Bequest value, 19, 20, 120, 133

Biodiversity, xxii, 20, 21, 123-138, 147, 175
    assessment of, 123-124
    defined, 123
    habitat value for, 130-132
    in a forest, 124-130
    reasons for conservation, 132-133
    public attitudes about effect of forestry on, 155-166
    valuation of, 133-135
    value of future planting for, 137
    benefits of Strategy for, 175
Birdsall, N., 16, 81
Bishop, R. C., 9, 19, 254
Bord Fáilte, 108, 109, 112, 113
Bowes, M. D., 9, 245, 246
Bowman, J., 97, 98, 104, 263
Boyd, R. G., 151
Bracken, J., 98
Brennan, M., 96, 98, 103, 109, 113, 114
Brookshire, D. S., 251, 253
Brown, G., 8, 250
Brown, T.C., 189
Bruce, J. P., 78
Bulfin, M., 10, 11, 261

Caldecott, J., 8
Calder, I. R., 94, 95
Cannell, M., 77, 78, 79
Cape, J., 77, 78, 79
CARBMOD, 86
Carbon seqestration, xx-xxi, xxvii, 8, 10, 19, 20, 21, 77-90, 185, 186, 195
    and Kyoto Agreement, 83
    and Luxembourg Agreement, 83
    valuation techniques for, 80

benefits of Strategy for, 88
modelling of, 86
and soil type, 79
Carson, R. T., 22, 236, 238, 250, 251, 252, 253, 254, 255, 257, 258, 259, 260
Chilton, S., 118, 120
Chopra, K., 8
Christie, J., 36
Ciriacy-Wantrup, S. V., 250
Clark, C. W., 245
Clawson, M., 9, 23
Clinch, J. P., 5, 11, 188
Cline, W., 16, 81, 82
COFORD, 2, 52, 53, 195
Cohesion Countries, 3
Coillte Teoranta, xx, xxvi, xxvii, xxviii, 4, 25, 27, 50, 51, 52, 57, 58, 63, 64, 67, 72, 75, 93, 104, 108, 109, 111, 113, 114, 115, 118, 125, 153, 186, 188, 193, 195, 196
and information, 195
and monopoly power, 63
and forest recreation, 113
Statutory objectives of, 63
Common Agricultural Policy, xxv, 3, 69, 192
Common, M. S., 10
Community Integrity, xxiii, 21, 149, 150-151, 153, 177, 195
Community Stability, 151
Community Strategy and Action Programme for the Forestry Sector, 29
Community Support Framework, 3, 30
Conlon, F., 4
Conservation Reconsidered, 19
Contingent Valuation, xxiii-xxiv, 11, 22-23, 99, 117, 118, 120, 134, 137, 143, 167-175, 183, 239, 249-260
and aggregation, 259
and bias, 253-256
and elicitation of bids, 255-256
and winners and losers, 167-169

criticisms of, 253-256
defined, 22
guidelines for, 257-260
history of, 250
NOAA judgement of, 258
responses to the critics of, 256-257
steps, 22-23
validity of, 252-253
welfare measures in, 250-252
zero and negative bids in, 167-169
Convery, F. J., 10, 11, 107, 108
Cooney, G., 151, 152, 153
Cooper, J., 9
Cost Benefit Analysis, xxiv, 13-19, 21, 177-182, 183, 187-189
defined, 13-14
history of, 14
of Strategy, 177-182
policy implications regarding, 187-189
and subsidies, 189
Crabbe, P. J., 63
Craig, S., 10
Cruz, W., 8
Curran, B., 8
Cuttle, S. P., 94
d'Arge, R., 253
Damage Avoided Approach, 80, 81-82
Davis, R. K., 250
Deans, J. D., 96
Desvousges, W. H., 253, 254, 255
Diamond, P. A., 253, 254, 256
Dickie, M., 254
Discounting, xx, 16-17, 239-243
Irish Government rate of discount, 16
problems with, 241-243
rationale for, 240-241
UK rate of discount, 16
USA rate of discount, 16
World Bank rate of discount, 16
Dively, D., 13, 234
Dixon, J. A., 8
Drèze, J., 17, 244

Duffield, J. W., 254
Dupuit, J., 236
Dynamic efficiency, 187

Economic Security, xx, 21, 35, 64-
    65, 66, 67, 182, 186
    value of Strategy, 66
Economies of scale, 1, 2
Edwards, P., 36
Emissions trading, 81, 82-86, 87,
    88, 89, 90
    permit price, 84, 85, 87, 88, 89,
    90
Englin, J., 9
Environment, Department of, 26,
    83
Environmental Designations, 28
Environmental Impact Assessment,
    26
Environmental regulations, 25-28
Equity, 15, 188, 233-234
    and Kaldor-Hicks test, 233-234
    and welfare criterion, 15, 233-
    234
Estate forestry, 2
EU funds
    cost of, xxv, xxviii, 182, 184,
        185-186, 191-192, 196, 268
Eurofortech, 30
Eutrophication, 104
Excess Burden, xxiv, 177, 178,
    179, 182, 184, 185
Existence value, xxii, 8, 9, 10, 19,
    20, 21, 22, 23, 133, 134, 137,
    138, 151, 249, 253, 257
    defined, 20
Externalities
    and optimal forest rotation, 247
    depletable, 18
    diminishing external benefits,
        166
    formal definition, 245
    informal definition, 17
    net external benefit of Strategy,
        xxiv, xxv, 179, 182, 184, 191
    pecuniary, 149, 245
    and subsidies, 267, 268

undepletable, 18
Extractive Value
    of tropical forestry, 8

Fankhauser, S., 77, 78, 81, 82, 87
Farming. See Agriculture
Farrell, E. P., 2, 149, 188
Faustmann, M., 7, 35, 37, 246, 247
Financial appraisal, 10, 11, 14, 65,
    194
Fiscal incentives, 29-33
Fiscal instruments, 30-33
Fitz Gerald, J., 70
Ford, E. D., 96
Forest benefits
    classification of, 21
Forest cover
    Ireland, 1, 3, 4, 13, 50
Forest estate
    EU, 39
    global, 38
    Ireland, 50
Forest investment
    favourable conditions for, 1, 2
Forest Service, xxvi, xxvii, 25, 26,
    27, 30, 31, 32, 57, 59, 64, 103,
    104, 114, 115, 117, 136, 139,
    140, 141, 149, 151, 152, 177,
    189, 193, 195
    role of, 25
    and information, 195
    Guidelines, 27
Freeman, A. M., 15, 18, 233, 234
Friedman, M., 19

Gallatin, A, 14
Garrod, G. D., 10, 141, 252
Giller, P. S., 94, 97, 99
Gillmor, 2
Glaister, S., 14, 15, 233, 234, 244
Godoy, R., 7, 8
Good, J., 18, 125, 126, 127, 128,
    129, 130, 131
Grandfathering, 84
Grants for forestry, 31-32, 115
    and recreation, 115
Gray, H. J., 10

Green Book, 14
Greene, W., 173
Greenhouse Effect, 4, 20, 77
Gregory, G. R., 7
Griliches, Z., 23
Grimes, A., 8
Gurnell, J., 133

Hammack, J., 250
Hanemann, W. M., 167, 172, 250,
    252, 254, 256
Hanley, N., 10, 14, 16, 63, 131,
    134, 135, 137, 189, 236, 240,
    242, 248, 249, 253, 255
Harriman, R., 94
Harrison, G. W., 259
Hartman, R., 7
Hausman, J. A., 253, 256
Hayden, T. J., 126, 127, 128, 133
Heal, G. M., 16
Hedonic Pricing, 23, 134, 143, 253
Henry, W., 8
Herberlein, T. A., 254
Hickey, B., 10
Hickie, D., 27, 28, 91, 93, 125,
    126, 127, 128, 129, 130, 136,
    262
Hicks, J., 15, 23, 149, 188, 233,
    234, 236
History
    of Irish forestry, 1, 2
Honohan, P., 14, 71, 177, 189, 190,
    265, 266, 267, 268
Hornung, M., 92, 93, 94, 95, 96,
    97, 99
Houghton, J. T., 78
Hudson, J. A., 96
Hulme, M., 78
Hunter Blair, P., 114
Hutchinson, R. W., 243
Hutchinson, W. G., 118, 120
Hyde, W. F., 151

Information, xxvii, 25, 195
    and Coillte Teoranta, 195
    and Forest Service, 195
Inputs, xx, 1, 21, 69-76, 184, 267

costs of Strategy, 76, 184
Ioris, E. M., 8

Johansson, P-O, 9, 22, 23, 237,
    238, 260
Johnson, J., 70
Johnson, R. C., 95, 96, 98, 102
Jones, P. D., 78

Kahneman, D., 254, 257
Kaldor, N., 15, 23, 149, 188, 233,
    234, 236, 260
Kaldor-Hicks test, 15, 149, 188,
    233, 234, 236, 260
    defined, 15, 233-234
Kangas, J., 123
Kearney, B., 11
Kennedy, J. J., 3
Kilroy, M., 92
Klaassen, G., 85, 87, 89
Knetsch, J., 9, 23, 254, 257
Kramer, R., 8
Kriström, B., 9, 19, 135, 167, 169,
    172, 173, 259, 260
Krutilla, J. V., 19, 20, 245, 246
Kula, E., 37, 243
Kumari, K., 8
Kuusipalo, J., 124

Labour, xx, 71-75, 76, 184, 190
    costs of Strategy, 74, 184
    shadow price of, xx, 71-73
Lampietti, J. A., 8
Land, xx, xxii, xxiii, 69-70, 149,
    189, 190, 267
    costs of Strategy, 70, 184
    price inflation of, 149, xxii-xxiii
    shadow price of, 69-70
Land price inflation, 149, xxii-xxiii
Landlordism, 2, 139
Landscape, xix, xxii, xxiii, xxiv,
    xxviii, 4, 20, 21, 26-27, 139-
    147, 155-166, 175, 179, 184,
    187, 188, 193, 194, 195
    assessing impact of forestry on,
        141-143
    benefits of Strategy, xxiv, 175

regulations regarding, 26-27,
140-141
public attitudes to forestry on,
144-147, 155-166
valuation of, 143
Law, F., 96
Layard, R., 14, 15, 233, 234, 244
Leamer, E. E., 257
Legislation, 25
Leslie, A. J., 16
Lind, R. C., 240, 243
Little, I., 14, 15, 98, 125, 234
Long, N. V., 63
Loomis, J. B., 9
Lucey, C., 150
Lynam, J., 107

Magrath, W., 8
Maitland, P. S., 91, 92, 93, 94, 95,
96, 97
Marglin, S., 14, 242
Markandya, A., 65, 243
Mattsson, L., 9
McCloskey, D., 256
McConnell, K. E., 20
McCormack, A., 112, 114, 141
McCusker, P., 3
McWilliams, B., 82
Mendelson, R. O., 8, 9
Milner, N. J., 100
Mirrlees, J. A., 14
Mishan, E. J., 14
Mitchell, F., 125
Mitchell, R. C., 22, 236, 238, 250,
251, 252, 253, 254, 255, 257,
258, 259, 260
Monopoly, xx, 17, 63, 65, 67, 186
Moran, D., 134, 135
Mori, S. A., 8
Mulloy, F., 3, 29, 30
Murphy, A., 160, 167
Murphy, G., 42
Murphy, M., 92

Nash, C., 14, 15, 16, 233, 234
National Economic and Social
Council, 11

Navrud, S., 134, 255
Neeson, E., 2
Newbery, D. M., 16, 17
Newson, M . D., 95, 96
Ní Dhubháin, A., 11
NOAA Panel, 145, 257, 258, 260
Non-market valuation, xix, 7-12,
13, 21-23, 118, 183, 195, 248-
260
literature review of forestry
studies on, 7-12
Non-market costs and benefits, 1,
7, 10, 11, 12, 17
Non-timber costs and benefits, xix,
7, 8, 9, 11, 12, 194
Non-use value, 19, 20, 133, 257
Nordhaus, W. D., 81, 82
Noss, R. F., 124

O'Connor, R., 11
O'Halloran, J., 94, 97, 99
Oates, W. E., 18, 149, 245
O'Connor, R., 4
Offset Approach, 80
Ohlin, B., 7
O'Leary. T., 112, 114, 141
Operational Programme
for forestry, 3, 4, 5, 11, 27, 29,
30, 32, 115, 116, 136, 139,
189
Option value, 17, 19, 20, 23, 120,
133, 134
defined, 19, 20
Organisational structure
of Irish forestry, 25
Other considerations, xxii-xxiii,
149-153
Ozanne, C. M. P., 130

Pareto Optimality, 15, 188, 233
defined, 15
potential, 15
Patterson, D. A., 254
Pearce, D. W., 7, 8, 9, 14, 15, 16,
19, 20, 21, 64, 65, 80, 134, 135,
150, 233, 234, 240, 241, 242,
243

Peat, 79, 88, 89, 90, 135, 195
    and carbon sequestration, 79-90,
        195
Peck, S., 81, 82
Pepper, H. W., 133
Peterken, G. F., 123, 126, 127,
    128, 129, 131
Peterson, G. L., 189
Pigou, A. C., 242
Pinedo-Vazquez, M., 8
Policy implications
    of Strategy, 187-196
Policy instruments, 25-33
Polinsky, A. M., 233
Portney, P. R., 257
Potential compensation principle,
    15, 233-234
Premium Scheme for forestry, 30,
    32
Preservation Value
    of tropical forestry, 8
Preßler, M. R., 7
Price incentives, 28
Price, C., 10, 13, 80, 86, 99, 100,
    143, 243
Prins, R., 8
Production Function Approaches,
    21-22, 99,134, 183, 248-249
    defined, 21-22, 248-249
Public attitudes, xxiii, 5, 144-147,
    155-166
    regional differences, 6, 144-147
Public funds
    cost of, xxviii, 177, 190, 196,
        266, 267
Public good, 17-19, 22, 167, 168,
    175, 237, 238, 250, 252, 253,
    255
    definition, 17-19,
Public bad, 18, 168, 175
Pyatt, D. G., 96

Radner, R., 257
Ramsey, F., 242
Randall, A., 132, 135, 236, 238,
    250, 251, 252
rate of return

private, 5, 10
    to Strategy, xxviii, 178, 182,
        196
Recreation, xxi-xxii, xxiii, xxiv, 3,
    4, 7, 8, 9, 10, 11, 17, 20, 21, 23,
    27, 99, 107-121, 133, 137, 155-
    166, 179, 184, 186, 187
    Coillte Teoranta and, 113
    domestic visits for, 110-111
    grants for, 115
    incentives for, 113-117
    public attitudes about effect of
        forestry on, 155-166
    types of, 107-108
    supply of, 113-117
    total visits for, 112-113, 186
    tourist visits for, 111-112
    trends in, 108-110
    valuation of, 117-121
    value for tourism for, 118-120
    value of future planting for,
        120-121
    benefits of Strategy, xxiv, 175,
        184
Research
    future areas for, xxvii, 193-195
Review Group on Forestry, 11, 17
Riera, P., 173
Rigby, M. W., 243
Roberts, G., 94
Rose, A., 84
Rosen, S., 23
Rotation of a forest
    optimal, 245-247
    optimal with externalities, 247
    proft maximising, 37
Rowe, R., 253
Ruffell, R., 10
Ruitenbeek, H. J., 8
Rural communities
    impact of forestry on, 11, 150-
        151

Samuelson, P., 7, 235, 236, 247,
    253
Schuman, H., 257
Scitovsky Paradox, 233

Scitovsky, T., 234
Scully, B., 110
Sedjo, R. A., 9
Sensitivity Analysis
    defined, 17
    of Strategy, 179-182
Shadow price, xx, 17, 37, 69, 70,
    71, 72, 73, 243, 244, 264, 266,
    267
    defined, 17, 244
    of capital, 243
    of labour, xx, 71-73, 181
    of land, 69-70
    of public funds. See Cost of
    of timber, 63-64
Shadow wage, 181
Sheehy, S. J., 4
Shogren, J., 253
Sinclair, J., 10, 62
Sitka spruce, xxii, 1, 2, 31, 35, 36,
    37, 52, 55, 67, 72, 73, 75, 79,
    80, 87, 96, 129, 130, 139
Smith, K., 96
Smith, V. K., 19, 253, 254
Smyth, P., 82
Social costs and benefits, 18
Social efficiency, xix, 1, 5, 10, 15,
    183, 233, 234
    defined, 1
Sodal, D., 9
Solow, R., 257
Spash, C., 14, 16, 131, 134, 135,
    137, 189, 236, 240, 242, 248,
    249, 255
Squire, L., 14
Steer, A., 16, 81
Stern, N., 17, 244
Stoll, J., 238, 250, 251, 252
Strategic goal of the Strategy, xix,
    xxvi, 13, 193
Strategic Plan for the Forestry
    Sector. See Strategy
Strategy
    actual vs recommended subsidy
        to, 5, 191, 265-268
    awareness and approval of, 145

carbon sequestration, benefits
    of, 88
concordance and, 188
Cost Benefit Analysis of, 177-
    182
dynamic efficiency of, 187
Economic Security value of, 66
effectiveness of, 188
finance of, 13
inputs, costs of, 76
labour, costs of, 74
land, costs of, 70
landscape, wildlife, recreation,
    benefits of, 175
net external benefits of, 179
policy implications regarding,
    187
principal elements of, 13
rate of return to, 182
recommended vs actual subsidy
    to, 191
species, 37
Strategic Goal, 13
sustainability of, xxvii, 188
water, costs of, 105
timber, benefits of, 66
Stretton, C., 100
Subsidies
    actual vs recommended subsidy
        to Strategy, xxv-xxvi, xxvii,
        5, 189-193, 191, 196, 265-
        268
    assessment of, 265-268
    Cost Benefit Analysis and, 189
    in a first-best world, 190-191
    in a second-best world, 191-193
Sustainability, xxvii, 188, 189, 243
    of Strategy, xxvii, 188
Swanson, T. M., 132
Swift, D. W., 94

Taxation, 32-33
Teisberg, T. J., 81, 82
Temple-Lang, J., 136
Thayer, M., 253
Thorbjarnarson, J. H., 8
Tickell, O., 128, 130

Tietenberg, T., 84
Timber, xx, xxi, xxiv, xxv, 20, 35-67, 73, 86, 105, 177
  benefits of Strategy, 65-67
  Economic Security value of, 64-65
  import substitution argument for, 64
  markets and prices, 37-64
  monopoly supply of, 63
  production functions for, 35-37
Tobias, D., 8
Total Economic Value,
  components of forestry, xx-xxiii, 20, 21
  defined, 19-21
  literature on regarding forestry, 7-12
Tourism, xxi, xxii, 107, 108, 112, 120
  revenue from, 120
  tourist numbers, 108, 112
  value of forestry for, 118
Tradeable permits. See Emissions Trading
Travel Cost, 23, 117, 118, 120, 134, 143, 253
Tree growth
  rate of, 1, 35-37
Turner, R. K., 9, 19, 20, 167, 254

Uncertainty, 17, 82, 183
US Flood Control Act, 14
Use value, 9, 10, 19, 23, 120, 133
  defined, 19

van der Sleesen, A., 111
van der Tak, H. G., 14
van Kooten, G. C., 9
Varallo, P. V., 100
Varian, H. R., 244
Vicarious value, 19
Visits to forests. See Recreation

Walsh, P. D., 96
Walsh, R. G., 9
Walter, J., 81, 82
Walters, A., 15, 234
Warford, R., 8
Water, xxi, xxvii, 4, 7, 8, 9, 10, 14, 20, 91-105, 177, 184, 186, 194, 195
  at establishment, 91-94
  at harvest, 98-99
  at maturity, 94-98
  costs of Strategy, 105, 177, 184, 186
  restriction costs of Strategy, 100-103
  pollution costs of Strategy, 103-105
  valuation of, 99-105
Watson, R. T., 78
Weisbrod, B. A., 19
Welfare criterion, 15, 233-234, 235
Welfare measures, 16, 168, 234-239, 250
Western Package, 29, 30
Whelan, B. J., 92, 155
Whiteman, A., 10, 47, 49, 62, 100, 102, 104
Wibe, S., 8, 9, 198
Wildlife. See Biodiversity
Wilkie, D. S., 8
Williams, J., 155
Willig, R. D., 250
Willingness to pay/accept
  and welfare measures, 16, 168, 169, 250
Willis, K., 10, 80, 86, 117, 120, 141, 252
Winners and losers, 167-169
Worrell, R., 240, 243

Yield Class, 35-37, 261

Zerbe, R., 13, 234